A BIBLIOGRAPHY OF PACIFIC NORTHWEST HERPETOLOGY

by

R. Wayne Campbell
Michael G. Shepard
Brigitta M. Van Der Raay
&
Patrick T. Gregory

BRITISH COLUMBIA PROVINCIAL MUSEUM

HERITAGE RECORD NO. 14

1982

---

published by

THE BRITISH COLUMBIA PROVINCIAL MUSEUM
VICTORIA

PROVINCE OF BRITISH COLUMBIA
MINISTRY OF THE PROVINCIAL SECRETARY
AND GOVERNMENT SERVICES

Provincial Secretary

Canadian Cataloguing in Publication Data
Main entry under title:
A Bibliography of Pacific Northwest herpetology

(Heritage record, ISSN 0701-9556 ; no. 14)

Includes indexes.
ISBN 0-7718-8288-2

1. Herpetology - British Columbia - Bibliography.
2. Herpetology - Alaska - Bibliography. 3. Herpe-
tology - Washington (State) - Bibliography. 4.
Herpetology - Yukon Territory - Bibliography. I.
Campbell, R. Wayne (Robert Wayne),   . II
British Columbia Provincial Museum. III. Series.

Z7996.R4B52   016.5976'09711   C82-092035-5

THIS BIBLIOGRAPHY IS DEDICATED TO

G. CLIFFORD CARL

and

JAMES R. SLATER

FOR THEIR CONTRIBUTIONS TO HERPETOLOGY
OF THE PACIFIC NORTHWEST

CONTENTS

v

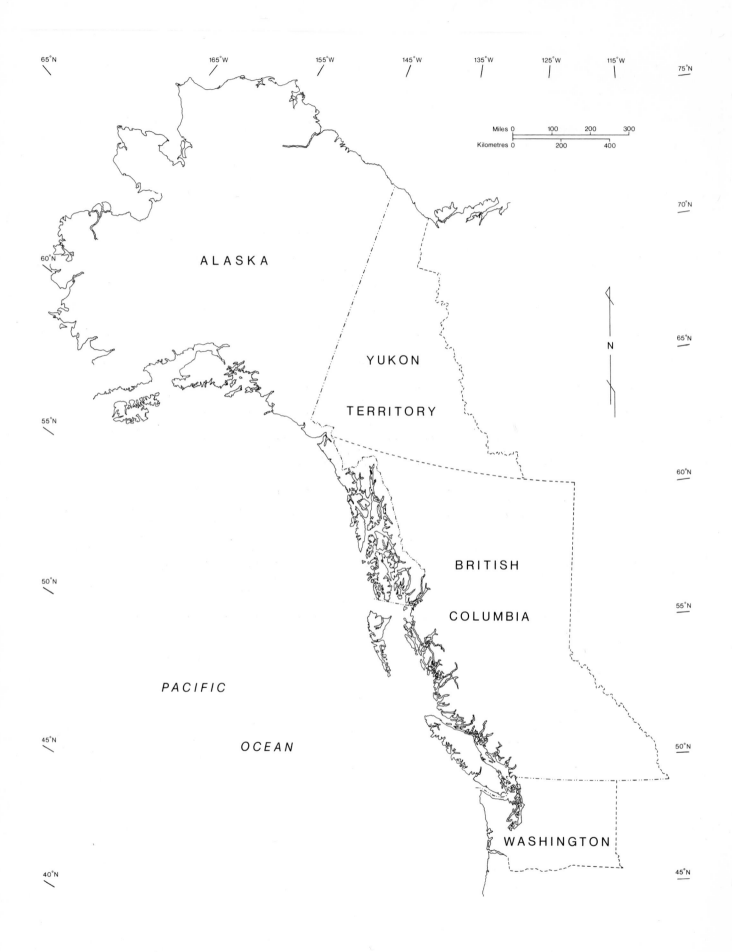

65°N   165°W   155°W   145°W   135°W   125°W   115°W   75°N

Miles 0   100   200   300
Kilometres 0   200   400

70°N

ALASKA

60°N

YUKON

65°N

N

TERRITORY

55°N

60°N

BRITISH

50°N

COLUMBIA

55°N

PACIFIC

OCEAN

45°N

50°N

WASHINGTON

40°N

45°N

INTRODUCTION

This book is the second in a series of four bibliographies on the mammals, birds, reptiles and amphibians of British Columbia. Unlike other volumes, the scope of this bibliography was expanded to include the Pacific Northwest (see map opposite), especially since many species of reptiles and amphibians have coastal distributions that extend from Alaska through Washington.

Our objective was to locate sources, and extract relevant information, for people interested in Pacific Northwest herpetology, whether professionals or amateurs. Also considered were sources (i.e. Biological Conservation, Journal of Range Management, etc.) that would be useful to conservationists, habitat protection biologists, land planners and wildlife managers.

The literature search is complete for British Columbia and fairly complete for Washington. References for Alaska and Yukon Territory were extracted incidental to the search for material on British Columbia and Washington and are included here because of their relevance to the area covered.

There were some problems deciding what references to select for wide-ranging species in North America. For example, the Painted Turtle (Chrysemys picta) is a popular experimental animal and has an extensive literature. In cases such as this we decided to include major references for the species and then select other papers that would be useful for life history information for species found in the Pacific Northwest. Most of these entries are listed in the "Additional Literature" category of this book.

Finally, we would appreciate knowing about sources we may have overlooked in searching material for this book.

ORGANIZATION

All sections in this book are set up either numerically or alphabetically, or a combination of both. The master list of entries is organized numerically. All articles were assigned a number as received, therefore, there is no specific order (i.e. by author, year, journal, etc.). Since computers were not available for data gathering, arrangement, or presentation of material, the present system allows flexibility to manually add to the list in the future.

Each entry is cross-referenced by species, geographic area and author. Species are listed alphabetically by scientific name. A LIST OF SPECIES of salamanders, frogs, toads, turtles, lizards and snakes covered by this bibliography is provided to assist with locating scientific names.

The GEOGRAPHIC INDEX includes six divisions (see page 119). Two of these, British Columbia and Washington, are further divided: British Columbia into 89 major grids following the National Topographic Grid System and Washington, by counties.

The titles for all entries have been typed in capital letters and are as they appeared in the reference. The source for each article has been underlined.

LIST OF SPECIES

CAUDATA - SALAMANDERS

Ambystoma gracile (Baird)	Northwestern Salamander
Ambystoma macrodactylum Baird	Long-toed Salamander
Ambystoma tigrinum (Green)	Tiger Salamander
Aneides ferreus Cope	Clouded Salamander
Dicamptodon copei Nussbaum	Cope's Giant Salamander
Dicamptodon ensatus (Eschscholtz)	Pacific Giant Salamander
Ensatina eschscholtzi Gray	Ensatina
Plethodon dunni Bishop	Dunn's Salamander
Plethodon larselli Burns	Larch Mountain Salamander
Plethodon vandykei Van Denburgh	Van Dyke's Salamander
Plethodon vehiculum Cooper	Western Redback Salamander
Rhyacotriton olympicus (Gaige)	Olympic Salamander
Taricha granulosa (Skilton)	Roughskin Newt

SALIENTIA - FROGS AND TOADS

Ascaphus truei Stejneger	Tailed Frog
Bufo boreas Baird and Girard	Western Toad
Bufo woodhousei Girard	Woodhouse's Toad
Hyla regilla Baird and Girard	Pacific Treefrog
Pseudacris triseriata (Wied)	Striped Chorus Frog
Rana aurora Baird and Girard	Red-legged Frog
Rana cascade Slater	Cascade's Frog
Rana catesbeiana Shaw	Bullfrog
Rana clamitans Latreille	Green Frog
Rana pipiens Schreber	Northern Leopard Frog
Rana pretiosa Baird and Girard	Spotted Frog
Rana sylvatica LeConte	Wood Frog
Scaphiopus intermontanus (Cope)	Great Basin Spadefoot

TESTUDINES - TURTLES

Chelonia mydas (Linnaeus)	Green Turtle
Chelydra serpentina Linnaeus	Snapping Turtle
Chrysemys picta (Sneider)	Painted Turtle
Clemmys marmorata (Baird and Girard)	Western Pond Turtle
Dermochelys coriacea (Linnaeus)	Leatherback

SAURIA - LIZARDS

Eumeces skiltonianus (Baird and Girard)	Western Skink
Gerrhonotus coeruleus (Wiegmann)	Northern Alligator Lizard
Gerrhonotus multicarinatus (Blainville)	Southern Alligator Lizard
Phrynosoma douglassi (Bell)	Short-horned Lizard
Phrynosoma platyrhinos (Girard)	Desert Horned Lizard
Sceloporus graciosus Baird and Girard	Sagebrush Lizard
Sceloporus occidentalis Baird and Girard	Western Fence Lizard
Uta stansburiana Baird and Girard	Side-blotched Lizard

SERPENTES - SNAKES

Charina bottae (Blainville)	Rubber Boa
Coluber constrictor Linnaeus	Racer
Contia tenuis (Baird and Girard)	Sharptail Snake
Crotalus viridis Rafinesque	Western Rattlesnake
Diadophis punctatus Linnaeus	Ringneck Snake
Hypsiglena torquata Gunther	Night Snake

<u>Lampropeltis</u> <u>zonata</u> Blainville	California Mountain Kingsnake
<u>Masticophis</u> <u>taeniatus</u> Hallowell	Striped Whipsnake
<u>Pituophis</u> <u>melanoleucus</u> Daudin	Gopher Snake
<u>Thamnophis</u> <u>elegans</u> Baird and Girard	Western Terrestrial Garter Snake
<u>Thamnophis</u> <u>ordinoides</u> Baird and Girard	Northwestern Garter Snake
<u>Thamnophis</u> <u>sirtalis</u> Linnaeus	Common Garter Snake

BIBLIOGRAPHIC SOURCES

The entries in this bibliography were gathered from 428 sources. Herpetological journals (i.e. <u>Copeia</u>, <u>Herpetologica</u>, <u>Journal of Herpetology</u>, etc.) were searched first followed by other major scientific journals dealing with vertebrates generally (i.e. <u>American Naturalist</u>, <u>Canadian Journal of Zoology</u>, <u>Ecology</u>, <u>Systematic Zoology</u>, etc.). Reference sections from these papers led to other more applied journals such as <u>Journal of Comparative Physiology</u> and <u>Journal of Morphology</u> and foreign journals (i.e. <u>Journal of Zoology</u>, <u>Oecologia</u>, etc.). Finally, journals dealing specifically with the biology of birds (i.e. <u>Auk</u>, <u>Condor</u>, etc.) and mammals (i.e. <u>Journal of Mammalogy</u>, etc.) were searched as often reptiles and amphibians of concern were included in papers on food habits.

It is important to note that if a single paper was referenced to any source, the <u>entire</u> source (i.e. all available issues) was searched for additional articles. A total of <u>148</u> journals, mostly North American, were searched.

Seventy-one sources were obtained from universities and colleges. These included student professional papers and Bachelor theses, which are not listed in Dissertation abstracts, as well as Master and Doctorate theses. Various scientific publications (i.e. <u>University of Washington Publications in Biology</u>) were also searched.

Zoological and natural history society publications (often regional) accounted for 63 sources while 56 museum publications, mostly from western North America, were searched.

Forty-five federal, provincial and state government publications are listed including an additional 31 unpublished sources, mostly from British Columbia and Washington.

The remaining sources were from consultant companies and a variety of miscellaneous sources such as publications of special committees (e.g. <u>Wildlife Report - The Canadian Scene</u>).

Not included in the list of sources are most of the references listed in "General Literature", which usually includes books, field guides and other individual publications.

The article "The" has been dropped from all sources and citations which follow. For example, <u>The Herptile</u> becomes <u>Herptile</u>. Sources below, marked with an asterisk (*) indicate that the literature search is complete from the first issue, through the latest issue (usually 1980) available to us.

*<u>Acta Zoologica</u> (International Journal for Zoology, Stockholm, Sweden):

- Vol. 1 (1920) through Vol. 52 (1971)

*<u>Acta Zoologica Fennica</u> (Societas Pro Fauna Et Flora Fennica, Helsinqforsiae):

- No. 1 (1926) through No. 160 (1979)

*<u>Advances in Ecological Research</u> (Academic Press, New York):

- Vol. 1 (1962) through Vol. 11 (1980)

*Advances in the Study of Behavior (Academic Press, New York):

- Vol. 1 (1965) through Vol. 10 (1979)

*Agro-Ecosystems (International Association for Ecology, Amsterdam, Holland):

- Vol. 1, No. 1 (1974) through Vol. 5, No. 3 (1979)

*Alaska Department of Fish & Game Information Leaflet (Alaska Department of Fish and Game, Juneau):

- No. 1 (1961) through No. 181 (1979)

*Alaska Department of Fish & Game Technical Data Report (Alaska Department of Fish and Game, Juneau):

- No. 1 (1972) through No. 41 (1978)

*Alaska Fish Tales and Game Trails (Alaska Department of Fish and Game, Juneau):

- No. 1 (1967) through Vol. 11, No. 5 (1979)

*American Committee for International Wild Life Protection Special Publication (American Committee for International Wild Life Protection, Bronx, New York):

- Vol. 1, No. 1 (1931) through No. 18 (1965)

*American Journal of Veterinary Research (American Veterinary Medical Association, Schaumburg, Illinois):

- Vol. 1, No. 1 (1940) through Vol. 39, No. 12 (1978)

*American Midland Naturalist (University of Notre Dame, Indiana):

- Vol. 1, No. 1 (1909) through Vol. 104, No. 1 (1980)

*American Museum Novitates (American Museum of Natural History, New York):

- No. 1 (1921) through No. 2696 (1980)

*American Naturalist (American Society of Naturalists, University of Chicago Press, Illinois):

- Vol. 1, No. 1 (1868) through Vol. 116, No. 3 (1980)

*American Scientist (Society of the Sigma Xi, New Haven, Conneticut):

- Vol. 30, No. 1 (1942) through Vol. 68, No. 5 (1980) (Succeeds Sigma X Quarterly in 1942)

*American Zoologist (American Society of Zoologists, Utica, New York):

- Vol. 1, No. 1 (1961) through Vol. 20, No. 2 (1980)

*Amphibia - Reptilia (Akademische Verlagsgesellschaft, Wiesbaden, Germany):

- Vol. 1, No. 1 (1980) through Vol. 1, No. 2 (1980)

*Animal Behaviour (Association for the Study of Animal Behaviour, Sussex, England):

- Vol. 6, No. 1 (1958) through Vol. 28, No. 3 (1980) (Succeeds British Journal of Animal Behaviour in 1958)

*Animal Behaviour Monographs (Animal Behaviour Society, London, England):

- Vol. 1, Part 1 (1968) through Vol. 6, Part 3 (1973)

Annals and Magazine of Natural History (London, England):

- miscellaneous issues from 1887 through 1919

*Annals of (the) Carnegie Museum (Museum of Natural History, Pittsburg, Pennsylvania):

- Vol. 1, No. 1 (1901) through Vol. 48, Article 18 (1979)

*Annual Report of the Michigan Academy of Science (Michigan Academy of Science, Lansing):

- First (1900) through Twenty-second (1921). (Discontinued in 1921; succeeded by Papers of the Michigan Academy of Science Arts and Letters in 1923)

*Annual Report of the United States National Museum (United States National Museum, Washington, District of Columbia):

- 1885 through 1965

*Annual Review of Ecology and Systematics (Annual Reviews Inc., Palo Alto, California):

- Vol. 1 (1970) through Vol. 10 (1979)

*Arctic (Arctic Institute of North America, Calgary):

- Vol. 1, No. 1 (1948) through Vol. 31, No. 4 (1978)

*Arctic Bibliography (Arctic Institute of North America, Montreal):

- Vol. 1 (1953) through Vol. 16 (1975)

Associated Engineering Services Ltd. Reports (Associated Engineering Services Ltd., Vancouver, British Columbia):

- 1966 only

*Auk (American Ornithologists' Union):

- Vol. 1, No. 1 (1884) through Vol. 96, No. 1 (1979)

*Bamfield Marine Station Reports (Bamfield Marine Station, Vancouver Island):

- 1972 through 1979

*Beaver (Magazine of the North, Winnipeg, Manitoba):

- Vol. 1, No. 1 (Outfit 1:1) (1920) through Outfit 309:2 (1978)

*Behavioral Ecology and Sociobiology (University of Konstanz, Federal Republic of Germany):

- Vol. 1, No. 1 (1976) through Vol. 6, No. 4 (1980)

*Behaviour Supplement (An International Journal of Comparative Ethology, Leiden, Netherlands):

- No. 1 (1950) through No. 20 (1977)

Big Bend Resource Society Reports (Big Bend Resource Society, Box 1946, Golden, British Columbia, V0A 1H0):

- 1979 only

*Biochemical Systematics (Pergamon Press, Oxford, England):

- Vol. 1, No. 1 (1973) through Vol. 8, No. 3 (1980)

*Biological Conservation (Applied Science Publishers, England):

- Vol. 1, No. 1 (1968) through Vol. 18, No. 3 (1980)

*Biological Journal of the Linnean Society (Linnean Society of London, England):

- Vol. 1, No. 1 & 2 (1969) through Vol. 13, No. 4 (1980)

*Biological Papers of the University of Alaska (University of Alaska, Anchorage):

- No. 1 (1957) through No. 19 (1978)

*Biological Reviews and Biological Proceedings of the Cambridge Philosophical Society (Cambridge Philosophical Society, London, England):

- Vol. 2, No. 1 (1926) through Vol. 9, No. 4 (1934). (Succeeds Proceedings of the Cambridge Philosophical Society (Biological Sciences; discontinued in 1934; succeeded by Biological Reviews of the Cambridge Philosophical Society in 1935).

*Biological Review of the Cambridge Philosophical Society (Cambridge Philosophical Society, London, England):

- Vol. 10, No. 1 (1935) through Vol. 55, No. 2 (1980). (Succeeds Biological Reviews and Biological Proceedings of the Cambridge Philosophical Society in 1935).

*Biological Symposia (The Jaques Cattell Press, Lancaster, Pennsylvania):

- Vol. 1 (1940) through Vol. 12 (1947)

*Blue Jay (Saskatchewan Natural History Society, Regina):

- Vol. 1, No. 1 (1942-43) through Vol. 38, No. 3 (1980)

*British Columbia Department of Recreation and Conservation Annual Report (British Columbia Department of Recreation and Conservation, Victoria):

- 1970 through 1976. (Succeeds British Columbia Provincial Museum Report of the Year in 1970; discontinued in 1976; succeeded by Ministry of Recreation and Conservation Annual Report in 1977).

*British Columbia Fish and Wildlife Branch (Atlin) Reports (British Columbia Fish and Wildlife Branch, Atlin, V0W 1A0):

- all reports from August 1974 through July, 1980

British Columbia Fish and Wildlife Branch (Cranbrook) Reports (British Columbia Fish and Wildlife Branch, Cranbrook):

- 1955, 1976 and 1977

British Columbia Fish and Wildlife Branch (Kamloops) Reports (British Columbia Fish and Wildlife Branch, Kamloops):

- miscellaneous reports from 1960 through 1980

British Columbia Fish and Wildlife Branch (Nanaimo) Reports (British Columbia Fish and Wildlife Branch, Nanaimo):

- miscellaneous reports in 1961, 1967, 1975, 1977 and 1980

British Columbia Fish and Wildlife Branch (Nelson) Reports (British Columbia Fish and Wildlife Branch, Nelson):

- 1979 only

British Columbia Fish and Wildlife Branch (Smithers) Reports (British Columbia Fish and Wildlife Branch, Smithers):

- miscellaneous reports from 1966 through 1980

British Columbia Fish and Wildlife Branch (Vancouver) Reports (British Columbia Fish and Wildlife Branch, Vancouver):

- miscellaneous reports in 1963, 1968, 1974

British Columbia Fish and Wildlife Branch (Victoria) Reports (British Columbia Fish and Wildlife Branch, Victoria):

- miscellaneous reports from 1935 through 1980

British Columbia Fish and Wildlife Branch (Williams Lake) Reports (British Columbia Fish and Wildlife Branch, Williams Lake):

- 1967 and 1979 only

*British Columbia Fish and Wildlife Branch Wildlife Management Reports (British Columbia Fish and Wildlife Branch, Victoria):

- No. 1 (1968) through No. 13 (1977)

British Columbia Forest Service (Victoria) Reports (British Columbia Forest Service, Victoria):

- miscellaneous wildlife section reports, from 1949 through 1955

British Columbia Hydro and Power Authority Reports (British Columbia Hydro and Power Authority, Vancouver):

- miscellaneous reports from 1974 through 1979

British Columbia Indian Language Project Reports (British Columbia Indian Language Project, Victoria):

- 1974 only

British Columbia Land Inventory Wildlife Division Reports (British Columbia Land Inventory, Victoria):

- 1973 only

*British Columbia Ministry of Environment Fish and Wildlife Reports (Province of British Columbia, Ministry of Environment, Fish and Wildlife Branch, Victoria):

- No. R-1 (1978) through No. R-3 (1979)

*British Columbia Ministry of Lands, Parks and Housing, Parks and Outdoor Recreation Division (Victoria) Reports. (British Columbia Ministry of Lands, Parks and Housing, Victoria):

- 1979 through June, 1981. (Succeeds British Columbia Parks Branch, Intepretation Assessment Division Reports in 1979).

*British Columbia Nature Council Newsletter:

- Vol. 1, No. 1 (1964) through Vol. 6, No. 3 (1969). (Discontinued in 1969; succeeded by Federation of British Columbia Naturalists Newsletter in 1969 with Vol. 7, No. 1)

British Columbia Parks and Outdoor Recreation Division (Kamloops) Reports (Ministry of Lands, Parks and Housing, Kamloops):

- 1980 (miscellaneous reports only)

*British Columbia Parks Branch Interpretation Assessment Section Reports (British Columbia Parks Branch, Victoria):

- Provincial Parks Interpretation Assessment Section Reports include: Alice Lake (1969-1974); Bowron Lake (1961-1977); Champion Lakes (1971-1976); Crooked River (1968-1975); Cultus Lake (1973-1978); Miracle Beach (1958-1978); Mitlenatch Island (1959-1978); Monck (1971-1977); Mount Assiniboine (1973-1974); Mount Edziza (1974); Elk Falls (1977-1978); Ellison (1965-1974); Englishman River (1968-1977); Garibaldi (1951-1974); Golden Ears (1963-1976); Goldstream (1962-1977); Haynes Point (1965-1977); Helliwell (1977-1978); Horn Lake Caves (1973); Kleanza Creek (1975-1976); Kokanee Creek (1966-1977); Mount Robson (1955-1977); Mount Seymour (1963-1976); Okanagan Falls (1972-1973); Okanagan Lake (1965-1977); Paul Lake (1975); Ralph River (1973-1974); Rathtrevor Beach (1968-1977); Shuswap Lake (1962-1977); Stagleap (1976); Strathcona (1973-1978); Syringa Creek (1973); Kokanee Glacier (1973); Lakelse Lake (1972-1977); Liard River Hotsprings (1971); Little Qualicum Falls (1968-1977); Maclure Lake (1976); Macmillian (1969-1974); Manning (1959-1974); Vaseux Lake (1972-1973); Wasa (1971-1978); Wells Gray (1962-1977); Whiskers Point (1968-1977); White Pelican (1971-1979); Wickaninnish (1964-1970). (Discontinued in 1978; succeeded by British Columbia Ministry of Lands, Parks and Housing, Parks and Outdoor Recreation Division (Victoria) Reports in 1979).

*British Columbia Parks Branch Resource Management Section (Wildlife Management Section) Reports (British Columbia Parks Branch, Victoria):

- Provincial Parks Resource Management Section Reports include: Atlin (1975-1978); Atsutla Range (1976); Bowron Lake (1978); Mount Assiniboine (1972-1978); Mount Edziza (1978-1979); Mount Robson (1974-1979); Buckinghorse Lake (1976); Burnie Lakes (1975); Cape Scott (1973); Cathedral Lakes (1960-1977); Fry Creek Canyon (1974); Gladys Lake (1975); Kokanee Glacier (1974); Kwadacha (1976-1978); Liard River Hot Springs (1975); Muncho Lake (1978); Spatsizi (1976-1980); Stone Mountain (1978); Strathcona (1966-1977); Tatlatui (1978-1979); Top-of-the-World (1974-1978); Tweedsmuir (1966-1978); Wells Gray (1956-1979).

*British Columbia Provincial Museum Handbook Series (British Columbia Provincial Museum, Victoria):

- No. 1 (1942) through No. 38 (1979)

*British Columbia Provincial Museum Heritage Record (British Columbia Provincial Museum, Victoria):

- No. 1 (1976) through No. 8 (1979)

*British Columbia Provincial Museum Occasional Papers Series (British Columbia Provincial Museum, Victoria):

- No. 1 (1939) through No. 20 (1978)

*British Columbia Provincial Museum Methods Manual (British Columbia Provincial Museum, Victoria):

- No. 1 (1973) through No. 7 (1979)

*British Columbia Provincial Museum Report of the Year (British Columbia Provincial Museum, Victoria):

- 1968 through 1969. (Succeeds Report of the Provincial Museum of Natural History and Anthroplogy for the Year in 1968; discontinued in 1969; succeeded by British Columbia Department of Recreation and Conservation Annual Report in 1970).

*British Columbia Provincial Museum Special Publications (British Columbia Provincial Museum, Victoria):

- 1898 through 1979

*British Columbia Provincial Museum Vertebrate Zoology Division Reports (British Columbia Provincial Museum, Victoria):

- 1932 through 1981

*British Columbia Resource Analysis Branch Bulletin (British Columbia Ministry of Environment, Assessment and Planning Division, Victoria):

- No. 1 (1977) through No. 20 (1980)

*British Columbia Resource Analysis Branch Technical Paper (British Columbia Ministry of Environment, Assessment and Planning Division, Victoria):

- No. 1 (1978) through No. 3 (1980)

*British Ecological Society Symposium (British Ecological Society, London):

- No. 1 (1960) through No. 15 (1975)

*British Journal of Animal Behaviour (Association for the Study of Animal Behaviour, Sussex, England):

- Vol. 1, No. 1 (1953) through Vol. 5, No. 4 (1957). (Discontinued in 1957; succeeded by Animal Behaviour in 1958).

*British Journal of Herpetology (British Herpetological Society, c/o Zoological Society of London, Regents Park, London, England):

- Vol. 1, No. 1 (1948) through Vol. 5, No. 9 (1977)

*Brookhaven Symposia in Biology (Brookhaven National Laboratory, Upton, New York):

- No. 1 (1948) through No. 28 (1976)

*Bulletins From the Ecological Research Committee (Swedish National Science Research Council, Stockholm):

- No. 1 (1968) through No. 19 (1976). (Discontinued with No. 19; succeeded by Ecological Bulletins with No. 20).

*Bulletin of the American Museum of Natural History (American Museum of Natural History, New York):

- Vol. 1, Article 1 (1881-86) through Vol. 165, Article 4 (1980)

*Bulletin of the Antivenin Institute of America (Antivenin Institute of America, Philadelphia, Pennsylvania):

- Vol. 1, No. 1 (1927) through Vol. 3, No. 4 (1930)

*Bulletin of the Biological Board of Canada (Minister of Fisheries, Ottawa, Ontario):

- No. 1 (1918) through No. 55 (1937). (Discontinued in 1937; succeeded by Bulletin of the Fisheries Research Board of Canada in 1939 with No. 56)

*Bulletin of the Buffalo Society of Natural History (Buffalo Society of Natural History, New York):

- Vol. 1, No. 1 (1873) through Vol. 28 (1976)

*Bulletin of Carnegie Museum of Natural History (Carnegie Museum of Natural History, Pittsburg, Pennsylvania):

- No. 1 (1976) through No. 13 (1979)

*Bulletin of the Chicago Academy of Sciences (Chicago Academy of Sciences, Illinois):

- Vol. 1, No. 1 (1883) through Vol. 11, No. 8 (1978)

*Bulletin of the Chicago Herpetological Society (Chicago Herpetological Society, Illinois):

- Vol. 1, No. 1 (1966) through Vol. 13, No. 3 (1978)

*Bulletin of the Fisheries Research Board of Canada (Fisheries and Environment, Ottawa, Ontario):

- No. 56 (1939) through No. 198 (1977). (Succeeds Bulletin of the Biological Board of Canada in 1939 with No. 56)

Bulletin of the Florida State Museum, Biological Sciences (Florida State Museum, University of Florida, Gainesville):

- miscellaneous issues in Vols. 3 and 6

*Bulletin of the Illinois Natural History Society (Illinois Natural History Survey, Urbana):

- Vol. 20, Article 1 (1932) through Vol. 24, Article 3 (1948). (Succeeds Bulletin of the Illinois State Natural History Survey in 1932).

*Bulletin of the Illinois State Laboratory of Natural History (Illinois State Laboratory of Natural History, Urbana):

- Vol. 1, No. 1 (1876) through Vol. 12, Article 6 (1918). (Discontinued in 1918; succeeded by Bulletin of the Illinois State Natural History Survey in 1922 with Vol. 13).

*Bulletin of the Illinois State Natural History Survey (Illinois State Natural History Survey, Urbana):

- Vol. 13, Article 1 (1922) through Vol. 19, Article 6 (1932). (Succeeds Bulletin of the Illinois State Laboratory in 1922; discontinued in 1932 with Vol. 19; succeeded by Bulletin of the Illinois Natural History Survey in 1932 with Vol. 20).

*Bulletin of the International Council (Committee) For Bird Preservation:

- No. 1 (1927) through No. 13 (1977)

Bulletin of the Jackson Park Branch of the Chicago Medical Society (Chicago Medical Society, Illinois):

- Vol. 15, No. 7 (1938) only

*Bulletin of the Museum of Comparative Zoology (Harvard University, Cambridge, Massachusetts):

- Vol. 1, No. 1 (1863-69) through Vol. 148, No. 10 (1979)

*Bulletin of the Museum of Natural History of the University of Oregon (University of Oregon, Eugene):

- No. 1 (1965) through No. 23 (1978)

*Bulletin of the Natural History Society of New Brunswick (Natural History Society of New Brunswick, Saint John):

- No. 1 (1882) through No. 30 (1913). (Discontinued in 1913).

*Bulletin of the Ohio Biological Survey New Series (Ohio State University, Columbus):

- Vol. 1, No. 1 (1959) through Vol. 5, No. 4 (1977). (Succeeds Ohio Biological Survey Bulletin in 1959).

*Bulletin of the Pacific Northwest Herpetological Society (Pacific Northwest Herpetological Society, Seattle, Washington):

- Vol. 1, No. 1 (1966) through Vol. 5, No. 2 (1972)

*Bulletin of the Philadelphia Herpetological Society (Philadelphia Herpetological Society, Pennsylvania):

- Vol. 1, No. 1 (1953) through Vol. 25, No. 4 (1978)

*Bulletin of the Scientific Laboratories of Dension University (Denison University, Granville, Ohio):

- Vol. 1, Part 1 (1886) through Vol. 18, Article 7 (1916). (Discontinued in 1916; succeeded by Journal of the Scientific Laboratories of Denison University in 1920).

*Bulletin of the Southern California Academy of Sciences (Southern California Academy of Sciences, Los Angelos):

- Vol. 1, No. 1 (1902) through Vol. 78, No. 1 (1979)

*Bulletin of the University of Utah Biological Series (University of Utah, Salt Lake City):

- Vol. 1, No. 1 (1929) through Vol. 11, No. 2 (1949). (Discontinued in 1949; succeeded by University of Utah Biological Series in 1951).

Bulletin of the Vancouver Natural History Society (Vancouver Natural History Society, British Columbia):

- No. 92 (1955) through No. 146 (1970). (Discontinued in May, 1970; succeeded by Vancouver Natural History Society Discovery in June, 1970 with No. 146).

*Bulletin of the Wildlife Diseases Association (Wildlife Disease Association, Chicago, Illinois):

- Vol. 1, No. 1 (1965) through Vol. 5, No. 4 (1969). (Discontinued in 1969; succeeded by Journal of Wildlife Disease in 1970).

Bulletins of the Zoological Society of San Diego (Zoological Society of San Diego, California):

- No. 15 (1939) through No. 27 (1952)

*California Fish and Game (Department of Fish and Game, Sacramento):

- Vol. 1, No. 1 (1914-15) through Vol. 66, No. 3 (1980)

*Canada Land Inventory Report (British Columbia Ministry of Environment, Assessment and Planning Division, Victoria):

- No. 1 (1970) through No. 7 (1973)

*Canadian Alpine Journal (Alpine Club of Canada):

- Vol. 1 (1907) through Vol. 61 (1978)

Canadian Amphibian and Reptile Conservation Society Newsletter (Canadian Amphibian and Reptile Conservation Society, Toronto, Ontario):

- Vol. 18, No. 2 (1980) only

*Canadian Audubon (Audubon Society of Canada, Toronto, Ontario):

- Vol. 20, No. 1 (1958) through Vol. 33, No. 45 (1971). (Succeeds Canadian Nature in 1958; discontinued in 1971; succeeded by Nature Canada in 1972).

*Canadian Field-Naturalist (Ottawa Field Naturalists' Club):

- Vol. 33, No. 1 (1919) through Vol. 94, No. 3 (1980). (Succeeds Ottawa Naturalist in 1919).

*Canadian Journal: A Repertory of Industry, Science and Art, and a Record of the Canadian Institute (The Canadian Institute, Toronto):

- Vol. 1 (1853) through Vol. 3 (1855). (Discontinued in 1855; succeeded by Canadian Journal of Industry, Science and Art in 1856).

*Canadian Journal of Forest Research (National Research Council of Canada, Ottawa):

- Vol. 1, No. 1 (1971) through Vol. 9, No. 3 (1979)

*Canadian Journal of Industry, Science and Art (The Canadian Institute, Toronto):

- Vol. 1 (new series) (1856) through Vol. 11 (new series) (1867). (Succeeds Canadian Journal: A Repertory of Industry, Science and Art, and a Record of the Canadian Institute in 1856; discontinued in 1867; succeeded by Canadian Journal of Science, Literature and History in 1870).

*Canadian Journal of Science, Literature and History (The Canadian Institute, Toronto):

- Vol. 12 (1870) through Vol. 15 (1878). (Succeeds Canadian Journal of Industry, Science and Art in 1870; discontinued in 1878).

*Canadian Journal of Research (National Research Council of Canada):

- Vol. 1, No. 1 (1929) through Vol. 28, No. 6 (1950). (Discontinued in 1950; succeeded by Canadian Journal of Zoology in 1951).

*Canadian Journal of Zoology (National Research Council of Canada, Ottawa):

- Vol. 29, No. 1 (1951) through Vol. 58, No. 9 (1980). (Succeeds Canadian Journal of Research in 1951).

*Canadian Naturalist (Committee of the Natural History Society of Montreal):

- Vol. 1, No. 1 (1857) through Vol. 10, No. 8 (1883). (Discontinued in 1883; succeeded by Canadian Record of Science in 1885).

*Canadian Nature (Audubon Society of Canada, Toronto, Ontario):

- Vol. 1, No. 1 (1939) through Vol. 19, No. 5 (1957). (Discontinued in 1957; succeeded by Canadian Audubon in 1958).

Canadian Nature Federation Special Publication (Canadian Nature Federation, 46 Elgin Street, Ottawa K1P 5K6):

- No. 6 (1976) only

*Canadian Record of Science (Natural History Society of Montreal):

- Vol. 1, No. 1 (1885) through Vol. 9 (1916). (Succeeds Canadian Naturalist in 1885; discontinued in 1916).

*Canadian Society of Wildlife and Fishery Biologists Occasional Papers (University of Alberta, Department of Biology, Calgary):

- No. 1 (1965) through No. 2 (1967)

*Canadian Wildlife Administration Reports (Canadian Wildlife Service, Ottawa):

- Vol. 1, No. 1 (1975) through Vol. 2, No. 4 (1979)

*Canadian Wildlife Service (Delta) Unpublished Reports (Delta, British Columbia):

- 1921 through 1979

*Canadian Wildlife Service (Ottawa) Unpublished Reports (Ottawa, Ontario):

- No. CWSC 1 (1921) through No. CWSC 2569 (1977)

*Canadian Wildlife Service (Qualicum Beach) Unpublished Reports (Marshall-Stevenson Wildlife Refuge, Qualicum, British Columbia):

- 1974 through 1980

*Catalogue of American Amphibians and Reptiles (Society for the Study of Amphibians and Reptiles, Bethesda, Maryland):

- No. 1.1 (1963) through No. 270.1 (1980)

*Catholic University of America Biological Series (Catholic University of America, Washington, District of Columbia):

- No. 1 (1903) through No. 41 (1942). (Discontinued in 1942; succeeded by Catholic University of America Contributions from the Biological Laboratory in 1942 with Vol. 42).

*Catholic University of America Contributions from the Biological Laboratory (Catholic University of America, Washington, District of Columbia):

- No. 42 (1942) through No. 45 (1943). (Succeeds Catholic University of America Biological Series with No. 42).

Cell and Tissue Research (Springer-Verlag, Germany):

- Vol. 181 (1977) only

*Central Washington University Department of Biology Theses (Central Washington University, Ellensburg, Washington):

- Masters and Doctorate Theses, 1966 through 1979

*Chicago Academy of Sciences Special Publications (Chicago Academy of Sciences, Illinois):

- No. 1 (1902) through No. 14 (1959)

Cleveland Museum of Natural History Zoological Series (Cleveland Museum of Natural History, Ohio):

- No. 1 (1934) only

*Comox-Strathcona Natural History Society Publications (Comox-Strathcona Natural History Society, Comox, British Columbia):

- 1976 only

*Comparative Biochemistry and Physiology (Pergamon Press, Oxford, England):

- Vol. 1, No. 1 (1960) through Vol. 67 A & B, No. 2 (1980)

*Condor (Cooper Ornithological Society):

- Vol. 1, No. 1 (1899) through Vol. 81, No. 2 (1979)

*Contributions of the Royal Ontario Museum of Zoology and Palaeontology (Royal Ontario Museum, Toronto):

- No. 33 (1952) through No. 51 (1959). (Succeeds Contributions of the Royal Ontario Museum of Zoology in 1952; discontinued in 1959 with No. 51; succeeded by Life Sciences Division Contribution, Royal Ontario Museum in 1960 with No. 52).

*Contributions of the Royal Ontario Museum of Zoology (Royal Ontario Museum, Toronto):

- No. 1 (1928) through No. 32 (1951). (Discontinued in 1951; succeeded by Contributions of the Royal Ontario Museum of Zoology and Palaeontology in 1952 with No. 33).

*Copeia (American Society of Ichthyologists and Herpetologists):

- No. 1 (1913) through No. 3 (1980)

*Current Topics in Developmental Biology (Academic Press, Inc., New York):

- Vol. 1 (1966) through Vol. 12 (1978)

*Eastern Washington State College Department of Biology Theses (Eastern Washington State College, Cheney):

- Masters and Doctorate Theses, 1949 through 1979

*Ecological Bulletins (Swedish National Science Research Council, Stockholm):

- No. 20 (1976) through No. 21 (1976). (Succeeds Bulletins from the Ecological Research Council in 1976 with No. 20).

*Ecological Monographs (Ecological Society of America, Durham, North Carolina):

- Vol. 1 (1931) through Vol. 50, No. 3 (1980)

*Ecology (Ecological Society of America, Durham, North Carolina):

- Vol. 1 (1920) through Vol. 61, No. 4 (1980)

*Environmental Conservation (Foundation for Environmental Conservation, Switzerland):

- Vol. 1, No. 1 (1974) through Vol. 2, No. 4 (1975)

*Evergreen State College Reports (Olympia, Washington):

- all student reports from 1970 through 1979

*Evolution (Society for the Study of Evolution, Lawrence, Kansas):

- Vol. 1, No. 1 (1947) through Vol. 34, No. 4 (1980)

*Federation of British Columbia Naturalists Newsletter (Federation of British Columbia Naturalists, Vancouver):

- Vol. 7, No. 1 (1969) through Vol. 17, No. 2 (1979). (Succeeds British Columbia Nature Council Newsletter in 1969 with Vol. 7, No. 1).

Federation of British Columbia Naturalists Reports (Federation of British Columbia Naturalists, Vancouver):

- 1973 only

*Fieldiana: Zoology (Chicago Natural History Museum, Illinois):

- Vol. 31 (1945) through Vol. 73, No. 3 (1979). (Succeeds Publications of the Field Museum of Natural History, Zoological Series, in 1945 with Vol. 31; discontinued in 1979 with Vol. 73, No. 3; succeeded by Fieldiana: Zoology New Series in December, 1979).

*Fieldiana: Zoology New Series (Chicago Natural History Museum, Illinois):

- No. 1 (1979) through No. 5 (1980). (Succeeds Fieldiana: Zoology in December, 1979).

*Fisheries Research Board of Canada Pacific Biological Station Circular (Pacific Biological Station, Nanaimo, British Columbia):

– No. 1 (1944) through No. 107 (1977)

*Fisheries Research Board of Canada Report (Fisheries and Environment, Ottawa, Ontario):

– No. 1 (1973) through No. 16 (1978)

*Fort Wright College Reports (Fort Wright College, Spokane, Washington):

– 1907 through 1980

*Freshwater Biology (Freshwater Biological Association, Oxford, England):

– Vol. 1, No. 1 (1971) through Vol. 10, No. 5 (1980)

*Gonzaga University Reports (Gonzaga University, Spokane, Washington):

– 1887 through 1980

*Great Basin Naturalist (Brigham Young University, Utah):

– Vol. 1, No. 1 (1939–40) through Vol. 40, No. 2 (1980)

*Growth (Society for the Study of Development and Growth, Worcester, Massachusetts):

– Vol. 1, No. 1 (1937) through Vol. 44, No. 2 (1980)

Hedlin Menzies & Associated Reports Hedlin Menzies & Associates Ltd., Vancouver, British Columbia):

– 1967 only

*Heredity (An International Journal of Genetics, Oliver and Boyd, Edinburgh):

– Vol. 1, Part 1 (1947) through Vol. 43, Part 2 (1979)

*Herp (New York Herpetological Society, New York):

– Vol. 1, No. 1 (1964) through Vol. 8, No. 4 (1972)

Herptile (International Herpetological Society, Birmingham, England):

– Vol. 2, No. 3 (1979) only

*Herpetologica (The Herpetologist's League, Lawrence, Kansas):

– Vol. 1, No. 1 (1936–40) through Vol. 36, No. 4 (1980)

*Herpetological Information Search Systems Publications in Herpetology HISS, Box 5L, 2 Washington Square Village, New York, New York, 10012):

– No. 1 (1968) through No. 8 (1975)

*Herpetological Review (Society for the Study of Amphibians and Reptiles, c/o University of Kansas, Lawrence):

– Vol. 1, No. 1 (1967) through Vol. 11, No. 4 (1980)

*Holarctic Ecology (Scandinavian Society Oikos, Department of Animal Ecology, Lund, Sweden):

– Vol. 1, No. 1 (1978) through Vol. 3, No. 3 (1980)

Howard Paish and Associates Limited Reports (Howard Paish and Associates Limited, Vancouver):

– 1973 only

*Journal of Animal Behavior (Henry Holt and Co., Boston, Massachusetts):

– Vol. 1 (1911) through Vol. 7 (1917)

*Journal of Animal Ecology (British Ecological Society, Oxford):

- Vol. 1 (1932) through Vol. 49, No. 2 (1980)

*Journal of Applied Ecology (British Ecological Society, Oxford):

- Vol. 1 (1964) through Vol. 17, No. 1 (1980)

*Journal of Biogeography (Blackwell Scientific Publications, London, England):

- Vol. 1, No. 1 (1974) through Vol. 4, No. 4 (1977)

*Journal of Comparative Physiology (International Journal on Comparative Physiology, Springer-Verlag, Heidelberg, Germany):

- Vol. 77, No. 1 (1972) through Vol. 138 A & B, No. 2 (1980). (Succeeds Zeitschrift fur Vergleichende Physiologie in 1972 with Vol. 77, No. 1).

*Journal of Entomology and Zoology (Pomona College Department of Zoology, Claremont, California):

- Vol. 5, No. 1 (1913) through Vol. 42, Nos. 3 and 4 (1951). (Succeeds Pomona College Journal of Entomology in 1913; discontinued in 1951 with Vol. 42).

*Journal of Herpetology (Society for the Study of Amphibians and Reptiles):

- Vol. 1, No. 1 (1968) through Vol. 1, No. 3 (1980). (Succeeds Journal of the Ohio Herpetological Society in 1968).

*Journal of Immunology (American Association of Immunologists, Williams and Williams Co., Baltimore, Maryland):

- Vol. 1, No. 1 (1916) through Vol. 125, No. 5 (1980)

*Journal of Mathematical Biology (Springer-Verlag, Berlin):

- Vol. 1, No. 1 (1974) through Vol. 10, No. 1 (1980)

*Journal of Morphology (Wistar Institute of Anatomy and Biology, Philadelphia, Pennsylvania):

- Vol. 1, No. 1 (1887) through Vol. 165, No. 3 (1980)

*Journal of Natural History (International Journal of Taxonomic and General Biology, c/o British Museum (Natural History), London, England):

- Vol. 1, No. 1 (1967) through Vol. 14, No. 5 (1980)

*Journal of Parasitology (American Society of Parasitologists):

- Vol. 1, No. 1 (1914-15) through Vol. 66, No. 4 (1968)

*Journal of Range Management (Society for Range Management, Denver, Colorado):

- Vol. 1, No. 1 (1948) through Vol. 31, No. 6 (1978)

*Journal of Wildlife Diseases (Wildlife Disease Association, Chicago):

- Vol. 6, No. 1 (1970) through Vol. 16, No. 3 (1980). (Succeeds Bulletin of the Wildlife Disease Association in 1970).

*Journal of Zoology (Zoological Society of London, England):

- Vol. 146 (1966) through Vol. 192, Part 1 (1980). (Succeeds Proceedings of the Zoological Society of London).

*Journal of the Academy of Natural Sciences of Philadelphia (Academy of Natural Sciences of Philadelphia, Pennsylvania):

- Vol. 1, Part 1 (1817) through Vol. 7, Part 2 (1837); Vol. 1 (Second Series), Part 1, Article 1 (1847) through Vol. 16 (Second Series) Part 4, Article 6 (1918). (Discontinued in 1918).

*Journal of the Biological Board of Canada (Biological Board of Canada, Ottawa):

- Vol. 1, No. 1 (1934) through Vol. 3, No. 5 (1937). (Discontinued in 1937; succeeded by Journal of the Fisheries Research Board of Canada in 1938).

*Journal of the Entomological Society of British Columbia (Entomological Society of British Columbia, Vancouver):

- No. 63 (1966) through No. 76 (1979). (Succeeds Proceedings of the Entomological Society of British Columbia in 1965).

*Journal of the Fisheries Research Board of Canada (Fisheries Research Board of Canada, Ottawa):

- Vol. 4, No. 1 (1938) through Vol. 36, No. 3 (1979). (Succeeds Journal of the Biological Board of Canada in 1938).

*Journal of the Linnean Society, Zoology (Linnean Society, Burlington, Piccadilly, England):

- Vol. 9 (1868) through Vol. 35, No. 238 (1924). (Succeeds Journal of the Proceedings of the Linnean Society, Zoology in 1868; discontinued in 1924; succeeded by Journal of the Linnean Society of London, Zoology in 1924 with Vol. 36, No. 239).

*Journal of the Linnean Society of London, Zoology (Linnean Society, Burlington House, Piccadilly, England):

- Vol. 35, No. 239 (1924) through Vol. 47, No. 313 (1968). (Succeeds Journal of the Linnean Society, Zoology in 1924 with Vol. 36, No. 239).

*Journal of Mammalogy (American Society of Mammalogists):

- Vol. 1, No. 1 (1920) through Vol. 60, No. 4 (1979)

*Journal of the Ohio Herpetological Society (Ohio Herpetological Society):

- Vol. 1, No. 1 (1958) through Vol. 5, No. 4 (1966). (Discontinued in 1966; succeeded by Journal of Herpetology in 1968).

*Journal of the Proceedings of the Linnean Society, Zoology (Linnean Society, Burlington House, Piccadilly, England):

- Vol. 1 (1857) through Vol. 8 (1864). (Discontinued in 1864; succeeded by Journal of the Linnean Society, Zoology in 1868 with Vol. 9).

*Journal of the Scientific Laboratories of Denison University (Denison University, Granville, Ohio):

- Vol. 19, Article 1 (1920) through Vol. 45, Article 3 (1975). (Succeeds Bulletin of the Scientific Laboratories of Denison University in 1920).

*Journal of the Washington Academy of Sciences (Washington Academy of Sciences, Menasha, Wisconsin):

- Vol. 1, No. 1 (1911) through Vol. 69, No. 1 (1979). (Succeeds Proceedings of the Washington Academy of Sciences in 1911 with Vol. 1, No. 1).

*Journal of Wildlife Management (The Wildlife Society, Washington, D.C.):

- Vol. 1, No. 1 (1937) through Vol. 43, No. 1 (1979)

*Kansas University Science Bulletin (Kansas University, Lawrence):

- Vol. 1, No. 1 (1902) through Vol. 26, No. 15 (1939). (Discontinued in 1939; succeeded by University of Kansas Sciences Bulletin in 1941 with Vol. 27).

*Kirtlandia (Cleveland Museum of Natural History, Ohio):

- No. 1 (1967) through No. 30 (1979)

Kootenay Advertiser (1510 2nd Street North, Cranbrook, British Columbia):

- November 3, 1980 issue only

*Kirtlandia (Cleveland Museum of Natural History, Ohio):
- No. 1 (1967) through No. 30 (1979)

Kootenay Advertiser (1510 2nd Street North, Cranbrook, British Columbia):
- November 3, 1980 issue only

Lake Windermere Valley Echo (P.O. Box 70, Invermere, British Columbia):
- December 11, 1980 issue only

LGL Limited (LGL Limited, Environmental Research Associates, Vancouver, British Columbia):
- miscellaneous reports from 1971 through 1979

*Life Sciences Division Contribution, Royal Ontario Museum (Royal Ontario Museum, Toronto):
- No. 52 (1960) through No. 119 (1979). (Succeeds Contribution of the Royal Ontario Museum of Zoology and Palaeontology in 1960 with No. 52).

*Living Bird (Laboratory of Ornithology, Cornell University):
- First (1962) through Fifteenth (1976)

*Lutheran Bible Institute of Seattle Reports (Lutheran Bible Institute of Seattle, Issaquah, Washington):
- 1979 through 1980

*Malaspina College Reports (Malaspina College, Nanaimo, British Columbia):
- 1975 through 1978

*Mammalia (Museum National D'Histoire Naturelle, Paris, France):
- Vol. 1 (1937) through Vol. 33, No. 2 (1979)

*Mammal Review (The Mammal Society, London, England):
- Vol. 1, No. 1 (1970) through Vol. 9, No. 2 (1979)

*Marine Pollution Bulletin (Pergamon Press Limited, Oxford, England);
- Vol. 1 (NS), No. 1 (1970) through Vol. 11, No. 10 (1980)

Massachusetts Department of Agriculture Publications (Boston):
- 1929 only

*McGill University Publication Series XI (Zoology) (McGill University, Montreal):
- No. 1 (1917) through No. 23 (1932). (Discontinued in 1932).

*Memoirs of the Museum of Comparative Zoology at Harvard College (Harvard College, Cambridge, Massachusetts):
- Vol. 1, No. 1 (1864) through Vol. 55 (1938)

*Memoirs of the University of Michigan Museums (University of Michigan, Ann Arbor):
- Vol. 1 (1928) through Vol. 2 (1929)

*Memoirs of the Southern California Academy of Sciences (Los Angeles County Museum of Natural History, California):
- Vol. 1 (1938) through Vol. 7 (1968)

*Ministry of Recreation and Conservation Annual Report (Ministry of Recreation and Conservation, Victoria):
- 1977 and 1978. (Succeeds British Columbia Department of Recreation and Conservation Annual Report in 1977).

17

*Miscellaneous Publications Museum of Zoology University of Michigan (University of Michigan, Ann Arbor):

- No. 1 (1916) through No. 154 (1977)

*Monographs of the Academy of Natural Sciences of Philadelphia (Academy of Natural Sciences of Philadelphia, Pennsylvania):

- No. 1 (1935) through No. 20 (1979)

Mt. Rainier National Park Nature Notes (United States Department of the Interior National Park Service, Mount Rainier National Park, Washington):

- Vol. 14, No. 1 (1936) through Vol. 14, No. 4 (1936)

*Murrelet (Pacific Northwest Bird and Mammal Society):

- Vol. 1, No. 1 (1920) through Vol. 59, No. 3 (1978)

*Museology The Museum Texas Tech University (Texas Tech University, Lubbock):

- No. 1 (1975) through No. 5 (1979)

*National Audubon Society Research Reports (National Audubon Society, New York):

- No. 1 (1942) through No. 7 (1978)

*National Museum of Canada Anthropology Papers (National Museum of Canada, Ottawa):

- No. 1 (1961) through No. 3 (1963)

*National Museum of Canada Bulletin (National Museum of Canada, Ottawa):

- No. 1 (1913) through No. 237 (1968). (Includes early publications listed under Geological Survey and Victoria Memorial Museum and includes the Anthropological Biological and Geological Series).

National Museums of Canada Herpetology Section Reports (National Museums of Canada, Ottawa, Ontario, K1A 0M8):

- unpublished reports, 1980 only

*National Museum of Canada Natural History Papers (National Museum of Canada, Ottawa):

- No. 1 (1958) through No. 45 (1969). (Discontinued in 1969 with No. 45).

*National Museum of Canada Publications in Zoology (National Museum of Canada, Ottawa, Ontario):

- No. 1 (1969) through No. 13 (1977)

*National Museum of Natural Sciences Publications in Zoology (National Museum of Canada, Ottawa):

- No. 1 (1969) through No. 13 (1977)

Nature (Macmillan Journals Limited, London, England):

- Vol. 255, No. 5503 (1975) through Vol. 255, No. 5511 (1975)

*Nature and Resources (Official Bulletin of Man and the Biosphere Program, International Hydrological Program and International Geological Correlation Program, Paris, France):

- Vol. 1, No. 1 (1965) through Vol. 15, No. 2 (1979)

*Nature Canada (Canadian Nature Federation, Ottawa):

- Vol. 1, No. 1 (1972) through Vol. 9, No. 4 (1980). (Succeeds Canadian Audubon in 1972).

*Naturegraph Pocket Keys (Naturegraph Company, Los Alta, California):

- Vol. 1 (1948) through Vol. 2 (1949)

*Nemouria (Delaware Museum of Natural History, Greenville, Delaware):

- No. 1 (1970) through No. 24 (1980)

*Nevada Department of Fish and Game Biological Bulletin (Nevada Department of Fish and Game, Reno):

- No. 1 (1954) through No. 6 (1978)

New Brunswick Museum Publications (New Brunswick Museum, Saint John):

- 1974 only

North Okanagan Naturalists Club Newsletter (North Okanagan Naturalists Club, Vernon, British Columbia):

- No. 1 (1953) through

*Northwest College Reports (Northwest College, Kirkland, Washington):

- 1934 through 1980

*Northwest Science (Northwest Scientific Association, Washington):

- Vol. 1, No. 1 (1927) through Vol. 51, No. 4 (1977)

Northwood Pulp and Timber Limited Unpublished Reports (Northwood Pulp and Timber Limited, P.O. Box 9000, Prince George, British Columbia, V2L 4W2):

- 1980 only

*Occasional Papers Department of Biology College of Puget Sound (College of Puget Sound, Department of Biology, Tacoma, Washington):

- No. 1 (1939) through No. 16 (1955). (Discontinued in 1955; succeeded by Occasional Papers Department of Biology University of Puget Sound in 1962).

*Occasional Papers Department of Biology University of Puget Sound (University of Puget Sound, Department of Biology, Tacoma, Washington):

- No. 17 (1962) through No. 53 (1978). (Succeeds Occasional Papers Department of Biology College of Puget Sound in 1962).

*Occasional Papers of the Bell Museum of Natural History (Bell Museum of Natural History, University of Minnesota, Minneapolis):

- No. 1 (1916) through No. 16 (1980)

*Occasional Papers of the California Academy of Sciences (California Academy of Sciences, San Francisco):

- No. 1 (1890) through No. 133 (1979)

*Occasional Papers of the Idaho State College Museum (Idaho State College Museum, Pocatello):

- No. 1 (1958) through No. 10 (1962). (Discontinued in 1962; succeeded by Occasional Papers of the Idaho State University Museum in 1963).

*Occasional Papers of the Idaho State University Museum (Idaho State University Museum, Pocatello):

- No. 11 (1963) through No. 30 (1973). (Succeeds Occasional Papers of the Idaho State College Museum in 1963).

*Occasional Papers of the Museum of Natural History University of Kansas (University of Kansas, Lawrence):

- No. 1 (1971) through No. 85 (1980) University of Kansas Publications Museum of Natural History in 1971).

*Occasional Papers of the Museum of Zoology Louisiana State University (Louisiana State University, Baton Rouge):

- No. 1 (1938) through No. 56 (1979)

*Occasional Papers of the Museum of Zoology University of Michigan (University of Michigan, Ann Arbor):

- No. 1 (1913) through No. 689 (1979)

*Occasional Papers of the Natural History Museum of Stanford University (Natural History Museum of Stanford University, California):

- No. 1 (1956) through No. 10 (1962)

*Occasional Papers of the San Diego Society of Natural History (San Diego Society of Natural History, California):

- No. 1 (1936) through No. 15 (1968)

*Occasional Papers of the Western Foundation of Vertebrate Zoology (Western Foundation of Vertebrate Zoology, Los Angeles, California):

- No. 1 (1968) through No. 2 (1970)

*Occasional Papers The Museum Texas Tech University (Texas Tech University, Lubbock):

- No. 1 (1972) through No. 62 (1979)

*Oceanography and Marine Biology Annual Review (Aberdeen University Press, Scotland):

- Vol. 1 (1963) through Vol. 16 (1978)

*Oecologia (Springer-Verlag, Heidelberg, Germany):

- Vol. 1 (1968) through Vol. 46, No. 2 (1980)

*Ohio Biological Survey Bulletin (University of Ohio, Columbus):

- Vol. 1, No. 1 (1913) through Vol. 8, No. 3 (1954). (Discontinued in 1954; succeeded by Bulletin of the Ohio Biological Survey New Series in 1959).

Ontario Ministry of Natural Resources Reports (Ontario Ministry of Natural Resources, Ottawa):

- 1978 only

*Oryx (Journal of the Fauna Preservation Society, c/o Zoological Society of London, England):

- Vol. 1 (1950) through Vol. 15, No. 4 (1980)

*Ottawa Field-Naturalists' Club Transactions (Ottawa Field-Naturalists' Club, Ontario):

- Vol. 1, No. 1 (1879-80) through Vol. 2, No. 3 (1886). (Discontinued in 1886 with Vol. 2, No. 3; succeeded by Ottawa Naturalist in 1887 with Vol. 1).

*Ottawa Naturalist (Ottawa Field-Naturalists Club, Ontario):

- Vol. 1 (1887-88) through Vol. 32, No. 9 (1918-19). (Succeeds Ottawa Field-Naturalist's Club Transactions in 1887-88; discontinued in 1918-19 with Vol. 32, No. 9; succeeded by Canadian Field-Naturalist in 1919 with Vol. 33, No. 1).

*Pacific Lutheran University Theses (Pacific Lutheran University, Tacoma, Washington):

- Masters and Doctorate Theses, 1955 through 1978

*Pacific Naturalist (Beaudette Foundation for Biological Research, Solvang, California):

- Vol. 1, No. 1 (1958) through Vol. 4, No. 3 (1964)

*Pacific Northwest (Pacific Search Press, Seattle, Washington):

- Vol. 14, No 1 (1980) through Vol. 14, No. 2 (1980). (Succeeds Pacific Search in 1980).

*Pacific Search (Pacific Search Press, Seattle, Washington):

- Vol. 1, No. 1 (1966) through Vol. 13, No. 9 (1979). (Discontinued in 1979; succeeded by Pacific Northwest in 1980 with Vol. 14, No. 1).

*Pacific Science (University of Hawaii, Honolulu):

- Vol. 1, No. 1 (1947) through Vol. 33, No. 4 (1979)

*Papers of the Michigan Academy of Science Arts and Letters (University of Michigan, Lansing):

- Vol. 1 (1923) through Vol. 53, Part 3 (1968). (Succeeds Annual Report of the Michigan Academy of Science in 1923).

Parks Canada (Kootenay) Reports (Kootenay National Park, Radium Hotsprings, British Columbia):

- miscellaneous reports from 1965 through 1977

Parks Canada (Mount Revelstoke-Glacier National Parks) Reports (Mount Revelstoke-Glacier National Parks, Revelstoke, British Columbia):

- 1963 through 1980 (miscellaneous reports)

Parks Canada (Ottawa) Reports (National Parks Branch, Ottawa, Ontario):

- miscellaneous reports from 1944 through 1977

*Parks Canada (Pacific Rim National Park) Reports (Pacific Rim National Park, Ucluelet, British Columbia):

- 1970 through 1979

*Peabody Museum of Natural History (Yale University) Bulletins (Yale University, New Haven, Connecticut):

- No. 1 (1929) through No. 40 (1975)

*Pomona College Journal of Entomology (Department of Biology (Zoology) of Pomona College, Claremont, California):

- Vol. 1, No. 1 (1909) through Vol. 4, No. 4 (1912). (Discontinued in 1912; succeeded by Journal of Entomology and Zoology in 1913).

*Postilla (Yale Peabody Museum of Natural History, New Haven, Connecticut):

- No. 1 (1950) through No. 173 (1978)

*Proceedings and Transactions of the Royal Society of Canada (Royal Society of Canada, Montreal):

- Vol. 1 (1883) through Vol. 11 (1894). (Discontinued in 1894; succeeded by Proceedings and Transactions of the Royal Society of Canada (Second Series) in 1895).

Proceedings and Transactions of the Royal Society of Canada (Second Series) (Royal Society of Canada, Montreal):

- Vol. 1 (1895) through Vol. ( ). (Succeeds Proceedings and Transactions of the Royal Society of Canada in 1895).

*Proceedings of the Academy of Natural Sciences of Philadelphia (Academy of Natural Sciences of Philadelphia, Pennsylvania):

- Vol. 1 (1841) through Vol. 131 (1979)

*Proceedings of the Alaska(n) Science Conference (American Association for the Advancement of Science (Alaska Division), Anchorage:

- First (1950) through Twenty-third (1972)

Proceedings of the American Academy of Arts and Sciences (American Academy of Arts and Sciences, Boston, Massachusetts):

- 1920 only

*Proceedings of the American Association of Museums (c/o The Charleston Museum, South Carolina):

- Vol. 1 (1907) through Vol. 8 (1914)

*Proceedings of the American Philosophical Society (American Philosophical Society, Philadelphia, Pennsylvania):

- Vol. 1, No. 1 (1840) through Vol. 123, No. 4 (1979)

*Proceedings of the Annual Biology Colloquium (Oregon State University Press, Corvalis):

- First (1939) through Thirty-fourth (1976)

*Proceedings of the Biological Society of Washington (Biological Society of Washington, District of Columbia):

- Vol. 1 (1882) through Vol. 93, No. 2 (1980)

*Proceedings of the Boston Society of Natural History (Boston Society of Natural History, Massachusetts):

- Vol. 1 (1841) through Vol. 42, No. 8 (1941-42). (Discontinued in 1942 with Vol. 42, No. 8).

*Proceedings of the California Academy of Sciences (Fourth Series) (California Academy of Sciences, San Francisco):

- Vol. 1, No. 1 (1907) through Vol. 42, No. 8 (1980)

*Proceedings of the Cambridge Philosophical Society (Biological Sciences) (Cambridge University Press, London, England):

- Vol. 1, No. 1 (1923) through Vol. 1, No. 4 (1925). (Discontinued in 1925; succeeded by Biological Review and Biological Proceedings of the Cambridge Philosophical Society in 1926).

Proceedings of the Canadian Institute (New Series) (The Canadian Institute, Toronto):

- Vol. 1 (new series) (1898) through

Proceedings of the Canadian Institute (Third Series) (The Canadian Institute, Toronto):

- Vol. 1 (1884) through

*Proceedings of the Colorado Museum of Natural History (Colorado Museum of Natural History, Fort Collins):

- Vol. 1, No. 1 (1915) through Vol. 18, No. 2 (1948)

*Proceedings of the International Congress of Zoology (Locations vary throughout the world):

- First Congress (1899 - Paris) through Seventeenth Congress (1972 - Monte Carlo)

*Proceedings of the Linnaean Society of New York (Linnaen Society of New York, New York):

- No. 1 (1888-89) through No. 71 (1970)

*Proceedings of the Louisiana Academy of Sciences (Louisiana Academy of Sciences, Baton Rouge):

- Vol. 1, No. 1 (1932) through Vol. 41 (1978)

*Proceedings of the New England Zoological Club (New England Zoological Club, Cambridge, Massachusetts):

- Vol. 1 (1921) through Vol. 24 (1947)

*Proceedings of the North American Wildlife Conference (Committee on Conservation of Wildlife Resources, Washington, District of Columbia):
- First (1936) only. (Discontinued in 1936; succeeded by Transactions of the North American Wildlife Conference in 1937).

*Proceedings of the United States National Museum (United States National Museum, Washington, D.C.):

- Vol. 1, No. 1 (1978) through Vol. 125, No. 3668 (1968)

*Proceedings of the Washington Academy of Sciences (Washington Academy of Sciences, Menasha, Wisconsin):

- Vol. 1 (1899) through Vol. 13 (1911). (Discontinued in 1911 with Vol. 13; succeeded by Journal of the Washington Academy of Sciences in 1911 with Vol. 1, No. 1).

*Proceedings of the West Virginia Academy of Sciences (West Virginia Academy of Sciences, Morgantown):

- Series 1, No. 1 (1926) through Vol. 45, No. 3 (1973)

*Proceedings of the Zoological Society of London (Zoological Society of London, England):

- Part 1 (1830) through Vol. 145 (1965). (Discontinued in 1965; succeeded by Journal of Zoology in 1966).

*Publications of the Field Columbian Museum Zoological Series (Field Columbian Museum, Chicago, Illinois):

- Vol. 1, No. 1 (1895) through Vol. 8 (1907). (Discontinued in 1907; succeeded by Publications of the Field Museum of Natural History Zoological Series in 1909 with Vol. 9).

*Publications of the Field Museum of Natural History Zoological Series (Field Museum of Natural History, Chicago, Illinois):

- Vol. 9 (1909) through Vol. 30 (1944). (Succeeds Publications of the Field Columbian Museum Zoological Series in 1909; discontinued in 1944; succeeded by Fieldiana: Zoology in 1945 with Vol. 31).

*Publications of the Museum Biological Series Michigan State University (The Museum, Michigan State University, East Lansing):

- Vol. 1, No. 1 (1957) through Vol. 4, No. 5 (1977)

*Publications of the University of California at Los Angeles in Biological Sciences (University of California, Berkeley):

- Vol. 1, No. 1 (1933) through Vol. 2 (1940)

*Publication Puget Sound Biological Station (Puget Sound Biological Station, University of Washington, Seattle):

- Vol. 2 (1918) through Vol. 7 (1931). (Succeeds Puget Sound Marine Station Publication in 1918; discontinued in 1931; succeeded by University of Washington Publications in Oceanography in 1932).

*Puget Sound College of the Bible Reports (Puget Sound College of the Bible, Edmonds, Washington):

- 1950 through 1980

*Puget Sound Marine Station Publication (Puget Sound Marine Station, University of Washington, Seattle):

- Vol. 1 (1915 to 1917). (Discontinued in 1917; succeeded by Publication Puget Sound Biological Station in 1918).

*Quarterly Review of Biology (Published by Stony Brook Foundation, Inc., New York):

- Vol. 1, No. 1 (1926) through Vol. 55, No. 3 (1980)

*Rachelwood Wildlife Research Preserve Publication (Rachelwood Wildlife Research Preserve, New Florence, Pennsylvania):

- No. 1 (1971) only

*Report of the Provincial Museum of Natural History for the Year: (British Columbia Provincial Museum, Victoria):

- 1912 through 1939. (Discontinued in 1939; succeeded by Report of the Provincial Museum of Natural History and Anthropology for the Year in 1940).

*Report of the Provincial Museum of Natural History and Anthropology for the Year: (British Columbia Provincial Museum, Victoria):

- 1940 through 1967. (Succeeds Report of the Provincial Museum of Natural History for the Year in 1940; discontinued in 1967; succeeded by British Columbia Provincial Museum Report of the Year in 1968).

*Research Studies of the State College of Washington (State College of Washington, Pullman):

- Vol. 1, No. 1 (1929) through Vol. 26, No. 4 (1958). (Discontinued in 1957; succeeded by Research Studies of the Washington State University in 1959 with Vol. 27, No. 1).

*Research Studies of the Washington State University (Washington State University, Pullman):

- Vol. 27, No. 1 (1959) through Vol. 46, No. 3 (1978). (Succeeds Research Studies of the State College of Washington in 1959).

*Roosevelt Wild Life Annals (New York State College of Forestry, Syracuse University):

- Vol. 1, No. 1-2 (1926) through Vol. 4, No. 2 (1936)

*Roosevelt Wild Life Bulletin (New York State College of Forestry, Syracuse University):

- Vol. 1, No. 1 (1921) through Vol. 9, No. 1 (1950)

Ross Allen's Reptile Institute Special Publications (The Reptile Institute, Silver Springs, Florida):

- No. 1 (1950) only

*Santa Barbara Museum of Natural History Occasional Papers (Santa Barbara Museum of Natural History, California):

- No. 1 (1932) through No. 9 (1974)

*Science (American Association for the Advancement of Science, Washington, District of Columbia):

- Vol. 1, No. 1 (1883) through Vol. 203, No. 4386 (1979)

Scientific Monthly

- Vol. 50 (1940) only

*Scientific Report of the Laboratory for Amphibian Biology (Hiroshima University, Department of Zoology, Japan):

- Vol. 1 (1972) through Vol. 3 (1978)

*Seattle Pacific University Reports (Seattle Pacific University, Seattle, Washington):

- 1891 through 1980

Selkirk College Reports (Selkirk College, Castlegar, British Columbia):

- only 1973

Sierra Club of Western Canada Reports (Sierra Club of Western Canada, Victoria, British Columbia):

- miscellaneous reports, 1980

*Sigma Xi Quarterly (Society of Sigma Xi, Chicago):

- Vol. 1 (1913) through Vol. 29, No. 3, 4 (1941). (Discontinued in 1941; succeeded by American Scientist in 1942).

*Simon Fraser University, Department of Biological Sciences Theses (Simon Fraser University, Department of Biological Sciences, Burnaby, British Columbia):

- all Master of Science and Doctor in Philosophy Theses and Master of Pest Management Professional Papers from 1965 through 1980

*Simon Fraser University, Department of Geography Theses (Simon Fraser University, Department of Geography, Burnaby, British Columbia):

- all Master of Science and Doctorate in Philosophy Theses from 1965 through 1980

*Smithsonian Contributions to Zoology (Smithsonian Institution, Washington, District of Columbia):

- No. 1 (1969) through No. 278 (1978)

Society for the Study of Amphibians and Reptiles Facsimile Reprints in Herpetology (Society for the Study of Amphibians and Reptiles, Ohio University, Athens):

- 1971 through 1976

*Society for the Study of Amphibians and Reptiles Herpetological Circulars (Society for the Study of Amphibians and Reptiles, Department of Zoology, Ohio University, Athens):

- No. 1 (1973) through No. 10 (1980)

*Spatsizi Association for Biological Research Reports (Spatsizi Association for Biological Research, Vancouver, British Columbia):

- No. 1 (1979)

*Special Publications of the Academy of Natural Sciences of Philadelphia (Academy of Natural Sciences of Philadelphia, Pennsylvania):

- No. 1 (1922) through No. 5 (1963)

*Special Publications The Museum Texas Tech University (Texas Tech University, Lubbock):

- No. 1 (1972) through No. 16 (1979)

*Spolia Zodogica Musei Hauniensis (Univesitetets Zoologiske Museum, Copenhagen):

- No. 1 (1941) through No. 29 (1969)

*Stanford University Publications Biological Sciences (Stanford University, California):

- Vol. 1, No. 1 (1920) through Vol. 9, No. 2 (1944)

Summary Report of the Geological Survey (Geological Survey, Department of Mines, Ottawa):

- 1906 Sessional Paper No. 26, No. 947 through No. 1927

Swan Wooster Engineering Co. Ltd. Reports (Swan Wooster Engineering Co. Ltd., Vancouver, British Columbia):

- 1966 only

*Syesis (British Columbia Provincial Museum, Victoria):

- Vol. 1 (1968) through Vol. 12 (1979)

*Symposia of the Zoological Society of London (Zoological Society of London, England):

- No. 1 (1960) through No. 44 (1979)

*Systematic Zoology (Society of Systematic Zoology, Washington, District of Columbia):

- Vol. 1, No. 1 (1952) through Vol. 29, No. 2 (1980)

*Terrace Naturalist Newsletter (Terrace Naturalist's Club, British Columbia):

- 1978 (five issues, March through November)

*Thomas Burke Memorial Washington State Museum Research Report (Thomas Burke Memorial Museum, University of Washington, Seattle):

- No. 1 (1965) through No. 3 (1968)

*Transactions of the Academy of Science of St. Louis (Academy of Science of St. Louis, Missouri):

- Vol. 1 (1856) through Vol. 31, No. 9 (1958)

Transactions of the American Fisheries Society (American Fisheries Society, Lawrence, Kansas):

- Vol. 24 (1895) through Vol. 106, No. 6 (1977)

Transactions of the Canadian Institute (The Canadian Institute, Toronto):

- Vol. 1 (1892) through Vol. 9 (1913). (Discontinued in 1913; succeeded by Transactions of the Royal Canadian Institute in 1913-15).

Transactions of the Kansas Academy of Science (Kansas Academy of Science, Lawrence):

- Vol. 38 (1935) and Vol. 80, No. 1 and 2 (1977) only

*Transactions of the Linnaean Society of New York (Linnaean Society of New York, New York):

- Vol. 1 (1882) through Vol. 8 (1962)

*Transactions of the North American Wildlife and Natural Resources Conference (Wildlife Management, Washington, District of Columbia):

- Twenty-fifth (1960) through Forty-third (1978). (Succeeds Transactions of the North American Wildlife Conference in 1960).

*Transactions of the North American Wildlife Conference (Wildlife Management Institute, Washington, District of Columbia):

- Second (1937) through Twenty-fourth (1959). (Succeeds Proceedings of the North American Wildlife Conference in 1937; discontinued with Twenty-fourth Conference in 1959; succeeded by Transactions of the North American Wildlife and Natural Resources Conference in 1960).

Transactions of the Royal Canadian Institute (The Canadian Institute, Toronto):

- Vol. 10, Part 1 (1913-1915) through Vol. 34, No. 71, Part 2. (Succeeds Transactions of the Canadian Institute in 1913-15 with Vol. 10).

*Transactions of the San Diego Society of Natural History (San Diego Society of Natural History, California):

- Vol. 1, No 1 (1907) through Vol. 19, No. 11 (1979)

*Transactions of the Zoological Society of London (Zoological Society of London, England):

- Vol. 1, Part 1 (1835) through Vol. 35, Part 3 (1980)

*United States Department of Agriculture Bureau of Biological Survey Circular (United States Department of Agriculture, Washington, District of Columbia):

- No. 1 (1894) through No. 94 (1913)

*United States Department of Agriculture Bureau of Biological Survey Wildlife Research and Management Leaflet (United States Department of Agriculture, Bureau of Biological Survey, Washington, District of Columbia):

- BS-1 (1935) through BS-140 (1939). (Discontinued in 1939; succeeded by United States Department of the Interior Bureau of Biological Survey Wildlife Leaflet in 1939 with BS-141).

*United States Department of Agriculture (Department) Bulletin (United States Department of Agriculture, Washington, District of Columbia):

- No. 1 (1913) through No. 1500 (1929)

*United States Department of Agriculture (Division of) Biological Survey Bulletin (United States Department of Agriculture, Washington, District of Columbia):

- No. 8 (revised) (1897) through No. 45 (1913). (Succeeds United States Department of Agriculture Division of (Economic) Ornithology and Mammalogy Bulletin in 1897 with No. 8 (revised).

*United States Department of Agriculture, Division of (Economic) Ornithology and Mammalogy Bulletin (United States Department of Agriculture, Washington, District of Columbia):

- No 1 (1889) through No. 8 (1896). (Discontinued in 1896; succeeded by United States Department of Agriculture (Division of) Biological Survey Bulletin in 1897 with No. 8 (revised)).

*United States Department of Agriculture Division (Bureau) of Biological Survey North American Fauna (United States Department of Agriculture, Washington, District of Columbia):

- No. 13 (1897) through No. 56 (1938). (Succeeds United States Department of Agriculture Division of Ornithology and Mammalogy North American Fauna in 1897; discontinued in 1938; succeeded by United States Department of the Interior Fish and Wildlife Service North American Fauna in 1941 with No. 57).

*United States Department of Agriculture Forest Service General Technical Report Pacific Northwest (Pacific Northwest Forest and Range Experimental Station, Portland, Oregon):

- No. 1 (1972) through No. 82 (1979)

*United States Department of Agriculture Miscellaneous Publications (United States Department of Agriculture, Washington, District of Columbia):

- No. 1 (1927) through No. 1336 (1976)

*United States Department of Agriculture Technical Bulletin (United States Department of Agriculture, Washington, District of Columbia):

- No. 1 (1927) through No. 1577 (1978)

*United States Department of the Interior Bureau of Biological Survey Wildlife Leaflet (United States Department of the Interior, Bureau of Biological Survey, Washington, Distict of Columbia):

- BS-141 (1939) through BS-165 (1940). (Succeeds United States Department of Agriculture Bureau of Biological Survey Wildlife Research and Management in 1939; discontinued in 1940; succeeded by United States Department of the Interior Fish and Wildlife Service Wildlife Leaflet in 1940 with BS-166).

*United States Department of the Interior – Bureau of Land Management Technical Note Report (Habitat Management Series for Unique or Endangered Species) (United States Department of the Interior, Bureau of Land Management, Denver, Colorado):

- No. 1 (1972) through No. 14 (1975)

*United States Department of the Interior Fish and Wildlife Service Circulars (United States Department of the Interior, Fish and Wildlife Service, Washington, District of Columbia):

- No. 1 (1941) through No. 343 (1970)

*United States Department of the Interior Fish and Wildlife Service Conservation Bulletin (United States Department of the Interior, Fish and Wildlife Service, Washington, District of Columbia):

- No. 1 (1940) through No. 36 (1944)

2

*United States Department of the Interior Fish and Wildlife Service North American Fauna (United States Department of the Interior, Washington, District of Columbia):

- No. 57 (1941) through No. 72 (1978). (Succeeds United States Department of Agriculture Division (Bureau) of Biological Survey North American Fauna in 1941 with No. 57).

*United States Department of the Interior Fish and Wildlife Service Research Report (United States Department of the Interior, Fish and Wildlife Service, Washington, D.C.):

- No. 1 (1941) through No. 69 (1966)

United States Department of the Interior Fish and Wildlife Service Resource Publication (United States Department of the Interior, Fish and Wildlife Service, Washington, D.C.):

- No. 134 (1980) only

United States Department of the Interior Fish and Wildlife Service Special Scientific Report - Wildlife (United States Department of the Interior, Fish and Wildlife Service, Washington, D.C.):

- No. 228 (1980) only

*United States Department of the Interior Fish and Wildlife Service Wildlife Leaflet (United States Department of the Interior, Fish and Wildlife Service, Washington, District of Columbia):

- No. 166 (1940) through No. 512 (1977). (Succeeds United States Department of the Interior Bureau of Biological Survey Wildlife Leaflet in 1940).

*United States Department of the Interior Fish and Wildlife Service Wildlife Research Report (United States Department of the Interior, Fish and Wildlife Service, Washington, District of Columbia):

- Report 1 (1972) through Report 11 (1979)

*United States Department of the Interior National Park Service Fauna Series (United States Department of the Interior, National Park Service, Washington, District of Columbia):

- No. 1 (1932) through No. 5 (1944)

*United States National Museum Bulletin (Smithsonian Institution, Washington, District of Columbia):

- No. 1 (1875) through No. 297 (1970)

University of Alberta Department of Zoology Theses (University of Alberta, Edmonton):

- 1963 only

University of Alaska Department of Biology Theses (University of Alaska, Fairbanks):

- Master and Doctorate Theses, 1966 through 1977

*University of British Columbia Department of Agriculture (Departments of Animal and Plant Sciences) Theses (University of British Columbia, Vancouver):

- Bachelor, Master and Doctorate Theses, 1921 through 1978

*University of British Columbia Department of Zoology Theses (University of British Columbia, Vancouver):

- Bachelor, Masters and Doctorate Theses, 1922 through 1978

*University of British Columbia Faculty of Forestry Theses (University of British Columbia, Vancouver):

- Bachelor, Master and Doctorate Theses, 1923 through 1978

*University of Calgary Faculty of Environmental Design Theses (University of Calgary, Alberta):

- 1973 only

*University of California Publications in Physiology (University of California, Berkeley):

- Vol. 1, No. 1 (1903) through Vol. 7, No. 15 (1931)

*University of California Publications in Zoology (University of California, Berkeley):

- Vol. 1, No. 1 (1902) through Vol. 111 (1979)

*University of Kansas Museum of Natural History Miscellaneous Publications (Museum of Natural History, University of Kansas, Lawrence):

- No. 1 (1946) through No. 52 (1970)

*University of Kansas Publications Museum of Natural History (University of Kansas, Lawrence):

- Vol. 1, No. 1 (1946) through Vol. 20, No. 3 (1971). (Discontinued in 1971 with Vol. 20, No. 3; succeeded by Occasional Papers of the Museum of Natural History University of Kansas in 1970 with No. 1).

*University of Kansas Science Bulletin (University of Kansas, Lawrence):

- Vol. 27, No. 1 (1941) through Vol. 51, No. 24 (1979). (Succeeds Kansas University Science Bulletin in 1941 with Vol. 27).

University of Michigan Museum and Department of Zoology Theses (University of Michigan, Ann Arbor):

- 1972 only

*University of Michigan Studies Scientific Series (University of Michigan, Ann Arbor):

- Vol. 1 (1914) through Vol. 21 (1960)

University of Montana School of Forestry Reports/Theses (University of Montana, Missoula):

- 1977 only

*University of Puget Sound Department of Biology Theses (University of Puget Sound, Tacoma, Washington):

- Masters and Doctorate Theses, 1934 through 1979

*University of Toronto Studies Biological Series (University of Toronto, Ontario):

- No. 1 (1900) through No. 62 (1956)

*University of Utah Biological Series (University of Utah, Salt Lake City):

- Vol. 11, No. 3 (1951) through Vol. 12, No. 7 (1962). (Succeeds Bulletin of the University of Utah Biological Series in 1951).

*University of Victoria Department of Biology Theses (University of Victoria, British Columbia):

- Bachelor, Masters and Doctorate Theses; 1958 through 1979

*University of Washington College of Forest Resources Theses (University of Washington, Seattle):

- Bachelor, Masters and Doctorate Theses; 1904 through 1979

*University of Washington Department of Anthropology Reports in Archaeology (University of Washington, Seattle):

- No. 1 (1968) through No. 5 (1978)

*University of Washington Department of Zoology Theses (University of Washington, Seattle):

- Bachelor, Masters and Doctorate Theses; 1905 through 1978

*University of Washington Publications in Biology (University of Washington, Seattle):

- Vol. 1, No. 1 (1932) through Vol. 21 (1966)

*University of Washington Publications in Oceanography (University of Washington, Seattle):

- No. 1 (1932) through No. 200 (1957). (Succeeds Publication Puget Sound Biological Station in 1932).

*University of Washington Publications in Oceanography Contributions (University of Washington, Seattle):

- No. 80 (1939) through No. 99 (1941). (Succeeds University of Washington Publications in Oceanography Supplementary Series in 1939).

*University of Washington Publications in Oceanography Supplementary Series (University of Washington, Seattle):

- No. 1 (1931) through No. 79 (1938). (Discontinued in 1938; succeeded by University of Washington Publications in Oceanography Contributions in 1939).

*University of Wisconsin Studies (University of Wisconsin, Madison):

- No. 1 (1920) through No. 5 (1932)

*Vancouver City College Reports (City College, Vancouver, Washington):

- 1973 through 1980

*Vancouver Natural History Society Discovery (Vancouver Natural History Society, British Columbia):

- No. 147 (1970) through No. 153 (1971-72). (Succeeds Bulletin of the Vancouver Natural History Society in 1970 with No. 147; discontinued in 1971-72 with No. 153; succeeded by Vancouver Natural History Society Discovery, New Series in 1972 with Vol. 1, No. 1 (No. 154).

*Vancouver Natural History Society Discovery (New Series) (Vancouver Natural History Society, British Columbia):

- Vol. 1, No. 1 (1972) through Vol. 5, No. 2 (1976). (Succeeds Vancouver Natural History Society Discovery in 1972; discontinued in 1976 with Vol. 5, No. 2; succeeded by Discovery in 1976 with Vol. 5, No. 3).

*Vancouver Natural History Society Special Publications (Vancouver Natural History Society, British Columbia):

- 1972 through 1981

*Victoria Memorial Museum Memoirs Biological Series (Canada Department of Mines, Ottawa):

- No. 1, Memoir 14 (1910) through No. 4, Memoir 126 (1922)

*Victoria Natural History Society Special Publications (Victoria Natural History Society, British Columbia):

- 1959 through 1978

*Victoria Naturalist (Victoria Natural History Society, British Columbia):

- Vol. 1, No. 1 (1944) through Vol. 37, No. 3 (1980)

*Walla Walla College Department of Biology Reports (Walla Walla College, Walla Walla, Washington):

- Reports from 1950 through 1979

*Walla Walla College Publications (Department of Biological Sciences, College Place, Washington):

- No. 1 (1951) through No. 31 (1962)

Washington Department of Game (Olympia) Unpublished Reports (Washington Department of Game, Olympia):

- miscellaneous reports, 1976 through 1979

Washington Department of Game (Seattle) Unpublished Reports (Washington Department of Game, Seattle):

- miscellaneous reports, 1977 through 1979

*Washington Game Department Environmental Management Division Applied Research Section Bulletin (Washington Game Department, Olympia):

- No. 1 (1974) through No. 9 (1976)

*Washington State Game Bulletin (Washington State Game Department, (Seattle) Olympia):

- Vol. 1, No. 1 (1949) through Vol. 22, No. 1 (1970). (Discontinued in 1970; succeeded by Washington Wildlife in 1970 with Vol. 22, No. 2).

*Washington State University Department of Zoology Theses (Washington State University, Pullman):

- Masters and Doctorate Theses, 1919 through 1979

*Washington University Studies (New Series) Science & Technology (Washington University, St. Louis, Missouri):

- No. 1 (1928) through No. 12 (1941)

*Washington Wildlife (Washington State Game Department, Olympia):

- Vol. 22, No. 2 (1970) through Vol. 29, No. 4 (1977). (Succeeds Washington State Game Bulletin in 1970).

*Wasmann Collector (Wasmann Club, University of San Francisco, California):

- Vol. 1, No. 1 (1935) through Vol. 7, No. 6 (1949). (Discontinued in 1949; succeeded by Wasmann Journal of Biology in 1950).

*Wasmann Journal of Biology (University of San Francisco, California):

- Vol. 8, No. 1 (1950) through Vol. 32, No. 2 (1978). (Succeeds Wasmann Collector in 1950).

*West American Scientist (San Diego Society of Natural History, California):

- Vol. 1, No. 1 (1884) through Vol. 18 (1911)

*West Virginia Science Bulletin (West Virginia Scientific Society, Morgantown):

- Vol. 1, No. 1 (1922) through Vol. 2, No. 4 (1930)

*Western Washington University Department of Biology Theses (Western Washington University, Bellingham):

- Masters and Doctorate Theses, 1950 through 1979

*Western Washington University Department of Education Theses (Western Washington University, Bellingham):

- Masters and Doctorate Theses, 1950 through 1979

*White Rock-Surrey Naturalists' Newsletter (White Rock and Surrey Naturalists, British Columbia):

- 1976 (January) through 1980 (January)

*Whitman College Reports (Whitman College, Spokane, Washington):

- Senior theses, 1970 through 1979

*Whitworth College Reports (Whitworth College, Spokane, Washington):

- 1890 through 1980

*Wildlife Monographs (Wildlife Society, Washington, District of Columbia):

- No. 1 (1958) through No. 62 (1978)

Wildlife Report: The Canadian Scene (Canadian Wildlife Federation, 1673 Carling Avenue, Ottawa, Ontario K2A 1C4):

- January-February Issue only (1977)

*Wildlife Review (British Columbia Government, Victoria):

- Vol. 1, No. 1 (1954) through Vol. 8, No. 10 (1979)

*Wildlife Society Bulletin (The Wildlife Society, Washington, District of Columbia):

- Vol. 1, No. 1 (1973) through Vol. 7, No. 3 (1979). (Succeeds Wildlife Society News in 1973 with Vol. 1, No. 1).

*Wildlife Society News (The Wildlife Society, Washington, District of Columbia):

- No. 41 (1952) through No. 143 (1973). (Succeeds Wildlife Society Newsletter in 1952 with No. 41; discontinued in 1973 with No. 143; succeeded by Wildlife Society Bulletin in 1973 with Vol. 1, No. 1).

*Wildlife Society Newsletter (The Wildlife Society, Washington, District of Columbia):

- No. 1 (1947) through No. 40 (1952). (Discontinued in 1952 with No. 40, succeeded by Wildlife Society News in 1952 with No. 41).

*Wilson Bulletin (Wilson Ornithological Club):

- Vol. 1, No. 1 (1889) through Vol. 91, No. 2 (1979)

*Zeitschrift Fur Tierpsychologie (Journal of Comparative Ethology) (Verlag Paul Parey, Berlin and Hamburg):

- Vol. 1, No. 1 (1943) through Vol. 53, No. 1 (1980)

*Zeitschrift Fur Vergleichende Physiologie (International Journal on Comparative Physiology, Springer-Verlag, Heidelberg, Germany):

- Vol. 1, No. 1 (1924) through Vol. 76, No. 4 (1972). (Discontinued in 1972 with Vol. 76, No. 4; succeeded by Journal of Comparative Physiology in 1972 with Vol. 77, No. 1).

Zeitschrift fur Zellforschung und Mikroskopische Anatomie (Springer-Verlag, Berlin, Germany):

- Vol. 84 (1968) through Vol. 112 (1971)

*Zoe (San Francisco, California):

- Vol. 1, No. 1 (1890) through Vol. 5, No. 11 (1906)

*Zoologica (New York Zoological Society, New York):

- Vol. 1, No. 1 (1907) through Vol. 58, No. 4 (1973)

*Zoological Scripta (Royal Swedish Academy of Sciences, Stockholm):

- Vol. 1, No. 1 (1972) through Vol. 9, No. 3 (1980)

*Zoon (Department of Zoology, Uppsala University, Sweden):

- Vol. 1, No. 1 (1973) through Vol. 7, No. 1 (1979)

A complete copy of <u>every</u> reference in this book (indexed by its number) is in the literature file for British Columbia vertebrates in the <u>Vertebrate Zoology Division</u>, <u>British Columbia Provincial Museum</u> in Victoria.

ACKNOWLEDGEMENTS

Since its inception in 1979 many people have been involved in the preparation and production of this bibliography. The following agencies or institutions, and people, provided source material and assistance: American Museum of Natural History, New York; British Columbia Ministry of Environment, Fish and Wildlife Branch, Victoria (Ray Halliday, Bill Munro and Don Eastman), and Terrestrial Studies Branch, Victoria (Andy Stewart); British Columbia Ministry of Lands, Parks and Housing, Parks and Outdoor Recreation Division, Victoria (David Stirling, Kerry Joy and Peggy McIntosh); British Columbia Ministry of Provincial Secretary and Government Services, Provincial Museum Branch; British Columbia Provincial Library, Victoria (Rod Carswell); Canadian Wildlife Service, Delta (Neil K. Dawe and Nolan Perret); National Museums of Canada, Ottawa; Parks Canada, Pacific Rim National Park (Bill McIntyre, Barry Campbell and Frank Camp); Simon Fraser University, Department of Biological Sciences (Ann MacDonald); Simon Fraser University, Main Library; United States National Museum, Washington, D.C.; University of British Columbia, Department of Zoology (G. G. E. Scudder and W. W. Coward), Faculty of Forestry (Margaret Logan), MacMillan Library (Kathy Neill), and Woodward Bio-Medical Library (Anna Leith); University of Victoria, Department of Biology (J. McInerney); University of Victoria, Main Library; University of Washington, Department of Zoology, Forest Resources Library (Barbara Gordon), Natural Sciences (Suzzallo) Library (Nancy Blase, and Sophia Smith) and Washington Department of Game (Siobhan Sullivan and Betty Roderick).

Although most of the literature search, photo-copying and cross-referencing was done by the compilers, assistance was received from Allister Bell, Douglas Bertram, Eileen Campbell, Neil K. Dawe, Heather M. Garrioch, Brian Goodacre, David M. Green, Tracey Hooper, Stan Orchard, Christopher D. Shepard, James R. Slater and Elizabeth M. Taylor. Most Washington university and college sources were searched by Siobhan Sullivan and Brigitta Van Der Raay.

Keith Taylor provided all artwork for pages 35 through 88 and Brigitta Van Der Raay for pages 89 through 109. The cover design and artwork was done by Rennie Knowlton and Clover Tobin. All maps were prepared by Elizabeth M. Taylor.

The manuscript was typed by Erica Gillard. Harold Hosford provided editorial assistance and Yorke Edwards provided encouragement and support.

This project was supported, in part, by the British Columbia Ministry of Environment, Fish and Wildlife Branch, British Columbia Ministry of Lands, Parks and Housing, Parks and Outdoor Recreation Division, and Washington Department of Game, Nongame Wildlife Program.

We are deeply indebted to them all.

BIBLIOGRAPHY

1. Grant, James. 1961. THE TAILED TOAD IN SOUTHEASTERN BRITISH COLUMBIA. Canadian Field-Naturalist 75(3):165.

2. Cook, Francis R. 1970. RARE OR ENDANGERED CANADIAN AMPHIBIANS AND REPTILES. Canadian Field-Naturalist 84(1):9-16.

3. Herreid, Clyde F. 1963. RANGE EXTENSION FOR Bufo boreas boreas. Herpetologica 19(3):218.

4. Henderson, Bryan A. 1973. THE SPECIALIZED FEEDING BEHAVIOR OF Ambystoma gracile IN MARION LAKE, BRITISH COLUMBIA. Canadian Field-Naturalist 87(2):151-154.

5. Ferguson, Denzel E. 1956. THE DISTRIBUTION OF Rana sylvatica cantabrigensis BAIRD IN WESTERN CANADA AND ALASKA. Herpetologica 12(2):132.

6. Patch, Clyde L. 1929. SOME AMPHIBIANS OF WESTERN NORTH AMERICA. Canadian Field-Naturalist 53(6):137-138.

7. Loomis, Richard B. and J. Knox Jones, Jr. 1953. RECORDS OF THE WOOD FROG, Rana sylvatica, FROM WESTERN CANADA AND ALASKA. Herpetologica 9(3):149-151.

8. Carl, G. Clifford. 1950. THE SHARP-TAILED SNAKE IN BRITISH COLUMBIA. Herpetologica 6:116.

9. Mills, R. Colin. 1948. A CHECK LIST OF THE REPTILES AND AMPHIBIANS OF CANADA. Herpetologica 4 (second supplement):1-15.

10. Evenden, Fred G., Jr. 1948. DISTRIBUTION OF THE TURTLES OF WESTERN OREGON. Herpetologica 4(6):201-204.

11. Mittleman, M. B. 1948. AMERICAN CAUDATA: II. GEOGRAPHIC VARIATION IN Ambystoma macrodactylum. Herpetologica 4(3):81-95.

12. Carl, G. Clifford. 1949. EXTENSION OF KNOWN RANGES OF SOME AMPHIBIANS IN BRITISH COLUMBIA. Herpetologica 5:139-140.

13. Carl, G. Clifford. 1943. THE AMPHIBIANS OF BRITISH COLUMBIA. _British Columbia Provincial Museum Handbook_ No. 2, Victoria. 63 pages.

14. Carl, G. Clifford. 1944. THE REPTILES OF BRITISH COLUMBIA. _British Columbia Provincial Museum Handbook_ No. 3, Victoria. 65 pages.

15. Patch, Clyde L. 1934. _Eumeces_ IN CANADA. _Copeia_ 1934(1):50-51.

16. Ricker, William E. and E. B. S. Logier. 1935. NOTES ON THE OCCURRENCE OF THE RIBBED TOAD (_Ascaphus truei_ STEJNEGER) IN CANADA. _Copeia_ 1935(1):46.

17. Hart, John Lawson. 1934. MELANISTIC GARTER SNAKE RECORDED FROM VANCOUVER ISLAND. _Copeia_ 1934(3):142.

18. Storer, Tracy I. 1937. FURTHER NOTES ON THE TURTLES OF THE NORTH PACIFIC COAST OF NORTH AMERICA. _Copeia_ 1937(1):66-67.

19. Watney, Gertrude Smith. 1938. A NEW RECORD OF _Plethodon vehiculus_ (COOPER) FROM VANCOUVER, BRITISH COLUMBIA. _Copeia_ 1938(2):89.

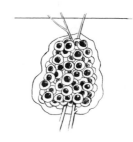

20. Cowan, Ian McTaggart. 1938. DISTRIBUTION OF TURTLES IN COASTAL BRITISH COLUMBIA. _Copeia_ 1938(2):91.

21. Patch, Clyde L. 1939. NORTHERN RECORDS OF THE WOOD FROG. _Copeia_ 1939(4):235.

22. Watney, Gertrude M. Smith. 1941. NOTES ON THE LIFE HISTORY OF _Ambystoma gracile_ BAIRD. _Copeia_ 1941(1):14-17.

23. Cowan, Ian McTaggart. 1941. LONGEVITY OF THE RED-LEGGED FROG. _Copeia_ 1941(1):48.

24. Carl, G. Clifford. 1942. THE LONG-TOED SALAMANDER ON VANCOUVER ISLAND. _Copeia_ 1942(1):56.

25. Carl, G. Clifford. 1942. THE WESTERN SPADEFOOT TOAD IN BRITISH COLUMBIA. _Copeia_ 1942(2):129.

26. Slipp, John W. and G. Clifford Carl. 1943. NORTHWARD EXTENSIONS OF THE RANGE OF _Ascaphus_. _Copeia_ 1943(2):127.

27. Dunn, Emmett Reid. 1944. NOTES ON THE SALAMANDERS OF THE _Ambystoma gracile_ GROUP. _Copeia_ 1944(3):129-130.

28. Carl, G. Clifford and Ian McTaggart Cowan. 1945. NOTES ON THE SALAMANDERS OF BRITISH COLUMBIA. _Copeia_ 1945(1):43-44.

29. Carl, G. Clifford and Ian McTaggart Cowan. 1945. NOTES ON SOME FROGS AND TOADS OF BRITISH COLUMBIA. _Copeia_ 1945(1):52-53.

30. Carl, G. Clifford. 1940. THE RED SALAMANDER (_Ensatina eschscholtzii_ GRAY) ON VANCOUVER ISLAND. _Copeia_ 1940(2):129.

31. Johnson, Murray L. and James R. Slater. 1949. ON THE VALIDITY OF _Thamnophis elegans nigrescens_ JOHNSON. _Copeia_ 1949(4):288.

32. Hebard, William B. 1951. OBSERVATIONS ON GARTERSNAKES IN THE PUGET SOUND REGION. _Copeia_ 1951(1):53-55.

33. MacAskie, I. B. and C. R. Forrester. 1962. PACIFIC LEATHERBACK TURTLES (Dermochelys) OFF THE COAST OF BRITISH COLUMBIA. Copeia 1962(3):646.

34. Efford, Ian E. and Jack A. Mathias. 1969. A COMPARISON OF TWO SALAMANDER POPULATIONS IN MARION LAKE, BRITISH COLUMBIA. Copeia 1969(4):723-730.

35. Cowan, Ian McTaggart. 1939. THE VERTEBRATE FAUNA OF THE PEACE RIVER DISTRICT OF BRITISH COLUMBIA. British Columbia Provincial Museum Occasional Paper No. 1, Victoria. 102 pages.

36. Dumas, Philip C. 1966. STUDIES OF THE Rana SPECIES COMPLEX IN THE PACIFIC NORTHWEST. Copeia 1966(1):60-74.

37. Campbell, R. Wayne. 1969. NOTES ON SOME FOODS OF THE WANDERING GARTER SNAKE ON MITLENATCH ISLAND, BRITISH COLUMBIA. Syesis 2(1/2):183-187.

38. Carl, G. Clifford. 1961. AMPHIBIAN MIGRATION. Victoria Naturalist 18(3):36.

39. Hardy, George A. 1956. THE FROG AND THE CENTIPEDE. Victoria Naturalist 12(9):101.

40. Guiguet, C. J. 1955. THE GREEN FROG. Victoria Naturalist 11(8):85.

41. Campbell, R. Wayne and D. Stirling. 1971. A PHOTODUPLICATE FILE FOR BRITISH COLUMBIA VERTEBRATE RECORDS. Syesis 4(1/2):217-222.

42. Guppy, Richard. 1953. SOME NOTES ON VANCOUVER ISLAND SALAMANDERS. Victoria Naturalist 10(2):13-15; 10(3):25-27.

43. Carl, G. Clifford. 1952. THE WESTERN PAINTED TURTLE GETS AROUND. Victoria Naturalist 9(3):25-26.

44. Merrick, George. 1951. RED-LEGGED FROGS. Victoria Naturalist 8(6):71.

45. Carl, G. Clifford. 1951. WHAT TO LOOK FOR IN FEBRUARY. Victoria Naturalist 7(8):90-91.

46. Anonymous. 1950. TOAD TADPOLES IN FAST WATER. Victoria Naturalist 7(6):65.

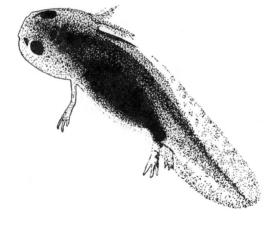

47. Ainscough, Brian. 1949. THE NORTHERN ALLIGATOR LIZARD (Gerrhonotus coeruleus principis). Victoria Naturalist 6(3):35.

48. Anonymous. 1947. A GARTER SNAKE RECORD. Victoria Naturalist 4(4):38.

49. Watson, Mary R. 1944. THE PACIFIC COAST NEWT (Triturus granulosus). Victoria Naturalist 1(4):51-52.

50. Guppy, Richard. 1946. SOME SALAMANDER OBSERVATIONS. Victoria Naturalist 3(3):45.

51. Carl, G. C. 1947. LEATHER-BACK TURTLE OFF DENMAN ISLAND. Victoria Naturalist 4(4):45.

52. Guppy, R. 1947. AQUARIUM REARING OF LARVAL NEWTS. Victoria Naturalist 4(6):63-65.

53. Carl, G. Clifford. 1952. WHAT TO LOOK FOR IN MARCH: FROGS - HERALDS OF SPRING. Victoria Naturalist 8(9):97-98.

54. Licht, Lawrence E. 1969. COMPARATIVE BREEDING BEHAVIOUR OF THE RED-LEGGED FROG (Rana aurora aurora) AND THE WESTERN SPOTTED FROG (Rana pretiosa pretiosa) IN SOUTHWESTERN BRITISH COLUMBIA. Canadian Journal of Zoology 47:1287-1299.

55. Johnson, T. S., E. J. Dornfeld and F. P. Conte. 1967. CELLULAR RENEWAL OF INTESTINAL EPITHELIUM IN THE WESTERN FENCE LIZARD, Sceloporus occidentalis. Canadian Journal of Zoology 45(1):63-71.

56. Friedmann, G. B. 1970. A COMPARISON OF SOME VALUES OF BLOOD SAMPLES FROM HEART AND TAIL VESSELS OF THE URODELE, Taricha granulosa. Canadian Journal of Zoology 48(3):900-901.

57. Friedmann, G. B. 1970. DIFFERENTIAL WHITE BLOOD CELL COUNTS FOR THE URODELE Taricha granulosa. Canadian Journal of Zoology 48(2):271-274.

58. Forbes, Richard B. and Dorothy McKey-Fender. 1968. A GREEN TURTLE FROM THE OREGON COAST. Canadian Journal of Zoology 46(5):1079.

59. Smith, Hobart M. 1946. HANDBOOK OF LIZARDS. Comstock Publishing Associates, Ithaca, New York. 557 pages.

60. Licht, Lawrence E. 1973. BEHAVIOR AND SOUND PRODUCTION BY THE NORTH-WESTERN SALAMANDER, Ambystoma gracile. Canadian Journal of Zoology 51(10):1055-1056.

61. Licht, Lawrence E. 1969. UNUSUAL ASPECTS OF ANURAN SEXUAL BEHAVIOUR AS SEEN IN THE RED-LEGGED FROG, Rana aurora aurora. Canadian Journal of Zoology 47(4):505-509.

62. Carr, Archie. 1952. HANDBOOK OF TURTLES. Comstock Publishing Associates, Ithaca, New York. 542 pages.

63. Wright, Albert Hazen and Anna Allen Wright. 1949. HANDBOOK OF FROGS AND TOADS (THIRD EDITION). Comstock Publishing Associates, Ithaca, New York. 640 pages.

64. Logier, E. B. S. and G. C. Toner. 1955. CHECK-LIST OF THE AMPHIBIANS AND REPTILES OF CANADA AND ALASKA. Contributions of the Royal Ontario Museum of Zoology and Palaeontology No. 41, Toronto. 88 pages.

65. Bols, N. C. and H. E. Kasinsky. 1973. AN ELECTROPHORETIC COMPARISON OF HISTONES IN ANURAN TESTES. Canadian Journal of Zoology 51(2):203-208.

66. Carl, G. Clifford. 1955. NORTHWARD EXTENSION OF KNOWN RANGE OF THE TAILED FROG, Ascaphus truei Stejneger. Herpetologica 11:202.

67. Carl, G. Clifford. 1971. RECORD OF THE SHARP-TAILED SNAKE FROM SOUTH PENDER ISLAND, BRITISH COLUMBIA. Syesis 4(1 & 2):267.

68. Savage, Jay M. 1952. THE DISTRIBUTION OF THE PACIFIC GIANT SALAMANDER, Dicamptodon ensatus, EAST OF THE CASCADE MOUNTAINS. Copeia 1952(3):183.

69. Snyder, Richard C. 1956. COMPARATIVE FEATURES OF THE LIFE HISTORIES OF Ambystoma gracile (BAIRD) FROM POPULATIONS AT LOW AND HIGH ALTITUDES. Copeia 1956(1):41-50.

70. Snyder, Richard C. 1960. THE EGG MASSES OF NEOTENIC Ambystoma gracile. Copeia 1960(3):267.

71. Anonymous. 1928. AMPHIBIA OF BRITISH COLUMBIA: ADDITIONAL NOTES AND CORRECTIONS. Report of the Provincial Museum of Natural History for the Year 1927, Victoria. Page 17.

72. Cowan, Ian McTaggart. 1937. A REVIEW OF THE REPTILES AND AMPHIBIANS OF BRITISH COLUMBIA. Report of the British Columbia Provincial Museum of Natural History for the Year 1936, Victoria. Pages 16-25.

73. Williams, M. Y. 1933. FAUNA OF THE FORMER DOMINION PEACE RIVER BLOCK, BRITISH COLUMBIA. Report of the Provincial Museum of Natural History for the Year 1932, Victoria. Pages 14-22.

74. Anonymous. 1929. ACCESSIONS. Report of the Provincial Museum of Natural History for the Year 1928, Victoria. Pages 23-25.

75. Carl, G. Clifford, C. J. Guiguet and George A. Hardy. 1951. BIOLOGY OF THE SCOTT ISLAND GROUP, BRITISH COLUMBIA. Report of the Provincial Museum of Natural History and Anthropology for the Year 1950, Victoria. Pages 21-63.

76. Kermode, F. 1932. A REMARKABLE CAPTURE OF LEATHERBACK TURTLES OFF BAJO REEF, NEAR NOOTKA SOUND, WEST COAST OF VANCOUVER ISLAND, BRITISH COLUMBIA. Report of the Provincial Museum of Natural History for the Year 1931, Victoria. Pages 6-7.

77. Carl, G. Clifford and Charles J. Guiguet. 1956. NOTES ON THE FLORA AND FAUNA OF BUNSBY ISLANDS, B.C. Report of the Provincial Museum of Natural History and Anthropology for the Year 1955, Victoria. Pages 31-44.

78. Hardy, G. A. 1949. A REPORT ON A STUDY OF JORDON MEADOWS, VANCOUVER ISLAND. Report of the Provincial Museum of Natural History and Anthropology for the Year 1948, Victoria. Pages 20-46.

79. Carl, G. Clifford. 1944. THE NATURAL HISTORY OF THE FORBIDDEN PLATEAU AREA, VANCOUVER ISLAND, BRITISH COLUMBIA. Report of the Provincial Museum of Natural History and Anthropology for the Year 1943, Victoria. Pages 18-40.

80. Carl, G. Clifford and George A. Hardy. 1943. REPORT ON A COLLECTING TRIP TO THE LAC LA HACHE AREA, BRITISH COLUMBIA. Report of the Provincial Museum of Natural History and Anthropology for the Year 1942, Victoria. Pages 25-49.

81. Dunn, Emmett Reid. 1940. THE RACES OF Ambystoma tigrinum. Copeia 1940(3):154-162.

82. Thacker, T. L. 1924. NOTES ON BELL'S PAINTED TURTLES (Chrysemys marginata bellii) IN BRITISH COLUMBIA. Canadian Field-Naturalist 38(9):164-167.

83. Stebbins, Robert C. 1966. A FIELD GUIDE TO WESTERN REPTILES AND AMPHIBIANS. Houghton Mifflin Company, Boston, Massachussetts. 279 pages.

84. Ryder, Glen R. 1971. PELICAN PARK-NATURALIST REPORT FOR 1971. Unpublished Report, British Columbia Parks Branch, Victoria. 91 pages.

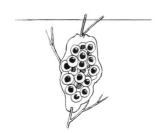

85. Gregson, J. D. 1942. THE COAST TICK (Ixodes californicus BANKS) PROBLEM IN BRITISH COLUMBIA. Canadian Entomologist 74(1):3-5.

86. Johansen, Kjell. 1962. OBSERVATIONS ON THE WOOD FROG Rana sylvatica IN ALASKA. Ecology 43(2):146-147.

87. Zweifel, Richard G. 1977. UPPER THERMAL TOLERANCES OF ANURAN EMBRYOS IN RELATION TO STAGE OF DEVELOPMENT AND BREEDING HABITS. American Museum Novitates 2617:1-21.

88. Ferguson, Denzel E. 1961. THE GEOGRAPHIC VARIATION OF Ambystoma macrodactylum BAIRD, WITH THE DESCRIPTION OF TWO NEW SUBSPECIES. American Midland Naturalist 65(2):311-338.

89. Kessel, Brina. 1965. BREEDING DATES OF Rana sylvatica AT COLLEGE, ALASKA. Ecology 46(2):206-208.

90. Dumas, Philip C. 1964. SPECIES-PAIR ALLOPATRY IN THE GENERA Rana AND Phrynosoma. Ecology 45(2):178-180.

91. Stull, Olive Griffith. 1935. A CHECK LIST OF THE FAMILY BOIDAE. Proceedings of the Boston Society of Natural History 40(8):387-408.

92. Edwards, Stephen R. and George R. Pisani (editors). 1976. ENDANGERED AND THREATENED AMPHIBIANS AND REPTILES IN THE UNITED STATES. Society for the Study of Amphibians and Reptiles Herpetological Circular No. 5:1-65.

93. Collins, Joseph T., James E. Huheey, James L. Knight and Hobart M. Smith. 1978. STANDARD COMMON AND CURRENT SCIENTIFIC NAMES FOR NORTH AMERICAN AMPHIBIANS AND REPTILES. Society for the Study of Amphibians and Reptiles Herpetological Circular No. 7:1-36.

94. Committee on Resources in Herpetology. 1975. COLLECTIONS OF PRESERVED AMPHIBIANS AND REPTILES IN THE UNITED STATES. Society for the Study of Amphibians and Reptiles Herpetological Circular No. 3:1-22.

95. Lindsey, C. C. 1966. TEMPERATURE-CONTROLLED MERISTIC VARIATION IN THE SALAMANDER Ambystoma gracile. Nature 209(5028):1152-1153.

96. Dickman, Mike. 1968. THE EFFECT OF GRAZING BY TADPOLES ON THE STRUCTURE OF A PERIPHYTON COMMUNITY. Ecology 49:1188-1190.

97. Neish, I. C. 1971. COMPARISON OF SIZE, STRUCTURE, AND DISTRIBUTIONAL PATTERNS OF TWO SALAMANDER POPULATIONS IN MARION LAKE, BRITISH COLUMBIA. Journal of the Fisheries Research Board of Canada 28(1):49–58.

98. Efford, Ian E. and Kanji Tsumura. 1969. OBSERVATIONS ON THE BIOLOGY OF THE TREMATODE Megalodiscus microphagus IN AMPHIBIANS FROM MARION LAKE, BRITISH COLUMBIA. American Midland Naturalist 82(1):197–203.

99. Henderson, Bryan A. 1970. SOME BIOLOGY AND THE FEEDING BEHAVIOR OF Ambystoma gracile IN MARION LAKE, B.C. M.Sc. Thesis, University of British Columbia, Department of Zoology, Vancouver. 37 pages.

100. Landesman, Richard H. 1966. AN ANALYSIS OF THE ROLE OF THE TISSUE ENVIRONMENT IN THE REGIONAL DIFFERENTIATION OF THE CENTRAL NERVOUS SYSTEM IN THE AMPHIBIAN Ambystoma gracile (BAIRD). Ph.D. Thesis, University of British Columbia, Department of Zoology, Vancouver. 92 pages.

101. Adams, Ellen. 1964. THE ONTOGENY OF ISOZYMES OF LACTIC DEHYDROGENASE IN TWO AMPHIBIAN SPECIES. M.A. Thesis, University of British Columbia, Department of Zoology, Vancouver. 28 pages.

102. Kennedy, Murray James. 1971. FOOD AND FEEDING HABITS OF THE NORTHWESTERN TOAD Bufo boreas boreas. B.Sc. Thesis, University of British Columbia, Department of Zoology, Vancouver. 27 pages.

103. Licht, Lawrence Edward. 1971. THE ECOLOGY OF COEXISTENCE IN TWO CLOSELY RELATED SPECIES OF FROGS (Rana). Ph.D. Thesis, University of British Columbia, Department of Zoology, Vancouver. 155 pages.

104. Hick, William Bernard Martin. 1947. A COMPARATIVE STUDY OF THE MYOLOGY OF THE HEAD REGION IN Thamnophis sirtalis tetrataenia, Thamnophis ordinoides vagrans, Thamnophis ordinoides ordinoides BASED ON A DETAILED DESCRIPTION OF THE CONDITION FOUND IN Thamnophis sirtalis tetrataenia. B.Sc. Thesis, University of British Columbia, Department of Zoology, Vancouver. 87 pages.

105. Calef, George Waller. 1971. AN ANALYSIS OF MORTALITY IN A POPULATION OF TADPOLES OF THE RED-LEGGED FROG (Rana aurora). Ph.D. Thesis, University of British Columbia, Department of Zoology, Vancouver. 74 pages.

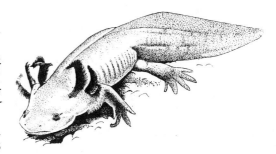

106. Gregson, John Douglas. 1934. THE BIONOMICS OF THE KEELED LIZARD, Gerrhonotus multicarinatus (BLAINVILLE) IN BRITISH COLUMBIA. B.A. Thesis, University of British Columbia, Department of Zoology, Vancouver. 75 pages.

107. Holland, George Pearson. 1937. LIFE HISTORY AND DISTRIBUTIONAL STUDIES OF BELL'S PAINTED TERRAPIN, Chrysemys picta bellii (GRAY). M.A. Thesis, University of British Columbia, Department of Zoology, Vancouver. 146 pages.

108. McLeay, Donald James. 1966. A CYTOCHEMICAL ANALYSIS OF TAIL DEVELOPMENT IN Ambystoma gracile. B.Sc. Thesis, University of British Columbia, Department of Zoology, Vancouver. 33 pages.

109. Preston, William Barton. 1964. THE IMPORTANCE OF THE FACIAL PIT OF THE NORTHERN PACIFIC RATTLESNAKE (Crotalus ciridis oreganus) UNDER NATURAL CONDITIONS IN SOUTHERN BRITISH COLUMBIA. B.Sc. Thesis, University of British Columbia, Department of Zoology, Vancouver. 64 pages.

110. Maguire, Frances Margaret. 1933. A THESIS ON THE ANATOMY OF Bufo boreas. B.A. Thesis, University of British Columbia, Department of Zoology, Vancouver. 129 pages.

111. Pope, Clifford H. 1939. TURTLES OF THE UNITED STATES AND CANADA. Alfred A. Knopf, Inc., New York, New York. 343 pages.

112. Smith, Harlan I. 1920. EMBELLISHED GARTER SNAKE IN BRITISH COLUMBIA. Copeia 88:102.

113. Van Winkle, Katherine. 1922. EXTENSION OF THE RANGE OF Ascaphus truei STEJNEGER. Copeia 102:4-6.

114. Blanchard, Frank N. 1921. A COLLECTION OF AMPHIBIANS AND REPTILES FROM NORTHEASTERN WASHINGTON. Copeia 90:5-6.

115. Patch, Clyde L. 1922. SOME AMPHIBIANS AND REPTILES FROM BRITISH COLUMBIA. Copeia 111:74-79.

116. Slater, James R. 1930. Ambystoma decorticatum COPE REDISCOVERED IN WASHINGTON. Copeia 1930(3):87.

117. Dunn, E. R. 1930. NOTE ON Ambystoma decorticatum. Copeia 1930(3):87-88.

118. Slater, James R. 1931. THE MATING OF Ascaphus truei STEJNEGER. Copeia 1931(2):62-63.

119. Noble, G. K. and Phillips G. Putnam. 1931. OBSERVATIONS ON THE LIFE HISTORY OF Ascaphus truei STEJNEGER. Copeia 1931(3):97-101.

120. Dunn, Emmett Reid. 1931. THE HERPETOLOGICAL FAUNA OF THE AMERICAS. Copeia 1931(3):106-119.

121. Svihla, Arthur. 1931. AN EXTENSION OF THE RANGE OF Dicamptodon ensatus. Copeia 1931(3):143.

122. Storer, Tracy I. 1932. THE WESTERN LIMIT OF RANGE FOR Chrysemys picta bellii. Copeia 1932(1):9-11.

123. Svihla, Arthur and Ruth Dowell Svihla. 1932. ANOTHER RECORD FOR THE MARBLED SALAMANDER IN WASHINGTON. Copeia 1932(1):38.

124. Svihla, Arthur and Ruth Dowell Svihla. 1933. NOTES ON Ascaphus truei IN KITTITAS COUNTY, WASHINGTON. Copeia 1933(1):37-38.

125. Svihla, Arthur. 1933. EXTENSION OF THE RANGES OF SOME WASHINGTON AMPHIBIA. Copeia 1933(1):39.

126. Slater, James R. 1933. NOTES ON WASHINGTON SALAMANDERS. Copeia 1933(1):44.

127. Svihla, Arthur and Ruth Dowell Svihla. 1933. AMPHIBIANS AND REPTILES OF WHITMAN COUNTY, WASHINGTON. Copeia 1933(3):125-128.

128. Slater, James R. 1934. NOTES ON NORTHWESTERN AMPHIBIANS. Copeia 1934(3):140-141.

129. Fitch, Henry S. 1934. A SHIFT OF SPECIFIC NAMES IN THE GENUS Gerrhonotus. Copeia 1934(4):172-173.

130. Eaton, Theodore H., Jr. 1934. THE AFFINITIES OF Dicamptodon AND Rhyacotriton. Copeia 1934(4):182.

131. Slater, James R. 1934. Ambystoma tigrinum IN THE STATE OF WASHINGTON. Copeia 1934(4):189-190.

132. Alcorn, Gordon D. 1935. THE WESTERN YELLOW-BELLIED RACER IN WESTERN WASHINGTON. Copeia 1935(2):103.

133. Svihla, Arthur. 1935. NOTES ON THE WESTERN SPOTTED FROG, Rana pretiosa pretiosa. Copeia 1935(3):119-122.

134. Svihla, Arthur. 1936. AN ABNORMALLY COLORED GARTER SNAKE. Copeia 1936(4):234-236.

135. Wood, Sherwin F. 1936. COURTING BEHAVIOUR OF SOME WESTERN LIZARDS. Copeia 1936(3):177.

136. Slater, James R. 1936. NOTES ON Ambystoma gracile BAIRD AND Ambystoma macrodactylum BAIRD. Copeia 1936(4):234-236.

137. Svihla, Arthur. 1938. OCCURRENCE OF THE RING-NECKED SNAKE IN THE STATE OF WASHINGTON. Copeia 1938(1):47.

138. Janes, Ralph G. 1939. STUDIES ON THE AMPHIBIAN DIGESTIVE SYSTEM, IV. THE EFFECT OF DIET ON THE SMALL INTESTINE OF Rana sylvatica. Copeia 1939(3):134-140.

139. Svihla, Arthur and Cameron Knox. 1940. THE SPOTTED NIGHT SNAKE Hypsiglena IN WASHINGTON. Copeia 1940(1):52.

140. Rahn, Hermann. 1940. SPERM VIABILITY IN THE UTERUS OF THE GARTER SNAKE, Thamnophis. Copeia 1940(2):109-115.

141. Owen, Robert P. 1940. A LIST OF THE REPTILES OF WASHINGTON. Copeia 1940(3):169-172.

142. Henry, Wilbur V. and Victor C. Twitty. 1940. CONTRIBUTIONS TO THE LIFE HISTORIES OF Dicamptodon ensatus AND Ambystoma gracile. Copeia 1940(4):247-250.

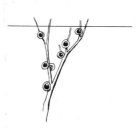

143. Mayr, Ernst. 1941. WHAT IS AN ARTEN-KREIS? Copeia 1941(2):115-116.

144. Johnson, Murray L. 1942. A DISTRIBU-TIONAL CHECK-LIST OF THE REP-TILES OF WASHINGTON. Copeia 1942(1):15-18.

145. Svihla, Arthur. 1942. MATING BEHAVIOR OF THE NORTHERN ALLIGATOR LIZARD. Copeia 1942(1):54.

146. Myers, George S. 1942. NOTES ON PACIFIC COAST Triturus. Copeia 1942(2):77-82.

147. Lewis, Thomas H. 1942. ADDITIONAL RECORDS OF WASHINGTON SNAKES. Copeia 1942(2):129.

148. Svihla, Arthur. 1943. NOTES ON YOUNG RUBBER SNAKES. Copeia 1942(2):128.

149. Schonberger, Clinton F. 1945. FOOD OF SOME AMPHIBIANS AND REPTILES OF OREGON AND WASHINGTON. Copeia 1945(2):120-121.

150. Fitch, Henry S. and Howard Twining. 1946. FEEDING HABITS OF THE PACIFIC RATTLESNAKE. Copeia 1946(2):64-71.

151. Licht, Lawrence E. 1975. GROWTH AND FOOD OF LARVAL Ambystoma gracile FROM A LOWLAND POPULATION IN SOUTHWESTERN BRITISH COLUMBIA. Canadian Journal of Zoology 53(11):1716-1722.

152. Licht, Lawrence E. 1975. COMPARATIVE LIFE HISTORY FEATURES OF THE WESTERN SPOTTED FROG, Rana pretiosa, FROM LOW- AND HIGH-ELEVATION POPULATIONS. Canadian Journal of Zoology 53(9):1254-1257.

153. Calef, George W. 1973. SPATIAL DIS- TRIBUTION AND "EFFECTIVE" BREED- ING POPULATION OF RED-LEGGED FROGS (Rana aurora) IN MARION LAKE, BRITISH COLUMBIA. Canadian Field-Naturalist 87(3):279-284.

154. McIntosh, A. G. Duncan and Patrick T. Gregory. 1976. PREDATION ON A BAT BY A WESTERN YELLOW-BELLIED RACER. Canadian Field-Naturalist 90(1):73.

155. Carl, G. Clifford. 1968. TREE-FROG TAD- POLES IN WINTER. Victoria Naturalist 24(7):90-91.

156. Carl, G. Clifford and C. J. Guiguet. 1958. ALIEN ANIMALS IN BRITISH COLUMBIA. British Columbia Provincial Museum Handbook No. 14, Victoria. 103 pages.

157. Hodge, Robert Parker. 1976. AMPHIBIANS AND REPTILES IN ALASKA, THE YUKON AND NORTHWEST TERRITORIES. Alaska Northwest Publishing Company, Anchorage. 89 pages.

158. Oliver, Marlene Gail. 1974. HABITAT SELECTION AND ITS RELATION TO REPRODUCTIVE DEVELOPMENT OF THE ROUGH-SKINNED NEWT, Taricha granulosa (SKILTON) ON SOUTHERN VANCOUVER ISLAND. M.Sc. Thesis, University of Victoria, Department of Biology, Victoria. 80 pages.

159. Antonelli, Arthur L., Ronald A. Nussbaum and Stamford D. Smith. 1972. COMPARATIVE FOOD HABITS OF FOUR SPECIES OF STREAM-DWELLING VERTEBRATES (Dicamptodon ensatus, D. copei, Cottus tenuis, Salmo gairdneri). Northwest Science 46(4):277-289.

160. Nussbaum, Ronald A. and Glen W. Clothier. 1973. POPULATION STRUCTURE, GROWTH, AND SIZE OF LARVAL Dicamptodon ensatus (ESCHSCHOLTZ). Northwest Science 47(4):218-277.

161. Nussbaum, Ronald A. and Richard F. Hoyer. 1974. GEOGRAPHIC VARIATION AND THE VALIDITY OF SUBSPECIES IN THE RUBBER BOA, Charina bottae (BLAINVILLE). Northwest Science 48(4):219-229.

162. Brown, Herbert A. 1975. REPRODUCTION AND DEVELOPMENT OF THE RED-LEGGED FROG, Rana aurora, IN NORTHWESTERN WASHINGTON. Northwest Science 49(4):241-252.

163. Harris, Martin J. 1976. HERPETOFAUNA OF YAKAWAWA CANYON, WASHINGTON. Northwest Science 50(2):114-121.

164. Nussbaum, Ronald A. and Lowell V. Diller. 1976. THE LIFE HISTORY OF THE SIDE-BLOTCHED LIZARD, Uta stansburiana BAIRD AND GIRARD, IN NORTH- CENTRAL OREGON. Northwest Science 50(4):243-260.

165. White, Robert L. 1977. PREY SELECTION BY THE ROUGH SKINNED NEWT (Taricha granulosa) IN TWO POND TYPES. Northwest Science 51(2):114-118.

166. Lewis, Thomas H. 1946. NOTES ON REPTILES FROM THE STATE OF WASHINGTON. Copeia 1946(3):155-159.

167. Fitch, Henry S. 1948. FURTHER REMARKS CONCERNING Thamnophis ordinoides AND ITS RELATIVES. Copeia 1948(2):121-126.

168. Gnaedinger, Leslie McKay and Charles A. Reed. 1948. CONTRIBUTION TO THE NATURAL HISTORY OF THE PLETHODONT SALAMANDER Ensatina eschscholtzii. Copeia 1948(3):187-196.

169. Lowe, Charles H., Jr. 1950. THE SYSTEMATIC STATUS OF THE SALAMANDER Plethodon hardii, WITH A DISCUSSION OF BIOGEOGRAPHICAL PROBLEMS IN Aneides. Copeia 1950(2):93-99.

170. Hebard, William B. 1950. A DIMORPHIC COLOR PATTERN OF THE GARTER SNAKE Thamnophis elegans vagrans IN THE PUGET SOUND REGION. Copeia 1950(3):217-219.

171. Fox, Wade. 1951. THE STATUS OF THE GARTERSNAKE, Thamnophis sirtalis tetrataenia. Copeia 1951(4):257-267.

172. Svihla, Arthur. 1953. DIURNAL RETREATS OF THE SPADE-FOOT TOAD Scaphiopus hammondi. Copeia 1953(3):186.

173. Storm, Robert M. 1955. NORTHERN AND SOUTHERN RANGE LIMITS OF DUNN'S SALAMANDER, Plethodon dunni. Copeia 1955(1):64-65.

174. Svihla, Arthur. 1955. STATUS OF THE STRIPED RACER Masticophis taeniatus taeniatus IN WASHINGTON. Copeia 1955(1):65.

175. Kezer, James and Donald S. Farner. 1955. LIFE HISTORY PATTERNS OF THE SALAMANDER Ambystoma macrodactylum IN THE HIGH CASCADE MOUNTAINS OF SOUTHERN OREGON. Copeia 1955(2):127-131.

176. Brattstrom, Bayard H. and James W. Warren. 1955. OBSERVATIONS ON THE ECOLOGY AND BEHAVIOUR OF THE PACIFIC TREEFROG, Hyla regilla. Copeia 1955(3):181-191.

177. Jameson, David L. 1956. GROWTH, DISPERSAL AND SURVIVAL OF THE PACIFIC TREE FROG. Copeia 1956(1):25-29.

178. Committee. 1956. COMMON NAMES FOR NORTH AMERICAN AMPHIBIANS AND REPTILES. Copeia 1956(3):172-185.

179. Hudson, George E. 1957. LATE PARTURITION IN THE RUBBER SNAKE. Copeia 1957(1):51-52.

180. Jameson, David L. 1957. POPULATION STRUCTURE AND HOMING RESPONSES IN THE PACIFIC TREE FROG. Copeia 1957(3):221-228.

181. Svihla, Arthur. 1959. A SIMPLE METHOD OF COLLECTING Ascaphus truei TAD-POLES. Copeia 1959(1):72.

182. Knudsen, Jens W. 1960. THE COURTSHIP AND EGG MASS OF Ambystoma gracile AND Ambystoma macrodac-tylum. Copeia 1960(1):44-46.

183. Stebbins, Robert C. 1960. EFFECTS OF PINEALECTOMY IN THE WESTERN FENCE LIZARD Sceloporus occiden-talis. Copeia 1960(4):276-283.

184. Batts, Billy S. 1961. INTERTIDAL FISHES AS FOOD OF THE COMMON GARTER SNAKE. Copeia 1961(3):350-351.

185. Burns, Douglas M. 1962. THE TAXONOMIC STATUS OF THE SALAMANDER Plethodon vandykei larselli. Copeia 1962(1):177-181.

186. Musacchia, X. J. and Walter Grundhauser. 1962. SEASONAL AND INDUCED ALTERATIONS OF WATER CONTENT IN ORGANS OF THE TURTLE Chrysemys picta. Copeia 1962(3):570-575.

187. Czopek, Juliusz. 1962. VASCULARIZATION OF RESPIRATORY SURFACES IN SOME CAUDATA. Copeia 1962(3):576-587.

188. Metter, Dean E. 1964. A MORPHOLOGICAL AND ECOLOGICAL COMPARISON OF TWO POPULATIONS OF THE TAILED FROG, Ascaphus truei STEJNEGER. Copeia 1964(1):181-195.

189. Valentine, Barry D. and David M. Dennis. 1964. A COMPARISON OF THE GILL-ARCH SYSTEM AND FINS OF THREE GENERA OF LARVAL SALAMANDERS, Rhyacotriton, Gyrinophilus, AND Ambystoma. Copeia 1964(1):196-201.

190. Davis, William C. and Victor C. Twitty. 1964. COURTSHIP BEHAVIOR AND REPRODUCTIVE ISOLATION IN THE SPECIES OF Taricha (AMPHIBIA, CAUDATA). Copeia 1964(4):601-610.

191. Etheridge, Richard. 1964. THE SKELETAL MORPHOLOGY AND SYSTEMATIC RELATIONSHIPS OF SCELOPORINE LIZARDS. Copeia 1964(4):610-631.

192. Metter, Dean E. 1964. ON BREEDING AND SPERM RETENTION IN Ascaphus. Copeia 1964(4):710-711.

193. Snyder, Wade F. and David L. Jameson. 1965. MULTIVARIATE GEOGRAPHIC VARIATION OF MATING CALL IN POPULATIONS OF THE PACIFIC TREE FROG (Hyla regilla). Copeia 1965(2):129-142.

194. Metter, Dean E. 1967. VARIATION IN THE RIBBED FROG Ascaphus truei STEJNEGER. Copeia 1967(3):634-649.

195. Brodie, Edmund D., Jr. 1968. INVESTIGATIONS ON THE SKIN TOXIN OF THE ADULT ROUGH-SKINNED NEWT, Taricha granulosa. Copeia 1968(2):307-313.

196. Presch, William. 1969. EVOLUTIONARY OSTEOLOGY AND RELATIONSHIPS OF THE HORNED LIZARD GENUS Phrynosoma (FAMILY IGUANIDAE). Copeia 1969(2):250-275.

197. Wiewandt, Thomas A. 1969. VOCALIZATION, AGGRESSIVE BEHAVIOR, AND TERRITORIALITY IN THE BULLFROG, Rana catesbeiana. Copeia 1969(2):276-285.

198. Metter, Dean E. and Robert J. Pauken. 1969. AN ANALYSIS OF THE REDUCTION OF GENE FLOW IN Ascaphus truei IN THE NORTHWEST U.S. SINCE THE PLEISTOCENE. Copeia 1969(2):301-307.

199. Rouf, M. A. 1969. HEMATOLOGY OF THE LEOPARD FROG, Rana pipiens. Copeia 1969(4):682-687.

200. Bury, R. Bruce. 1970. FOOD SIMILARITIES IN THE TAILED FROG, Ascaphus truei, AND THE OLYMPIC SALAMANDER, Rhyacotriton olympicus. Copeia 1970(1):170-171.

201. Nussbaum, Ronald A. 1970. Dicamptodon copei, n. sp., FROM THE PACIFIC NORTHWEST, U.S.A. (AMPHIBIA: CAUDATA: AMBYSTOMATIDAE). Copeia 1970(3):506-514.

202. Wood, Stephen C. 1972. METABOLIC RATE OF LARVAL AND ADULT PACIFIC GIANT SALAMANDERS, Dicamptodon ensatus (eschscholtz). Copeia 1972(1):177-179.

203. Parker, William S. and Eric R. Pianka. 1975. COMPARATIVE ECOLOGY OF POPULATIONS OF THE LIZARD Uta stansburiana. Copeia 1975(4):615-632.

204. Hollister, N. 1912. LIST OF REPTILES AND BATRACHIANS OF THE ALPINE CLUB EXPEDITION TO THE MOUNT ROBSON REGION. Canadian Alpine Journal 4(special number):45-46.

205. Clark, Glen W., Jack Bradford and Ronald Nussbaum. 1969. BLOOD PARASITES OF SOME PACIFIC NORTHWEST AMPHIBIANS. Bulletin of the Wildlife Disease Association 5(2):117-118.

206. Campbell, R. Wayne. 1975. THE PHOTODUPLICATE FILE - A VALUABLE VERTEBRATE RECORD. Federation of British Columbia Naturalists Newsletter 13(1):6.

207. Dawe, Neil K. 1976. SOME NOTES ON THE COMPARATIVE ECOLOGY OF GARTER SNAKES OF THE GENUS Thamnophis AT QUALICUM BEACH, B.C. Unpublished Report, Canadian Wildlife Service, Qualicum Beach. 17 pages.

208. Tanner, Vasco M. 1939. A STUDY OF THE GENUS Scaphiopus: THE SPADEFOOT TOADS. Great Basin Naturalist 1(1):3-26.

209. Tanner, V. M. and W. W. Tanner. 1939. NOTES ON Charina bottae IN UTAH: REPRODUCTION. Great Basin Naturalist 1(1):27-30.

210. Tanner, Wilmer W. 1940. NOTES ON THE HERPETOLOGICAL SPECIMENS ADDED TO THE BRIGHAM YOUNG UNIVERSITY VERTEBRATE COLLECTION DURING 1939. Great Basin Naturalist 1(3,4):138-146.

211. Tanner, Wilmer W. 1944. A TAXONOMIC STUDY OF THE GENUS Hypsiglena. Great Basin Naturalist 5(3,4):25-92.

212. Tanner, Vasco M. 1949. AMPHIBIANS AND REPTILES CONTRIBUTED TO BRIGHAM YOUNG UNIVERSITY BY OWEN BRYANT. Great Basin Naturalist 9(3,4):47-49.

213. Tanner, Wilmer W. 1957. A TAXONOMIC AND ECOLOGICAL STUDY OF THE WESTERN SKINK (Eumeces skiltonianus). Great Basin Naturalist 17(3-4):59-94.

214. Morris, Ronald L. and Wilmer W. Tanner. 1969. THE ECOLOGY OF THE WESTERN SPOTTED FROG *Rana pretiosa pretiosa* BAIRD AND GIRARD, A LIFE HISTORY STUDY. *Great Basin Naturalist* 29(2):45-81.

215. Black, Jeffrey Howard and Royal Bruce Brunson. 1971. BREEDING BEHAVIOR OF THE BOREAL TOAD, *Bufo boreas boreas* (BAIRD AND GIRARD), IN WESTERN MONTANA. *Great Basin Naturalist* 31(2):109-113.

216. Waddick, James W. and Hobart M. Smith. 1974. THE SIGNIFICANCE OF SCALE CHARACTERS IN EVALUATION OF THE LIZARD GENERA *Gerrhonotus*, *Elgaria* AND *Barisia*. *Great Basin Naturalist* 34(4):257-266.

217. Fanghella, Charles, David F. Avery and Wilmer W. Tanner. 1975. *Urosaurus* AND ITS PHYLOGENETIC RELATION- SHIP TO *Uta* AS DETERMINED BY OSTEOLOGY AND MYOLOGY (REPTILIA: IGUANIDAE). *Great Basin Naturalist* 35(3):245-268.

218. Neal, G. Morley. 1934. THE ANATOMY OF THE KEELED LIZARD *Gerrhonotus multicarinatus* (BLAINVILLE). B.A. Thesis, *University of British Columbia, Department of Zoology*, Vancouver. 118 pages.

219. Adams, Ellen. 1962. AN INVESTIGATION OF EXTRACELLULAR PROTEIN AND NUCLEIC ACID IN *Taricha torosa* EMBRYOS. B.Sc. Thesis, *University of British Columbia, Department of Zoology*, Vancouver. 20 pages.

220. Gow, Jack A. 1962. A STUDY OF THE METACHROMATIC RESPONSE IN EMBRYOS AND EXPLANTED TISSUES OF *Taricha torosa*. B.Sc. Thesis, *University of British Columbia, Department of Zoology*, Vancouver. 27 pages.

221. Mathias, Jack A. 1964. SOME ASPECTS OF THE BIOLOGY OF *Taricha granulosa*. B.Sc. Thesis, *University of British Columbia, Department of Zoology*, Vancouver. 39 pages.

222. Clark, Winifred Heather. 1967. THE DIFFERENTIATION CAPACITY OF THE POSTERIOR NEURAL PLANT *in vitro* IN THE AMPHIBIAN *Ambystoma gracile* (BAIRD). B.Sc. Thesis, *University of British Columbia, Department of Zoology*, Vancouver. 26 pages.

223. Stelmock, James Joseph. 1976. LIFE HISTORY AND FEEDING STRATEGIES OF *Aneides ferreus* (COPE, 1869) (URODELA: PLETHODONTIDAE). B.Sc. Thesis, *University of British Columbia, Department of Zoology*, Vancouver. 66 pages.

224. Jaremovic, Renata V. 1978. DISTRIBUTION AND MOVEMENTS OF THE SALAMANDER *Aneides ferreus* (COPE, 1869) ON CLELAND ISLAND, B.C. B.Sc. Thesis, *University of British Columbia, Department of Zoology*, Vancouver. 47 pages.

225. Smith, Gertrude M. 1926. THE DETAILED ANATOMY OF *Triturus torosus*. M.A. Thesis, *University of British Columbia, Department of Zoology*, Vancouver. 82 pages.

226. Simpson, Robert Edward. 1941. A HISTOLOGICAL STUDY OF THE DIGESTIVE TRACT AND ASSOCIATED ORGANS OF THE NEWT *Triturus granulosus* SKILTON. M.A. Thesis, *University of British Columbia, Department of Zoology*, Vancouver. 139 pages.

227. O'Day, Danton H. 1969. ALKALINE PHOSPHATASE AND EMBRYOGENESIS IN TWO URODELE AMPHIBIAN SPECIES. M.Sc. Thesis, University of British Columbia, Department of Zoology, Vancouver. 55 pages.

228. Bols, Niels Christian. 1972. STUDIES ON SPERM HISTONES IN AMPHIBIA AND CHONDRICHTHYTES. M.Sc. Thesis, University of British Columbia, Department of Zoology, Vancouver. 74 pages.

229. Whitney, Carl Linn. 1973. THE ROLE OF VOCALIZATIONS IN SPACING OUT AND MATE SELECTION IN PACIFIC TREE FROGS. M.Sc. Thesis, University of British Columbia, Department of Zoology, Vancouver. 90 pages.

230. Neish, Iain Charles. 1970. A COMPARATIVE ANALYSIS OF THE FEEDING BEHAVIOUR OF TWO SALAMANDER POPULATIONS IN MARION LAKE, B.C. Ph.D. Thesis, University of British Columbia, Department of Zoology, Vancouver. 108 pages.

231. West, Nigel Hugh. 1974. VENTILATION AND DIVING APNOEA IN Rana pipiens. Ph.D. Thesis, University of British Columbia, Department of Zoology, Vancouver. 128 pages.

232. Langille, Brian Lowell. 1975. A COMPARATIVE STUDY OF CENTRAL CARDIOVASCULAR DYNAMICS IN VERTEBRATES. Ph.D. Thesis, University of British Columbia, Department of Zoology, Vancouver. 185 pages.

233. Milsom, William Kenneth. 1978. PULMONARY RECEPTORS AND THEIR ROLE IN THE CONTROL OF BREEDING IN TURTLES. Ph.D. Thesis, University of British Columbia, Department of Zoology, Vancouver. 127 pages.

234. Carl, G. Clifford. 1945. VANCOUVER ISLAND SNAKES. Victoria Naturalist 2(1):5-6.

235. Anonymous. 1949. WESTERN PAINTED TURTLE. Victoria Naturalist 6(1):2.

236. Carl, G. Clifford. 1949. SHARP-TAILED SNAKE IN BRITISH COLUMBIA. Victoria Naturalist 6(5):50-51.

237. Orrico, Leo. 1957. BRITISH COLUMBIA TURTLES. Victoria Naturalist 14(1):11-12.

238. Guppy, Richard. 1960. RAISING RED-LEGGED FROGS IN CAPTIVITY. Victoria Naturalist 16(7):87-89.

239. Draycot, W. M. 1962. A HELPFUL SNAKE. Victoria Naturalist 18(7):98.

240. Todd, Terese. 1966. A LONG WAY FROM HOME. Victoria Naturalist 22(9):116.

241. Oliver, M. G. 1973. THE WESTERN TOAD ON SOUTHERN VANCOUVER ISLAND. Victoria Naturalist 29(5):49-51.

242. Logier, E. B. S. 1932. SOME ACCOUNT OF THE AMPHIBIANS AND REPTILES OF BRITISH COLUMBIA. Transactions of the Royal Canadian Institute XVIII Part 2(53):311-336.

243. Gregson, J. D. 1935. A PRELIMINARY REPORT OF THE LIZARD-TICK RELATIONSHIP ON THE COAST OF BRITISH COLUMBIA. Proceedings of the Entomological Society of British Columbia 31:17-21.

244. Chandler, Asa C. 1919. ON A SPECIES OF HEDRURIS OCCURRING COMMONLY IN THE WESTERN NEWT, Notophthalmus torosus. Journal of Parasitology 5(3):116-123.

245. Lehmann, Donald L. 1954. SOME HELMINTHS OF WEST COAST URODELES. Journal of Parasitology 40(2):231.

246. Lehmann, Donald L. 1954. A NEW SPECIES OF TRYPANOSOME FROM THE SALAMANDER Ambystoma gracile WITH NOTES ON A COLLECTION OF AMPHIBIAN BLOOD SMEARS. Journal of Parasitology 40(4):656-659.

247. Lehmann, Donald L. 1956. SOME HELMINTHS OF OREGON URODELES. Journal of Parasitology 42(1):25.

248. McCurdy, Harriet M. 1971. MELANOPHORE ACTIVITY OF URODELE MELANOCYTES. Canadian Journal of Zoology 49(2):277-278.

249. Gradwell, Norman. 1971. Ascaphus TADPOLE: EXPERIMENTS ON THE SUCTION AND GILL IRRIGATION MECHANISMS. Canadian Journal of Zoology 49(3):307-332.

250. Friedmann, G. B. 1971. ALTITUDINAL VARIATIONS IN THE RED BLOOD CELL COUNT AND HAEMOGLOBIN CONTENT OF URODELE BLOOD. Canadian Journal of Zoology 49(4):565-568.

251. Winterbourn, Michael J. 1971. THE LIFE HISTORIES AND TROPHIC RELATIONSHIPS OF THE TRICHOPTERA OF MARION LAKE, BRITISH COLUMBIA. Canadian Journal of Zoology 49(5):623-635.

252. Oliphant, L. W. 1973. EPIDERMAL XANTHOPHORES IN A SALAMANDER. Canadian Journal of Zoology 51(9):1007-1009.

253. Bols, N. C. and H. E. Kasinsky. 1972. BASIC PROTEIN COMPOSITION OF ANURAN SPERM: A CYTOCHEMICAL STUDY. Canadian Journal of Zoology 50(2):171-177.

254. Sprules, W. Gary. 1974. THE ADAPTIVE SIGNIFICANCE OF PAEDOGENESIS IN NORTH AMERICAN SPECIES OF Ambystoma (AMPHIBIA: CAUDATA): AN HYPOTHESIS. Canadian Journal of Zoology 52(3):393-400.

255. Friedmann, G. B. 1974. THE ANNUAL CYCLE OF RED BLOOD CELL COUNT AND HAEMOGLOBIN LEVEL IN THE URODELE Taricha granulosa ON SOUTHERN VANCOUVER ISLAND. Canadian Journal of Zoology 52(4):487-494.

256. Oliver, M. G. and H. M. McCurdy. 1974. MIGRATION, OVERWINTERING, AND REPRODUCTIVE PATTERNS OF Taricha granulosa ON SOUTHERN VANCOUVER ISLAND. Canadian Journal of Zoology 52(4):541-545.

257. Licht, Lawrence E. 1974. SURVIVAL OF EMBRYOS, TADPOLES, AND ADULTS OF THE FROGS _Rana aurora aurora_ AND _Rana pretiosa pretiosa_ SYMPATRIC IN SOUTHWESTERN BRITISH COLUMBIA. _Canadian Journal of Zoology_ 52(5):613–627.

258. Algard, F. T., G. B. Friedmann and H. M. McCurdy. 1974. RESPONSES OF ADULT NEWTS (AMPHIBIA: URODELE) TO X RAYS. _Canadian Journal of Zoology_ 52(6):665–669.

259. Sprules, W. Gary. 1974. ENVIRONMENTAL FACTORS AND THE INCIDENCE OF NEOTENY IN _Ambystoma gracile_ (BAIRD) (AMPHIBIA: CAUDATA). _Canadian Journal of Zoology_ 52(12):1545–1552.

260. Whitney, Carl L. and John R. Krebs. 1975. SPACING AND CALLING IN PACIFIC TREE FROGS, _Hyla regilla_. _Canadian Journal of Zoology_ 53(11):1519–1527.

261. Carr, Catherine M. and Patrick T. Gregory. 1976. CAN TONGUE FLICKS BE USED TO MEASURE NICHE SIZES? _Canadian Journal of Zoology_ 54(8):1389–1394.

262. Eagleson, Gerald W. 1976. A COMPARISON OF THE LIFE HISTORIES AND GROWTH PATTERNS OF POPULATIONS OF THE SALAMANDER _Ambystoma gracile_ (BAIRD) FROM PERMANENT LOW-ALTITUDE AND MONTANE LAKES. _Canadian Journal of Zoology_ 54(12):2098–2111.

263. Fitch, Henry S. 1938. A SYSTEMATIC ACCOUNT OF THE ALLIGATOR LIZARDS (_Gerrhonotus_) IN THE WESTERN UNITED STATES AND LOWER CALIFORNIA. _American Midland Naturalist_ 20(2):381–424.

264. Fitch, Henry S. 1941. GEOGRAPHIC VARIATION IN GARTER SNAKES OF THE SPECIES _Thamnophis sirtalis_ IN THE PACIFIC COAST REGION OF NORTH AMERICA. _American Midland Naturalist_ 26(3):570–592.

265. Livezey, R. L. and A. H. Wright. 1945. DESCRIPTIONS OF FOUR SALIENTIAN EGGS. _American Midland Naturalist_ 34(3):701–706.

266. Tihen, J. A. 1949. THE GENERA OF GERRHONOTINE LIZARDS. _American Midland Naturalist_ 41(3):580–601.

267. Livezey, Robert L. and A. H. Wright. 1947. A SYNOPTIC KEY TO THE SALIENTIAN EGGS OF THE UNITED STATES. _American Midland Naturalist_ 37(1):179–222.

268. Orton, Grace L. 1952. KEY TO THE GENERA OF TADPOLES IN THE UNITED STATES AND CANADA. _American Midland Naturalist_ 47(2):382–395.

269. Wright, A. H. and A. A. Wright. 1952. LIST OF THE SNAKES OF THE UNITED STATES AND CANADA BY STATES AND PROVINCES. _American Midland Naturalist_ 48(3):574–603.

270. Farner, Donald S. and James Kezer. 1953. NOTES ON THE AMPHIBIANS AND REPTILES OF CRATER LAKE NATIONAL PARK. _American Midland Naturalist_ 50(2):448–462.

271. Hotton, Nicholas. 1955. A SURVEY OF ADAPTIVE RELATIONSHIPS OF DENTITION TO DIET IN THE NORTH AMERICAN IGUANIDAE. _American Midland Naturalist_ 53(1):88–114.

272. Dunlap, Donald G. 1955. INTER- AND INTRASPECIFIC VARIATION IN OREGON FROGS OF THE GENUS _Rana_. _American Midland Naturalist_ 54(2):314–331.

273. Turner, Frederick B. 1959. PIGMENTATION OF THE WESTERN SPOTTED FROG, _Rana p. pretiosa_, IN YELLOWSTONE PARK, WYOMING. _American Midland Naturalist_ 61(1):162–176.

274. Turner, Frederick B. 1959. AN ANALYSIS OF THE FEEDING HABITS OF _Rana p. pretiosa_ IN YELLOWSTONE PARK, WYOMING. _American Midland Naturalist_ 61(2):403–413.

275. Livezey, Robert L. and Gilbert A. Wyllie. 1961. MORPHOLOGICAL VARIATION BETWEEN LOCAL POPULATIONS OF _Taricha granulosa_ IN OREGON. _American Midland Naturalist_ 66(2):410–416.

276. Tihen, J. A. 1962. OSTEOLOGICAL OBSERVATIONS ON NEW WORLD _Bufo_. _American Midland Naturalist_ 67(1):157–183.

277. Licht, Lawrence E. 1969. PALATABILITY OF RANA AND HYLA EGGS. _American Midland Naturalist_ 82(1):296–298.

278. Altig, Ronald and Edmund D. Brodie, Jr. 1971. FOODS OF _Plethodon larselli_, _Plethodon dunni_ AND _Ensatina eschscholtzi_ IN THE COLUMBIA RIVER GORGE, MULTNOMAH COUNTY, OREGON. _American Midland Naturalist_ 85(1):226–228.

279. McLean, Robert G. 1972. SMALL MAMMALS AND OTHER PREY IN THE DIET OF THE PACIFIC GIANT SALAMANDER (_Dicamptodon ensatus_). _American Midland Naturalist_ 87(2):524–525.

280. Clarke, Raymond D. 1974. FOOD HABITS OF TOADS, GENUS _Bufo_ (AMPHIBIA: BUFONIDAE). _American Midland Naturalist_ 91(1):140–147.

281. Johnson, Judith A. and Edmund D. Brodie, Jr. 1975. THE SELECTIVE ADVANTAGE OF THE DEFENSIVE POSTURE OF THE NEWT, _Taricha granulosa_. _American Midland Naturalist_ 93(1):139–148.

282. Nussbaum, Ronald A. 1977. ASPECTS OF THE LIFE HISTORY AND ECOLOGY OF THE OLYMPIC SALAMANDER, _Rhyacotriton olympicus_ (GAIGE). _American Midland Naturalist_ 98(1):176–199.

283. Bennett, Wm. H. 1937. NOTES ON THE CARE AND HABITS OF SOME INTERESTING URODELES. _Canadian Field-Naturalist_ 51(2):17–20.

284. Whitehouse, F. C. 1947. MOUSE KILLS SNAKE. _Canadian Field-Naturalist_ 61(1):21.

285. Thacker, T. L. 1949. SNAKE'S METHOD OF SLOUGHING ITS SKIN. _Canadian Field-Naturalist_ 63(1):37–38.

286. Gorham, Stanley W. 1963. THE COMPARATIVE NUMBER OF SPECIES OF AMPHIBIANS IN CANADA AND OTHER COUNTRIES. III. SUMMARY OF SPECIES OF ANURANS. _Canadian Field-Naturalist_ 77(1):13–48.

287. Gorham, Stanley W. 1963. KEEPING SMALL AMPHIBIANS AND REPTILES IN HOME-MADE TERRARIA. _Canadian Field-Naturalist_ 77(3):162–168.

288. Carl, G. Clifford. 1963. A COASTAL RECORD OF THE GOPHER SNAKE (_Pituophis_). _Canadian Field-Naturalist_ 77(3):178.

289. Grant, James. 1969. EARLY EMERGENCE FROM HIBERNATION OF THE RUBBER BOA. _Canadian Field-Naturalist_ 83(3):281.

290. Grass, Al. 1972. ROBIN ATTACKS GARTER SNAKE. Canadian Field-Naturalist 86(3):292.

291. Butler, Robert W. 1974. THE FEEDING ECOLOGY OF THE NORTHWESTERN CROW ON MITLENATCH ISLAND, BRITISH COLUMBIA. Canadian Field-Naturalist 88(3):313-316.

292. McNicholl, Martin K. 1975. SIGHT RECORD OF A WESTERN SKINK ON VANCOUVER ISLAND. Canadian Field-Naturalist 89(1):79-80.

293. Cook, Francis R. 1977. RECORDS OF THE BOREAL TOAD FROM THE YUKON AND NORTHERN BRITISH COLUMBIA. Canadian Field-Naturalist 91(2):185-186.

294. Boulenger, George Albert. 1889. CATALOGUE OF THE CHELONIANS, RHYNCHOCEPHALIANS, AND CROCODILES IN THE BRITISH MUSEUM (NATURAL HISTORY). British Museum, (Natural History), London, England. 311 pages.

295. Dunn, Emmett Reid. 1926. THE SALAMANDERS OF THE FAMILY PLETHODONTIDAE. Smith College, Northampton, Massachussetts. 441 pages.

296. Ditmars, Raymond L. 1936. THE REPTILES OF NORTH AMERICA. Doubleday and Company, Inc., Garden City, New York. 476 pages.

297. Bishop, Sherman C. 1943. HANDBOOK OF SALAMANDERS. Comstock Publishing Company, Inc., Ithaca, New York. 555 pages.

298. Pickwell, Gayle. 1947. AMPHIBIANS AND REPTILES OF THE PACIFIC STATES. Stanford University Press, Stanford, California. 236 pages.

299. Stebbins, Robert C. 1951. AMPHIBIANS OF WESTERN NORTH AMERICA. University of California Press, Berkeley and Los Angeles, California. 539 pages.

300. Wright, Albert Hazen and Anna Allen Wright. 1957. HANDBOOK OF SNAKES, VOLUME I AND II. Comstock Publishing Associates, Ithaca, New York. 1105 pages.

301. Klauber, Laurence M. 1972. RATTLE-SNAKES (second edition, Volumes 1 and 2). University of California Press. Berkeley and Los Angeles, California. 1533 pages.

302. Froom, Barbara. 1972. THE SNAKES OF CANADA. McClelland and Stewart Limited, Toronto, Ontario. 128 pages.

303. Fitch, Henry S. 1963. NATURAL HISTORY OF THE RACER Coluber constrictor. University of Kansas Publications, Museum of Natural History 15(8):351-468.

304. Fitch, Henry S. 1965. AN ECOLOGICAL STUDY OF THE GARTER SNAKE, Thamnophis sirtalis. University of Kansas Publications, Museum of Natural History 15(10):493-564.

305. Blair, W. Frank. 1963. EVOLUTIONARY RELATIONSHIPS OF NORTH AMERICAN TOADS OF THE GENUS Bufo: A PROGRESS REPORT. Evolution 17(1):1-16.

306. Jameson, David L., William Taylor and John Mountjoy. 1970. METABOLIC AND MORPHOLOGICAL ADAPTATION TO HETEROGENOUS ENVIRONMENTS BY THE PACIFIC TREE TOAD, Hyla regilla. Evolution 24(1):75-89.

307. Turner, Frederick B. 1960. POPULATION STRUCTURE AND DYNAMICS OF THE WESTERN SPOTTED FROG, Rana p. pretiosa BAIRD AND GIRARD, IN YELLOWSTONE PARK, WYOMING. Ecological Monographs 30(3):251-278.

308. Keddie, Grant R. 1975. THE PACIFIC RUBBER SNAKE IN LOWER CHILCOTIN. Syesis 8:389.

309. Harestad, Alton. 1977. RANGE EXTENSION OF THE NORTHERN ALLIGATOR LIZARD, Gerrhonotus coeruleus princeps (BAIRD AND GIRARD) ON VANCOUVER ISLAND. Syesis 10:171.

310. Licht, Lawrence E. 1971. BREEDING HABITS AND EMBRYONIC THERMAL REQUIREMENTS OF THE FROGS, Rana aurora aurora AND Rana pretiosa pretiosa, IN THE PACIFIC NORTH- WEST. Ecology 52(1):116-124.

311. Calef, George Waller. 1973. NATURAL MORTALITY OF TADPOLES IN A POPULATION OF Rana aurora. Ecology 54(4):741-758.

312. de Villiers, C. G. S. 1934. STUDIES OF THE CRANIAL ANATOMY OF Ascaphus truei STEJNEGER, THE AMERICAN "LIOPELMID". Bulletin of the Museum of Comparative Zoology 77(1):1-38.

313. Stejneger, Leonard and Thomas Barbour. 1943. A CHECK LIST OF NORTH AMERICAN AMPHIBIANS AND REPTILES. Bulletin of the Museum of Comparative Zoology 93(1):1-260.

314. Myers, George S. 1930. NOTES ON SOME AMPHIBIANS IN WESTERN NORTH AMERICA. Proceedings of the Biological Society of Washington 43:55-64.

315. Smith, Philip W. 1956. THE STATUS, CORRECT NAME, AND GEOGRAPHIC RANGE OF THE BOREAL CHORUS FROG. Proceedings of the Biological Society of Washington 69:169-176.

316. Johnson, Myrtle E. 1913. THE CONTROL OF PIGMENT FORMATION IN AMPHIBIAN LARVAE. University of California Publications in Zoology 11(4):53-88.

317. Holmes, S. J. 1913. OBSERVATIONS ON ISOLATED LIVING PIGMENT CELLS FROM THE LARVAE OF AMPHIBIANS. University of California Publications in Zoology 11(7):143-154.

318. Holmes, S. J. 1913. BEHAVIOR OF ECTODERMIC EPITHELIUM OF TADPOLES WHEN CULTIVATED IN PLASMA. University of California Publications in Zoology 11(8):155-172.

319. Storer, Tracy I. 1925. A SYNOPSIS OF THE AMPHIBIA OF CALIFORNIA. University of California Publications in Zoology 27:1-342.

320. Storer, Tracy I. 1930. NOTES ON THE RANGE AND LIFE-HISTORY OF THE PACIFIC FRESH-WATER TURTLE, Clemmys marmorata. University of California Publications in Zoology 32(5):429-441.

321. Eaton, Theodore H., Jr. 1933. THE OCCURRENCE OF STREPTOSTYLY IN THE AMBYSTOMIDAE. University of California Publications in Zoology 37(17):521- 526.

322. Fitch, Henry S. 1940. A BIOGEOGRAPHICAL STUDY OF THE ORDINOIDES ARTENKREIS OF GARTER SNAKES (GENUS *Thamnophis*). *University of California Publications in Zoology* 44(1):1-150.

323. Schechtman, A. Mandel. 1942. THE MECHANISM OF AMPHIBIAN GASTRULATION. I. GASTRULATION-PROMOTING INTERACTIONS BETWEEN VARIOUS REGIONS OF AN ANURAN EGG (*Hyla regilla*). *University of California Publications in Zoology* 51(1):1-40.

324. Harris, Morgan. 1942. DIFFERENTIATION AND GROWTH OF GASTRULAR ANLAGEN IMPLANTED HOMOPLASTICALLY IN TADPOLES OF *Hyla regilla*. *University of California Publications in Zoology* 51(2):41-86.

325. Fernald, Robert L. 1943. THE ORIGIN AND DEVELOPMENT OF THE BLOOD ISLAND OF *Hyla regilla*. *University of California Publications in Zoology* 51(4):129-148.

326. Stebbins, Robert C. and Harry B. Robinson. 1946. FURTHER ANALYSIS OF A POPULATION OF THE LIZARD *Sceloporus graciosus gracilis*. *University of California Publications in Zoology* 48(3):149-168.

327. Burch, Arthur B. 1946. AN EXPERIMENTAL STUDY OF THE HISTOLOGICAL AND FUNCTIONAL DIFFERENTIATION OF THE EPITHELIAL HYPOTHYSIS IN *Hyla regilla*. *University of California Publications in Zoology* 51(7):185-214.

328. James, Miriam Stokes. 1946. THE ROLE OF THE BASIBRANCHIAL CARTILAGES IN THE EARLY DEVELOPMENT OF THE THYROID OF *Hyla regilla*. *University of California Publications in Zoology* 51(8):215-228.

329. Rodgers, Thomas L. and Henry S. Fitch. 1947. VARIATION IN THE SKINKS (REPTILIA: LACERTILIA) OF THE SKILTONIANUS GROUP. *University of California Publications in Zoology* 48(4):169-220.

330. Eakin, Richard M. 1947. DETERMINATION AND REGULATION OF POLARITY IN THE RETINA OF *Hyla regilla*. *University of California Publications in Zoology* 51(10):245-288.

331. Stebbins, Robert C. 1949. SPECIATION IN SALAMANDERS OF THE PLETHODONTID GENUS *Ensatina*. *University of California Publications in Zoology* 48(6):377-526.

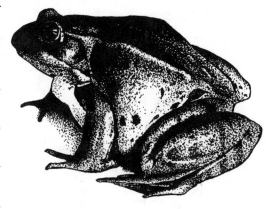

332. Stebbins, Robert C. and Charles H. Lowe, Jr. 1951. SUBSPECIFIC DIFFERENTIATION IN THE OLYMPIC SALAMANDER *Rhyacotriton olympicus*. *University of California Publications in Zoology* 50(4):465-484.

333. Fox, Wade. 1951. RELATIONSHIPS AMONG THE GARTER SNAKES OF THE *Thamnophis elegans* RASSENKREIS. *University of California Publications in Zoology* 50(5):485-530.

334. Stebbins, Robert C. 1954. NATURAL HISTORY OF THE SALAMANDERS OF THE PLETHODONTID GENUS *Ensatina*. *University of California Publications in Zoology* 54(2):47-124.

335. Riemer, William J. 1958. VARIATION AND SYSTEMATIC RELATIONSHIPS WITHIN THE SALAMANDER GENUS *Taricha*. *University of California Publications in Zoology* 56(3):301-390.

336. Peabody, Frank E. 1959. TRACKWAYS OF LIVING AND FOSSIL SALAMANDERS. *University of California Publications in Zoology* 63(1):1-72.

337. Karlstrom, Ernest L. 1962. THE TOAD GENUS Bufo IN THE SIERRA NEVADA OF CALIFORNIA. University of California Publications in Zoology 62(1):1-104.

338. Heath, James Edward. 1965. TEMPERATURE REGULATION AND DIURNAL ACTIVITY IN HORNED LIZARDS. University of California Publications in Zoology 64(3):97-136.

339. Brown, Charles W. 1974. HYBRIDIZATION AMONG THE SUBSPECIES OF THE PLETHODONTID SALAMANDER Ensatus eschscholtzi. University of California Publications in Zoology 98:1-62.

340. Van Denburgh, John. 1912. NOTES ON Ascaphus, THE DISCOGLOSSOID TOAD OF NORTH AMERICA. Proceedings of the California Academy of Sciences 3(11):259-264.

341. Van Denburgh, John and Joseph R. Slevin. 1918. GARTER-SNAKES OF WESTERN NORTH AMERICA. Proceedings of the California Academy of Sciences 8(6):181-270.

342. Van Denburgh, John and Joseph R. Slevin. 1919. THE GOPHER SNAKES OF WESTERN NORTH AMERICA. Proceedings of the California Academy of Sciences 9(6):197-220.

343. Van Denburgh, John. 1920. A FURTHER STUDY OF VARIATION IN THE GOPHER-SNAKES OF WESTERN NORTH AMERICA. Proceedings of the California Academy of Sciences 10(1):1-27.

344. Swarth, Harry S. 1936. ORIGINS OF THE FAUNA OF THE SITKAN DISTRICT, ALASKA. Proceedings of the California Academy of Sciences 23(3):59-78.

345. Miller, Malcolm R. 1966. THE COCHLEAR DUCT OF LIZARDS. Proceedings of the California Academy of Sciences (Fourth Series) XXXII(11):255-359.

346. Jameson, David L., James P. Mackey and Rollin C. Richmond. 1966. THE SYSTEMATICS OF THE PACIFIC TREE FROG, Hyla regilla. Proceedings of the California Academy of Sciences (Fourth Series) 33(19):551-620.

347. Miller, Malcolm R. and Michiko Kasahara. 1967. STUDIES ON THE CUTANEOUS INNERVATION OF LIZARDS. Proceedings of the California Academy of Sciences (Fourth Series) XXXIV(16):549-568.

348. Miller, Malcolm R. 1968. THE COCHLEAR DUCT OF SNAKES. Proceedings of the California Academy of Sciences (Fourth Series) XXXV(19):425-476.

349. Van Denburgh, John. 1897. THE REPTILES OF THE PACIFIC COAST AND GREAT BASIN: AN ACCOUNT OF THE SPECIES KNOWN TO INHABIT OREGON, WASHINGTON, IDAHO AND NEVADA. Occasional Papers of the California Academy of Sciences 5:1-236.

350. Van Denburgh, John. 1922. THE REPTILES OF WESTERN NORTH AMERICA — AN ACCOUNT OF THE SPECIES KNOWN TO INHABIT CALIFORNIA AND OREGON, WASHINGTON, IDAHO, UTAH, NEVADA, ARIZONA, BRITISH COLUMBIA, SONORA AND LOWER CALIFORNIA (VOLUME I — LIZARDS AND VOLUME II — SNAKES AND TURTLES.) Occasional Papers of the California Academy of Sciences No. 10, San Francisco. 1028 pages.

351. Slevin, Joseph R. 1928. THE AMPHIBIANS OF WESTERN NORTH AMERICA. California Academy of Sciences Occasional Paper 16:1-152.

352.   Anonymous. 1922. ACCESSIONS. Report of the Provincial Museum of Natural History for the Year 1921, Victoria. Pages 11-12.

353.   Hardy, G. A. 1925. AMPHIBIA OF BRITISH COLUMBIA. Report of the Provincial Museum of Natural History for the Year 1924, Victoria. Pages 21-24.

354.   Hardy, G. A. 1927. REPORT ON A COLLECTING TRIP TO GARIBALDI PARK, B.C. Report of the Provincial Museum of Natural History for the Year 1926, Victoria. Pages 15-26.

355.   Hardy, G. A. 1955. THE NATURAL HISTORY OF THE FORBIDDEN PLATEAU AREA VANCOUVER ISLAND, BRITISH COLUMBIA. Report of the Provincial Museum of Natural History and Anthropology for the Year 1954, Victoria. Pages 24-63.

356.   Carl, G. Clifford. 1955. THE GREEN TURTLE IN BRITISH COLUMBIA. Report of the Provincial Museum of Natural History and Anthropology for the Year 1954, Victoria. Pages 77-78.

357.   Thetis Park Nature Sanctuary Association. 1966. NATURAL HISTORY OF THETIS LAKE AREA NEAR VICTORIA, BRITISH COLUMBIA. Report of the Provincial Museum of Natural History and Anthropology for the Year 1965, Victoria. Pages 21-54.

358.   Campbell, R. Wayne and David Stirling. 1968. NOTES ON THE NATURAL HISTORY OF CLELAND ISLAND, BRITISH COLUMBIA, WITH EMPHASIS ON THE BREEDING BIRD FAUNA. Report of the Provincial Museum of Natural History and Anthropology for the Year 1967, Victoria. Pages 25-43.

359.   Thorson, Thomas Bertel. 1941. A COMPARATIVE STUDY OF THE EFFECTS OF EXSICCATION ON SELECTED SPECIES OF AMPHIBIA. M.Sc. Thesis, University of Washington, Department of Zoology. Seattle. 52 pages.

360.   Schmidt, Anthony John. 1954. THE THYROID AND THYROID FUNCTION IN THE NORTHWESTERN SALAMANDER, Ambystoma gracile (BAIRD). M.Sc. Thesis, University of Washington, Department of Zoology, Seattle. 62 pages.

361.   Manwell, Clyde Pat. 1955. A STUDY OF THE HEMOGLOBINS OF SOME SNAKES OF THE GENUS Thamnophis. M.Sc. Thesis, University of Washington, Department of Zoology, Seattle. 88 pages.

362.   Larsen, John Herbert. 1958. COMPARATIVE CRANIAL OSTEOLOGY OF THE AMBYSTOMID SALAMANDERS. M.Sc. Thesis, University of Washington, Department of Zoology, Seattle. 61 pages.

363.   Thorson, Thomas Bertel. 1952. THE RELATIONSHIP OF WATER ECONOMY OF AMPHIBIANS IN AIR TO TERRES-TRIALISM. Ph.D. Thesis, University of Washington, Department of Zoology, Seattle. 149 pages.

364.   Larsen, John Herbert. 1963. THE CRANIAL OSTEOLOGY OF NEOTENIC AND TRANSFORMED SALAMANDERS AND ITS BEARING ON INTERFAMILIAL RELATIONSHIPS. Ph.D. Thesis, University of Washington, Department of Zoology, Seattle. 205 pages.

365.   Pianka, Eric Rodger. 1965. SPECIES DIVERSITY AND ECOLOGY OF FLATLAND DESERT LIZARDS IN WESTERN NORTH AMERICA. Ph.D. Thesis, University of Washington, Department of Zoology, Seattle. 212 pages.

366. Stanwell-Fletcher, John F. and Theodora C. Stanwell-Fletcher. 1943. SOME ACCOUNTS OF THE FLORA AND FAUNA OF THE DRIFTWOOD VALLEY REGION OF NORTH CENTRAL BRITISH COLUMBIA. British Columbia Provincial Museum Occasional Paper No. 4, Victoria. 97 pages.

367. Carl, G. Clifford, C. J. Guiguet and George A. Hardy. 1952. A NATURAL HISTORY SURVEY OF THE MANNING PARK AREA, BRITISH COLUMBIA. British Columbia Provincial Museum Occasional Paper No. 9, Victoria. 130 pages.

368. Kennedy, Ken, Debra Le Brocq and Ian Dube. 1976. A PRELIMINARY REPORT ON THE WILDLIFE SURVEY AND ACTIVITIES ON THE MORRELL WILD-LIFE SANCTUARY DURING THE SUMMER OF 1975. Unpublished Report, Malaspina College, Nanaimo. 33 pages.

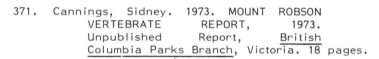

369. Shepard, Teresa. 1977. NATURALIST'S SUMMER REPORT, LAKELSE LAKE PARK. Unpublished Report, British Columbia Parks Branch, Victoria. 29 pages.

370. Butler, R. 1922. MOUNT ROBSON PARK NATURALIST PROGRAMME 1972. Unpublished Report, British Columbia Parks Branch, Victoria. 68 pages.

371. Cannings, Sidney. 1973. MOUNT ROBSON VERTEBRATE REPORT, 1973. Unpublished Report, British Columbia Parks Branch, Victoria. 18 pages.

372. van Tets, Gerard Frederick. 1963. A REPORT ON THE SEABIRD COLONY AT MITLENATCH ISLAND. Unpublished Report, British Columbia Parks Branch, Victoria. 133 pages.

373. Stirling, David. 1960. ANNUAL REPORT MIRACLE BEACH NATURE HOUSE 1960. Unpublished Report, British Columbia Parks Branch, Victoria. 6 pages.

374. Stirling, David. 1962. REPTILES AND AMPHIBIANS OF MIRACLE BEACH - 1962. Unpublished Report, British Columbia Parks Branch, Victoria. 2 pages.

375. Wade, Carson. 1964. THE REPTILES AND AMPHIBIANS OF MIRACLE BEACH PARK. Unpublished Report, British Columbia Parks Branch, Victoria. 7 pages.

376. Cannings, Rob and Ken Kennedy. 1965. A STUDY ON THE GARTER SNAKES OF MIRACLE BEACH. Unpublished Report, British Columbia Parks Branch, Victoria. 10 pages.

377. Westerborg, B. 1964. OBSERVATIONS ON THE FLORA AND FAUNA OF LONG BEACH PROVINCIAL PARK, AUG. 31 - SEPT. 2, 1964. Unpublished Report, British Columbia Parks Branch, Victoria. 6 pages.

378. Buffam, Frank. 1965. WICKANINNISH BEACH - SUMMER 1965. Unpublished Report, British Columbia Parks Branch, Victoria. 80 pages.

379. Campbell, R. Wayne. 1967. WICKANINNISH PROVINCIAL PARK SUMMER REPORT 1967. Unpublished Report, British Columbia Parks Branch, Victoria. 163 pages.

380. Campbell, R. Wayne. 1968. WICKANINNISH PROVINCIAL PARK SUMMER REPORT, 1968. Unpublished Report, British Columbia Parks Branch, Victoria. 104 pages.

381. Wolfe, Michael. 1977. HELLIWELL PARK - 1977 SUMMER REPORT. Unpublished Report, British Columbia Parks Branch, Victoria. 61 pages.

382. Wolfe, Michael. 1978. REPORT OF 1978 INTERPRETATION PROGRAM HELLIWELL PARK. Unpublished Report, British Columbia Parks Branch, Victoria. 15 pages.

383. Dawe, Neil K. 1971. NATURE INTERPRETATION REPORT ON WASA, MOYIE AND JIMSMITH PROVINCIAL PARKS, BRITISH COLUMBIA. Unpublished Report, British Columbia Parks Branch, Victoria. 97 pages.

384. Fitz-Gibbon, Joyce. 1977. WASA LAKE PARK – FAUNA RECORDS, 1977. Unpublished Report, British Columbia Parks Branch, Victoria. 43 pages.

385. Campbell, R. Wayne and Robert G. Foottit. 1969. NATURE INTERPRETATION SURVEY OF RATHTREVOR BEACH PROVINCIAL PARK (1969). Unpublished Report, British Columbia Parks Branch, Victoria. 24 pages.

386. Grass, Al. 1971. WELLS GRAY PARK NATURALIST'S REPORT – 1971. Unpublished Report, British Columbia Parks Branch, Victoria. 45 pages.

387. Wright, Richard T. 1972. NATURALIST'S REPORT – 1972 – WELLS GRAY PROVINCIAL PARK. Unpublished Report, British Columbia Parks Branch, Victoria. 55 pages.

388. Goldberg, Stephen R. 1975. YEARLY VARIATIONS IN THE OVARIAN CYCLE OF THE LIZARD Sceloporus occidentalis. Journal of Herpetology 9(2):187–189.

389. Jameson, E. W., Jr. 1974. FAT AND BREEDING CYCLES IN A MONTANE POPULATION OF Sceloporus graciosus. Journal of Herpetology 8(4):311–322.

390. Sottovia-Filho, Dagoberto. 1974. MORPHOLOGICAL AND HISTOCHEMICAL STUDY OF MAST CELLS IN LIZARDS AND FROGS, WITH SPECIAL REFERENCE TO THE SO-CALLED "SUMMER CELLS" OR "STILLING CELLS" OF AMPHIBIANS. Journal of Herpetology 8(4):305–309.

391. Vitt, Laurie J. 1974. REPRODUCTIVE EFFORT AND ENERGY COMPARISONS OF ADULTS, EGGS, AND NEONATES OF Gerrhonotus coeruleus principis. Journal of Herpetology 8(2):165–168.

392. Gaudin, Anthony J. 1974. AN OSTEOLOGICAL ANALYSIS OF HOLARCTIC TREE FROGS, FAMILY HYLIDAE. Journal of Herpetology 8(2):141–152.

393. Peacock, Robert L. and Ronald A. Nussbaum. 1973. REPRODUCTIVE BIOLOGY AND POPULATION STRUCTURE OF THE WESTERN RED-BACKED SALAMANDER, Plethodon vehiculum (COOPER). Journal of Herpetology 7(3):215–224.

3

394. Weiss, Burton A., Bradley H. Stuart and William F. Strother. 1973. AUDITORY SENSITIVITY IN THE Rana catesbeiana TADPOLE. Journal of Herpetology 7(3):211-214.

395. Maughan, O. Eugene and M. Gary Wickham. 1976. RECORDS OF THE PACIFIC GIANT SALAMANDER, Dicamptodon ensatus, (AMPHIBIA, URODELA, AMBYSTOMATIDAE) FROM THE ROCKY MOUNTAINS IN IDAHO. Journal of Herpetology 10(3):249-251.

396. Medica, Philip A. and Frederick B. Turner. 1976. REPRODUCTION BY Uta stansburiana (REPTILIA, LACER-TILIA, IGUANIDAE) IN SOUTHERN NEVADA. Journal of Herpetology 10(2):123-128.

397. Pisani, George R. 1976. COMMENTS ON THE COURTSHIP AND MATING MECHANICS OF Thamnophis (REPTILIA, SERPENTES, COLUBRI-DAE). Journal of Herpetology 10(2):139-142.

398. Weigman, Diana L. and Ronald Altig. 1975. ANAEROBIC GLYCOLYSIS IN TWO LARVAL AMPHIBIANS. Journal of Herpetology 9(4):355-357.

399. Schrode, C. J. 1972. EFFECT OF TEMPER-ATURE AND DISSOLVED OXYGEN CONCENTRATION ON THE RATE OF METAMORPHOSIS OF Ambystoma tigrinum. Journal of Herpetology 6(3-4):199-207.

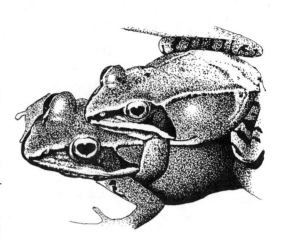

400. Garrick, Leslie D. 1972. TEMPERATURE INFLUENCES ON HIBERNATION IN Sceloporus occidentalis. Journal of Herpetology 6(3-4):195-198.

401. Anderson, James D. 1972. BEHAVIOR OF THREE SUBSPECIES OF Ambystoma macrodactylum IN A SOIL MOISTURE GRADIENT. Journal of Herpetology 6(3-4):191-194.

402. Altig, Ronald and Edmund D. Brodie, Jr. 1972. LABORATORY BEHAVIOR OF Ascaphus truei TADPOLES. Journal of Herpetology 6(1):21-24.

403. Whitaker, John O., Jr. 1971. A STUDY OF THE WESTERN CHORUS FROG, Pseudacris triseriata, IN VIGO COUNTY, INDIANA. Journal of Herpetology 5(3-4):127-150.

404. Guttman, Sheldon I. 1971. AN ELECTROPHORETIC ANALYSIS OF THE HEMOGLOBINS OF OLD AND NEW WORLD LIZARDS. Journal of Herpetology 5(1-2):11-16.

405. de Vlaming, Victor L. and R. Bruce Bury. 1970. THERMAL SELECTION IN TADPOLES OF THE TAILED-FROG, Ascaphus truei. Journal of Herpetology 4(3-4):179-189.

406. Mueller, Charles F. 1970. ENERGY UTILIZATION IN THE LIZARDS Sceloporus graciosus AND S. occidentalis. Journal of Herpetology 4(3-4):131-134.

407. Wernz, James G. 1969. SPRING MATING OF Ascaphus. Journal of Herpetology 3(3-4):167-169.

408. Metter, Dean E. 1968. THE INFLUENCE OF FLOODS ON POPULATION STRUCTURE OF Ascaphus truei STEJNEGER. Journal of Herpetology 1(1-4):105-106.

409. Stewart, Glenn R. 1968. SOME OBSERVATIONS ON THE NATURAL HISTORY OF TWO OREGON GARTER SNAKES (GENUS Thamnophis). Journal of Herpetology 2(3-4):71-86.

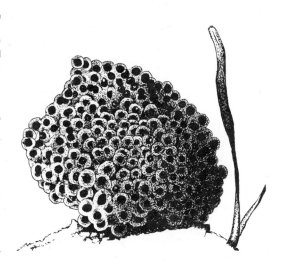

410. Vincent, Tom. 1975. BODY TEMPERATURES OF *Thamnophis sirtalis parietalis* AT THE DEN SITE. Journal of Herpetology 9(2):252-254.

411. Jameson, E. W., Jr. and Allen Allison. 1976. FAT AND BREEDING CYCLES IN TWO MONTANE POPULATIONS OF *Sceloporus occidentalis* (REPTILIA, LACERTILIA, IGUANIDAE). Journal of Herpetology 10(3):211-220.

412. Brown, Herbert A. 1977. A CASE OF INTERBREEDING BETWEEN *Rana aurora* AND *Bufo boreas* (AMPHIBIA, ANURA). Journal of Herpetology 11(1):92-94.

413. Bethea, Cynthia L. and Richard F. Walker. 1978. PARIETAL EYE-PINEAL GLAND INTERACTIONS IN THE LIZARD *Sceloporus occidentalis* (REPTILIA, LACERTILIS, IGUANIDAE). Journal of Herpetology 12(1):83-87.

414. Maxson, Linda R. 1978. IMMUNOLOGICAL EVIDENCE PERTAINING TO RELATIONSHIPS BETWEEN OLD WORLD *Hyla arborea* (AMPHIBIA, ANURA, HYLIDAE) AND NORTH AMERICAN *Hyla*. Journal of Herpetology 12(1):98-100.

415. McAuliffe, Joseph R. 1978. SEASONAL MIGRATIONAL MOVEMENTS OF A POPULATION OF THE WESTERN PAINTED TURTLE, *Chrysemys picta bellii* (REPTILIA, TESTUDINES, TESTUDINIDAE). Journal of Herpetology 12(2):143-149.

416. Vincent, T. K. and D. M. Secoy. 1978. THE EFFECTS OF ANNUAL VARIATION IN TEMPERATURE ON COLD RESISTANCE IN A NORTHERN POPULATION OF THE RED-SIDED GARTER SNAKE, *Thamnophis sirtalis parietalis* (REPTILIA, SERPENTES, COLUBRIDAE). Journal of Herpetology 12(3):291-294.

417. Horseman, Nelson D., Craig A. Smith and Dudley D. Culley, Jr. 1978. EFFECTS OF AGE AND PHOTOPERIOD ON OVARY SIZE AND CONDITION IN BULLFROGS (*Rana catesbeiana* SHAW) (AMPHIBIA, ANURA, RANIDAE). Journal of Herpetology 12(3):287-290.

418. Beiswenger, Ronald E. 1978. RESPONSES OF *Bufo* TADPOLES (AMPHIBIA, ANURA, BUFONIDAE) TO LABORATORY GRADIENTS OF TEMPERATURE. Journal of Herpetology 12(4):499-504.

419. Briggs, Jeffrey. 1978. AN ASYMPTOTIC GROWTH MODEL ALLOWING SEASONAL VARIATION IN GROWTH RATES, WITH APPLICATION TO A POPULATION OF THE CASCADE FROG, *Rana cascadae* (AMPHIBIA, ANURA, RANIDAE). Journal of Herpetology 12(4):559-564.

420. Vitt, Laurie. 1966. FIELD NOTES ON THE SPOTTED NIGHT SNAKE (*Hypsiglena torquata deserticola*). Bulletin of the Pacific Northwest Herpetological Society 1(1):10.

421. Carlson, Dennis S. 1967. A CHECKLIST OF AMPHIBIANS AND REPTILES OF WASHINGTON. Bulletin of the Pacific Northwest Herpetological Society 2(1):7-8.

422. Vitt, Laurie J. 1967. A PRELIMINARY SURVEY OF *Thamnophis ordinoides* (BAIRD AND GIRARD) FROM TWO REGIONS, LUMMI ISLAND AND CHUCKANUT DRIVE, WHATCOM COUNTY, WASHINGTON. Bulletin of the Pacific Northwest Herpetological Society 2(2):8-14.

423. Smith, Arnold J. M. 1968. GARTER SNAKES OF THE PACIFIC NORTHWEST. Bulletin of the Pacific Northwest Herpetological Society 3(1):16-19.

424. Wagner, Ernie. 1969. THE GEOLOGY OF RATTLESNAKE DENS IN WASHINGTON STATE. Bulletin of the Pacific Northwest Herpetological Society 4(1):9-12.

425. Lardie, Richard L. 1969. CHECKLIST OF THE REPTILES OF PIERCE COUNTY, WASHINGTON, WITH REFERENCE TO THOSE FOUND ON McCHORD AIR FORCE BASE. Bulletin of the Pacific Northwest Herpetological Society 4(1):18-23.

426. Vitt, Laurie. 1969. THE NORTHERN ALLIGATOR LIZARD, Gerrhonotus coeruleus principis FROM WEST OF THE CASCADE MOUNTAIN RANGE. Bulletin of the Pacific Northwest Herpetological Society 4(2):6-7.

427. Lardie, Richard L. 1969. CHECKLIST OF THE AMPHIBIANS OF PIERCE COUNTY, WASHINGTON WITH REFERENCE TO THOSE FOUND ON McCHORD AIR FORCE BASE. Bulletin of the Pacific Northwest Herpetological Society 4(2):17-21.

428. Paulson, Dennis. 1971. KEY TO WASHINGTON STATE REPTILES AND AMPHIBIANS. Bulletin of the Pacific Northwest Herpetological Society 5(1):27-33.

429. Paulson, Dennis. 1972. REPTILES AND AMPHIBIANS OF WASHINGTON. Bulletin of the Pacific Northwest Herpetological Society 5(2):13-15.

430. Kiester, A. Ross. 1971. SPECIES DENSITY OF NORTH AMERICAN AMPHIBIANS AND REPTILES. Systematic Zoology 20(2):127-137.

431. Pauken, Robert J. and Dean E. Metter. 1971. GEOGRAPHIC REPRESENTATION OF MORPHOLOGIC VARIATION AMONG POPULATIONS OF Ascaphus truei STEJNEGER. Systematic Zoology 20(4):434-441.

432. Maxson, Linda R. and A. C. Wilson. 1975. ALBUMIN EVOLUTION AND ORGANISMAL EVOLUTION IN TREE FROGS (HYLIDAE). Systematic Zoology 24(1):1-15.

433. Case, Susan M., Patricia G. Haneline and Margaret F. Smith. 1975. PROTEIN VARIATION IN SEVERAL SPECIES OF Hyla. Systematic Zoology 24(3):281-295.

434. Amaral, Afranio do. 1929. STUDIES OF NEARCTIC OPHIDIA V. ON Crotalus confluentus SAY, 1823, AND ITS ALLIED FORMS. Bulletin of the Antivenin Institute of America 2(4):86-97.

435. Martin, P. J. 1930. SNAKE HUNT NETS LARGE CATCH. Bulletin of the Antivenin Institute of America 4(3):77-78.

436. Storm, Robert M. 1966. AMPHIBIANS AND REPTILES. Northwest Science 40(4):138-141.

437. Slater, J. R. 1937. NOTES ON THE TIGER SALAMANDER, Ambystoma tigrinum, IN WASHINGTON AND IDAHO. Herpetologica 1(3):81-83.

438. Slater, James R. 1938. Rhyacotriton olympicus (GAIGE) IN NORTHERN OREGON AND SOUTHERN WASHINGTON. Herpetologica 1(5):136.

439. Slater, James R. 1939. DESCRIPTION AND LIFE HISTORY OF A NEW Rana FROM WASHINGTON. Herpetologica 1(6):145-149.

440. Slater, James R. 1939. Plethodon dunni IN OREGON AND WASHINGTON. Herpetologica 1(6):154.

441. Johnson, Murray L. 1947. THE STATUS OF THE elegans SUBSPECIES OF Thamnophis, WITH DESCRIPTION OF A NEW SUBSPECIES FROM WASHINGTON STATE. Herpetologica 3(5):159-165.

442. Storm, Robert M. and Alvin R. Allen. 1947. FOOD HABITS OF <u>Aneides ferreus</u>. <u>Herpetologica</u> 4(2):59–60.

443. Knowlton, G. F., E. J. Taylor and W. J. Hanson. 1948. INSECT FOOD OF <u>Uta</u> <u>stansburiana</u> <u>stansburiana</u> IN THE TIMPIE AREA OF UTAH. <u>Herpetologica</u> 4(6):197–198.

444. Hilton, William A. 1948. SALAMANDER NOTES FROM THE NORTHWEST. <u>Herpetologica</u> 4(3):120.

445. Hebard, William B. 1950. RELATIONSHIPS AND VARIATION IN THE GARTER SNAKES, GENUS <u>Thamnophis</u> OF THE PUGET SOUND REGION OF WASHINGTON STATE. <u>Herpetologica</u> 6(4):97–101.

446. Hilton, William A. 1950. REVIEW OF THE CHONDROCRANIUM OF TAILED AMPHIBIA. <u>Herpetologica</u> 6(5):125–135.

447. Hebard, William B. 1951. NOTES ON THE ECOLOGY OF GARTERSNAKES IN THE PUGET SOUND REGION. <u>Herpetologica</u> 7(2):61–62.

448. Hebard, William B. 1951. NOTES ON THE LIFE HISTORY OF THE PUGET SOUND GARTER SNAKE, <u>Thamnophis</u> <u>ordinoides</u>. <u>Herpetologica</u> 7(4):177–179.

449. Fox, Wade. 1952. NOTES ON FEEDING HABITS OF PACIFIC COAST GARTER SNAKES. <u>Herpetologica</u> 8(1):4–8.

450. Stokely, Paul S. and Paul A. Holle. 1953. VARIATION IN THE VERTEBRAL AXIS OF THE AMBYSTOMIDAE. <u>Herpetologica</u> 9(3):133–138.

451. Cunningham, John D. and Don P. Mullally. 1956. THERMAL FACTORS IN THE ECOLOGY OF THE PACIFIC TREEFROG. <u>Herpetologica</u> 12(1):68–79.

452. Storm, Robert M. 1960. NOTES ON THE BREEDING BIOLOGY OF THE RED-LEGGED FROG (<u>Rana</u> <u>aurora</u> <u>aurora</u>). <u>Herpetologica</u> 16(4):251–259.

453. Highton, Richard. 1962. REVISION OF NORTH AMERICAN SALAMANDERS OF THE GENUS <u>Plethodon</u>. <u>Bulletin of the Florida State Museum, Biological Sciences</u> 6(3):235–367.

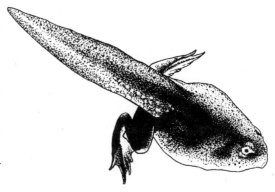

454. Van Denburgh, John. 1906. DESCRIPTION OF A NEW SPECIES OF THE GENUS <u>Plethodon</u> (<u>Plethodon</u> <u>vandykei</u>) FROM MOUNT RAINIER, WASHINGTON. <u>Proceedings of the California Academy of Sciences, Third Series</u> 4(4):61–63.

455. Nichols, Ray Janney. 1937. TAXONOMIC STUDIES ON THE MOUTH PARTS OF LARVAL ANURA. <u>Illinois Biological Monographs</u> 15(4):1–73.

456. Tihen, J. A. 1958. COMMENTS ON THE OSTEOLOGY AND PHYLOGENY OF AMBYSTOMATID SALAMANDERS. <u>Bulletin of the Florida State Museum, Biological Sciences</u> 3(1):1–50.

457. Bryant, Harold C. 1911. THE HORNED LIZARDS OF CALIFORNIA AND NEVADA OF THE GENERA <u>Phrynosoma</u> AND <u>Anota</u>. <u>University of California Publications in Zoology</u> 9(1):1–84.

458. Blanchard, Frank N. 1921. A REVISION OF THE KING SNAKES: GENUS <u>Lampropeltis</u>. <u>United States National Museum Bulletin</u> 114:1–260.

459. Moore, J. E. and E. H. Strickland. 1955. FURTHER NOTES ON THE FOODS OF ALBERTA AMPHIBIANS. American Midland Naturalist 54(1):253–255.

460. Millzner, Raymund. 1924. Megalodiscus ranophilus SP. NOV., A TREMATODE FROM THE RECTUM OF Rana pipiens. University of California Publications in Zoology 26(18):228–230.

461. Millzner, Raymund. 1924. A LARVAL ACANTHOCEPHALID, Centrorhynchus californicus SP. NOV., FROM THE MESENTERY OF Hyla regilla. University of California Publications in Zoology 26(17):225–227.

462. Wake, David B. 1966. COMPARATIVE OSTEOLOGY OF THE LUNGLESS SALAMANDERS, FAMILY PLETHODON-TIDAE. Memoirs of the Southern California Academy of Sciences 4:1–111.

463. Klauber, Laurence M. 1943. THE SUB-SPECIES OF THE RUBBER SNAKE, Charina. Transactions of the San Diego Society of Natural History 10(7):83–90.

464. Klauber, Laurence M. 1943. THE CORAL KING SNAKES OF THE PACIFIC COAST. Transactions of the San Diego Society of Natural History 10(6):75–82.

465. Rodgers, Thomas L. and Viola H. Memmler. 1943. GROWTH IN THE WESTERN BLUE-TAILED SKINK. Transactions of the San Diego Society of Natural History 10(3):61–68.

466. Van Denburgh, John. 1912. NOTES ON SOME REPTILES AND AMPHIBIANS FROM OREGON, IDAHO AND UTAH. Proceedings of the California Academy of Sciences, Fourth Series 3:155–160.

467. Miller, Malcolm R., Michiko Kasahara and Michael Mulroy. 1967. OBSERVATIONS ON THE STRUCTURE OF THE COCHLEAR DUCT LIMBUS OF REPTILES. Proceedings of the California Academy of Sciences, Fourth Series 35(3):37–52.

468. Fitch, Henry S. 1940. A FIELD STUDY OF THE GROWTH AND BEHAVIOR OF THE FENCE LIZARD. University of California Publications in Zoology 44(2):151–172.

469. Resnick, Linda E. and David L. Jameson. 1963. COLOR POLYMORPHISM IN PACIFIC TREE FROGS. Science 142(3595):1081–1083.

470. Mittleman, M. B. and George S. Myers. 1949. GEOGRAPHIC VARIATION IN THE RIBBED FROG, Ascaphus truei. Proceedings of the Biological Society of Washington 62(13):57–68.

471. Cowan, I. McT. and W. B. M. Hick. 1951. A COMPARATIVE STUDY OF THE MYOLOGY OF THE HEAD REGION IN THREE SPECIES OF Thamnophis (REPTILIA, OPHIDIA). Transactions of the Royal Society of Canada, Series Three 45(5):19–60.

472. Dickerson, Mary C. 1913. THE FROG BOOK. Doubleday, Page & Company, Garden City, New York. 253 pages.

473. Ditmars, Raymond L. 1908. THE REPTILE BOOK. Doubleday, Page & Company, New York, New York. 472 pages.

474. Stejneger Leonhard and Thomas Barbour. 1923. A CHECK LIST OF NORTH AMERICAN AMPHIBIANS AND REPTILES, SECOND EDITION. Harvard University Press, Cambridge, Massachusetts. 171 pages.

475. Stejneger, Leonhard and Thomas Barbour. 1939. A CHECK LIST OF NORTH AMERICAN AMPHIBIANS AND REPTILES, FOURTH EDITION. Harvard University Press, Cambridge, Massachusetts. 207 pages.

476. Schmidt, Karl P. and D. Dwight Davis. 1941. FIELD BOOK OF SNAKES OF THE UNITED STATES AND CANADA. G. P. Putnam's Sons, New York, New York. 365 pages.

477. Klauber, Laurence M. 1930. NEW AND RENAMED SUBSPECIES OF Crotalus confluentus SAY, WITH REMARKS ON RELATED SPECIES. Transactions of the San Diego Society of Natural History 6(3):95–144.

478. Klauber, Laurence M. 1936. A KEY TO THE RATTLESNAKES WITH SUMMARY OF CHARACTERISTICS. Transactions of the San Diego Society of Natural History 8(20):185–276.

479. Klauber, Laurence M. 1949. SOME NEW AND REVIVED SUBSPECIES OF RATTLESNAKES. Transactions of the San Diego Society of Natural History 11(6):61–116.

480. Northcutt, R. Glen. 1970. THE TELENCEPHALON OF THE WESTERN PAINTED TURTLE (Chrysemys picta belli). Illinois Biological Monographs No. 43:1–113.

481. Perkins, C. B. 1940. A KEY TO THE SNAKES OF THE UNITED STATES. Bulletins of the Zoological Society of San Diego 16:1–63.

482. Perkins, C. B. 1949. A KEY TO THE SNAKES OF THE UNITED STATES, SECOND EDITION. Bulletins of the Zoological Society of San Diego 24:1–79.

483. Klauber, Laurence M. 1947. CLASSIFICA-TION AND RANGES OF THE GOPHER SNAKES OF THE GENUS Pituophis IN THE WESTERN UNITED STATES. Bulletins of the Zoological Society of San Diego 22:1–81.

484. Marx, Hymen and George B. Rabb. 1972. PHYLETIC ANALYSIS OF FIFTY CHARACTERS OF ADVANCED SNAKES. Fieldiana: Zoology 63:1–321.

485. Pope, Clifford H. 1944. THE POISONOUS SNAKES OF THE NEW WORLD. New York Zoological Society, New York, New York. 47 pages.

486. Blanchard, Frank Nelson. 1942. THE RING-NECK SNAKES, GENUS Diadophis. Bulletin of the Chicago Academy of Sciences 7(1):1–144.

487. Wright, A. H. 1929. SYNOPSIS AND DESCRIPTION OF NORTH AMERICAN TADPOLES. Proceedings of the United States National Museum 74(2756):1–70.

488. Gloyd, Howard K. 1940. THE RATTLESNAKES, GENERA Sistrurus AND Crotalus. The Chicago Academy of Sciences, Special Publication 4:1–266.

489. Ruthven, Alexander G. 1908. VARIATION AND GENETIC RELATIONSHIPS OF THE GARTER-SNAKES. United States National Museum Bulletin 61:1–201.

490. Stull, Olive Griffith. 1940. VARIATIONS AND RELATIONSHIPS IN THE SNAKES OF THE GENUS Pituophis. United States National Museum Bulletin 175:1–225.

491. Cochran, Doris M. 1961. TYPE SPECIMENS OF REPTILES AND AMPHIBIANS IN THE UNITED STATES NATIONAL MUSEUM. United States National Museum Bulletin 220:1-291.

492. Klauber, Laurence M. 1940. A STATISTICAL STUDY OF THE RATTLESNAKES: VII – THE RATTLE, PART I. Occasional Papers of the San Diego Society of Natural History 6:1-62.

493. Klauber, Laurence M. 1937. A STATISTICAL STUDY OF THE RATTLESNAKES: IV – THE GROWTH OF THE RATTLESNAKES. Occasional Papers of the San Diego Society of Natural History 3:1-56.

494. Klauber, Laurence M. 1939. A STATISTICAL STUDY OF THE RATTLESNAKES: VI – FANGS. Occasional Papers of the San Diego Society of Natural History 5:1-61.

495. Klauber, Laurence M. 1938. A STATISTICAL STUDY OF THE RATTLESNAKES: V – HEAD DIMENSIONS. Occasional Papers of the San Diego Society of Natural History 4:1-53.

496. Klauber, Laurence M. 1936. A STATISTICAL STUDY OF THE RATTLESNAKES: I – INTRODUCTION; II – SEX RATIO IN RATTLESNAKE POPULATIONS; III – BIRTH RATE. Occasional Papers of the San Diego Society of Natural History 1:2-24.

497. Ditmars, Raymond L. 1939. A FIELD BOOK OF NORTH AMERICAN SNAKES. Doubleday, Doran & Company, Inc., New York. 356 pages.

498. Fitch, Henry S. 1935. NATURAL HISTORY OF THE ALLIGATOR LIZARDS. Transactions of the Academy of Science of St. Louis 29(1):1-38.

499. Stejneger, Leonhard. 1895. THE POISONOUS SNAKES OF NORTH AMERICA. Annual Report of the United States National Museum for 1892-1893:337-487.

500. Hansen, Ronald Rae. 1971. THE PACIFIC GIANT SALAMANDER Dicamptodon ensatus. Unpublished Manuscript, Washington State University, Pullman. 31 pages.

501. Cannings, Robert A. 1977. BIOLOGICAL INVESTIGATION OF THE BLUE RIVER HEADWATERS AREA, WELLS GRAY PARK. Unpublished Report, British Columbia Parks Branch, Victoria. 28 pages.

502. Mackie, Austin. 1944. RATTLESNAKES. Unpublished Manuscript by the author, Vernon, British Columbia. 23 pages.

503. Anonymous. 1973. AN ANNOTATED LIST OF THE AMPHIBIANS AND REPTILES OF KOKANEE CREEK PARK AND VICINITY. Unpublished Report, British Columbia Parks Branch, Victoria. 2 pages.

504. Underhill, J. E. 1967. REPORT OF A TRIAL PROGRAM OF INTERPRETATION, KOKANEE CREEK PARK – AUG. 1967. Unpublished Report, British Columbia Parks Branch, Victoria. 9 pages.

505. Henderson, N. Lydia. 1976. REPTILES AND AMPHIBIANS. Pages 37-44 in A NATURALIST GUIDE TO THE COMOX VALLEY AND ADJACENT AREAS INCLUDING CAMPBELL RIVER. Edited by Lydia Henderson and Phil Capes. Comox-Strathcona Natural History Society, Comox. 68 pages.

506. Campbell, R. Wayne and Robert G. Foottit. 1969. PRELIMINARY NATURE INTERPRETATION SURVEY OF THE ALICE LAKE PARK AREA, B.C. Unpublished Report, British Columbia Parks Branch, Victoria. 26 pages.

507. Goward, Trevor. 1973. NATURALIST'S REPORT 1973 – CHAMPION LAKES PROVINCIAL PARK. Unpublished Report, British Columbia Parks Branch, Victoria. 50 pages.

508. Stirling, David. 1961. A REPORT ON THE FLORA AND FAUNA OF SHUSWAP PARK – JULY, 1961. Unpublished Report, British Columbia Parks Branch, Victoria. 25 pages.

509. Nelson, R. Wayne. 1967. SHUSWAP LAKE PROVINCIAL PARK – 1967 SEASON REPORT. Unpublished Report, British Columbia Parks Branch, Victoria. 19 pages.

510. Barkley, William D. 1966. SHUSWAP LAKE NATURE HOUSE. 1966 SEASON REPORT. Unpublished Report, British Columbia Parks Branch, Victoria. 15 pages.

511. Buffam, Frank V. 1964. INTERIM ANNUAL REPORT – SHUSWAP LAKE NATURE HOUSE – JUNE, JULY 1964. Unpublished Report, British Columbia Parks Branch, Victoria. 2 pages.

512. Buffam, Frank V. 1963. ANNUAL REPORT: SHUSWAP LAKE NATURE HOUSE – 1963. Unpublished Report, British Columbia Parks Branch, Victoria. 9 pages.

513. Swift, Pat. 1976. PAUL LAKE PROVINCIAL PARK. Unpublished Report, British Columbia Parks Branch, Victoria. 24 pages.

514. Green, David. 1976. REPTILES AND AMPHIBIANS OF PARKSVILLE – QUALICUM REGION OF VANCOUVER ISLAND 1976. Unpublished Report, British Columbia Parks Branch, Victoria. 2 pages.

515. Hassell, S. 1972. LIST OF THE AMPHIBIANS FOUND IN GOLDEN EARS PARK. Unpublished Report, British Columbia Parks Branch, Victoria. 1 page.

516. Germyn, Dawn and Desmond Belton. 1975. MOUNT SEYMOUR ADDITIONS TO: FLORA AND FAUNA REPORT – SUMMER 1975. Unpublished Report, British Columbia Parks Branch, Victoria. 3 pages.

517. Germyn, D. 1974. REPTILES – MOUNT SEYMOUR PARK. Unpublished Report, British Columbia Parks Branch, Victoria. 1 page.

518. Stirling, David. 1961. A REPORT ON THE FLORA AND FAUNA OF COPPER ISLAND. Unpublished Report, British Columbia Parks Branch, Victoria. 2 pages.

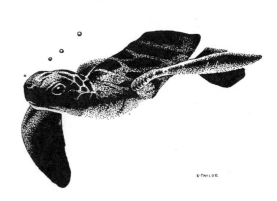

519. Green, David. 1974. REPTILES AND AMPHIBIANS OF SHUSWAP AREA – AN ANNOTATED LIST. Unpublished Report, British Columbia Parks Branch, Victoria. 2 pages.

520. Osmond-Jones, E., L. Bonner, M. Sather, B. Smith and M. MacColl. 1975. A FISHERIES AND WILDLIFE SURVEY OF THE BURNIE LAKES PARK PROPOSAL. Unpublished Report, British Columbia Parks Branch, Victoria. 44 pages.

521. Parkin, T. W. 1974. FRY CREEK CANYON RECREATION AREA. Unpublished Report, British Columbia Parks Branch, Victoria. 4 pages.

522. Swift, Pat. 1974. MISCELLANEOUS SIGHTINGS AT ELLISON PROVINCIAL PARK. Unpublished Report, British Columbia Parks Branch, Victoria. 1 page.

523. Reid, T. C. 1975. LIARD RIVER HOTSPRINGS PARK NATURAL HISTORY OBSERVATIONS (AUTUMN, 1975 AND WINTER-SPRING-SUMMER, 1975). Unpublished Report, British Columbia Parks Branch. 117 pages.

524. Sirk, George. 1972. THE FLORA AND FAUNA OF MONCK PARK. Unpublished Report, British Columbia Parks Branch, Victoria. 5 pages.

525. Stirling, David. 1962. ANNUAL REPORT SHUSWAP PARK NATURE HOUSE 1962. Unpublished Report, British Columbia Parks Branch, Victoria. 8 pages.

526. Parkin, T. W. 1974. KOKANEE GLACIER PROVINCIAL PARK – FISHERIES AND WILDLIFE INVENTORY, JULY - AUGUST 1974. Unpublished Report, British Columbia Parks Branch, Victoria. 38 pages.

527. Hazelwood, W. G. 1976. KWADACHA PARK 1976. Unpublished Report, British Columbia Parks Branch, Victoria. 19 pages.

528. Brown, Herbert A. 1977. OXYGEN CONSUMPTION OF A LARGE, COLD-ADAPTED FROG EGG (Ascaphus truei (AMPHIBIA: ASCAPHIDAE . Canadian Journal of Zoology 55(2):343-348.

529. Baker, M. R. 1977. REDESCRIPTION OF Oswaldocruzia pipiens WALTON, 1929 (NEMATODA: TRICHOSTRONGYLIDAE) FROM AMPHIBIANS OF EASTERN NORTH AMERICA. Canadian Journal of Zoology 55(1):104-109.

530. Friedmann, G. B. 1977. ANNUAL VARIATIONS OF RED AND WHITE CELL COUNT IN THE URODELE Taricha granulosa. Canadian Journal of Zoology 55(1):251-254.

531. Burggren, Warren. 1977. CIRCULATION DURING INTERMITTENT LUNG VENTILATION IN THE GARTER SNAKE Thamnophis. Canadian Journal of Zoology 55(10):1720-1725.

532. Dill, Lawrence M. 1977. 'HANDEDNESS' IN THE PACIFIC TREE FROG (Hyla regilla). Canadian Journal of Zoology 55(11):1926-1929.

533. Eagleson, G. W. and B. A. McKeown. 1978. CHANGES IN THYROID ACTIVITY OF Ambystoma gracile (BAIRD) DURING DIFFERENT LARVAL, TRANSFORMING, AND POSTMETAMORPHIC PHASES. Canadian Journal of Zoology 56(6):1377-1381.

534. Baker, M. R. 1978. DEVELOPMENT AND TRANSMISSION OF Oswaldocruzia pipiens WALTON, 1929 (NEMATODA: TRICHOSTRONGYLIDAE) IN AMPHIBIANS. Canadian Journal of Zoology 56(5):1026-1031.

535. Rauch, Josefine C. 1978. INTEGUMENTARY BLOODVASCULAR SYSTEM IN GARTER SNAKES (Thamnophis sirtalis parietalis AND Thamnophis radix). Canadian Journal of Zoology 56(3):469-476.

536. Cook, Sherburne F., Jr. 1960. ON THE OCCURRENCE AND LIFE HISTORY OF Contia tenuis. Herpetologica 16(3):163-173.

537. Seeliger, L. M. 1945. VARIATION IN THE PACIFIC MUD TURTLE. Copeia 1945(3):150-159.

538. Cope, E. D. 1867. A REVIEW OF THE SPECIES OF THE AMBLYSTOMIDAE. Proceedings of the Academy of Natural Sciences of Philadelphia 18(4):166-211.

539. Kennedy, Murray J. 1977. Aplectana lynae N.SP. (NEMATODA: COSMOCERCIDAE) FROM THE RED-LEGGED FROG, Rana aurora aurora, IN BRITISH COLUMBIA. Canadian Journal of Zoology 55(3):630-634.

540. Gentry, Alan F. 1885. A REVIEW OF THE GENUS Phrynosoma. Proceedings of the Academy of Natural Sciences of Philadelphia 36(Part 2):138-148.

541. Kirton, Michael Paul. 1974. FALL MOVEMENTS AND HIBERNATION OF THE WOOD FROG, Rana sylvatica, IN INTERIOR ALASKA. M.Sc. Thesis, University of Alaska, Department of Zoology, Fairbanks. 57 pages.

542. Hadley, Raymond S. 1969. THE EFFECTS OF SEASON AND TEMPERATURE ON CERTAIN ASPECTS OF THE PHYSIOLOGY OF THE ALASKAN WOOD FROG, Rana sylvatica. M.Sc. Thesis, University of Alaska, Department of Zoology, Fairbanks. 42 pages.

543. Kinney, Stephen Baldwin. 1966. DEVELOPMENTAL ADAPTATIONS AND BREEDING BEHAVIOR OF THE ALASKAN WOOD FROG, Rana sylvatica. M.Sc. Thesis, University of Alaska, Department of Zoology, Fairbanks. 57 pages.

544. Stejneger, Leonhard. 1890. ON THE SNAKES OF THE GENUS Charina. Proceedings of the United States National Museum 13(808):177-182.

545. Gaige, Helen Thompson. 1917. DESCRIPTION OF A NEW SALAMANDER FROM WASHINGTON. Occasional Papers of the Museum of Zoology, University of Michigan No. 40:1-3.

546. Stejneger, Leonhard. 1896. DESCRIPTION OF A NEW GENUS AND SPECIES OF DISCOGLOSSOID TOAD FROM NORTH AMERICA. Proceedings of the United States National Museum 21(1178):899-902.

547. Meek, S. E. and D. G. Elliot. 1899. NOTES ON A COLLECTION OF COLD-BLOODED VERTEBRATES FROM THE OLYMPIC MOUNTAINS. Publications of the Field Columbian Museum, Zoological Series 1(12):225-236.

548. Case, Susan M. 1978. BIOCHEMICAL SYSTEMATICS OF MEMBERS OF THE GENUS Rana NATIVE TO WESTERN NORTH AMERICA. Systematic Zoology 27(3):299-311.

549. Marx, Hymen. 1976. SUPPLEMENTARY CATALOGUE OF TYPE SPECIMENS OF REPTILES AND AMPHIBIANS IN FIELD MUSEUM OF NATURAL HISTORY. Fieldiana: Zoology 69(2):33-94.

550. Hock, Raymond J. 1956. ALASKAN ZOO-GEOGRAPHY AND ALASKAN AMPHIBIA. Proceedings of the IV Alaskan Science Conference, Anchorage. Pages 201-206.

551. Karlstrom, Ernest L. 1966. THE NORTH-WESTERN TOAD, Bufo boreas boreas IN CENTRAL COASTAL ALASKA - A STUDY OF AN ECTOTHERM AT THE NORTHERN LIMIT OF ITS SPECIES RANGE (ABSTRACT ONLY). Proceedings of the XVII Alaskan Science Conference, Anchorage. Page 64.

552. Johansen, Kjell. 1962. OBSERVATIONS ON THE WOOD FROG Rana sylvatica IN ALASKA. Ecology 43(1):146-147.

553. Kessel, Brina. 1965. BREEDING DATES OF Rana sylvatica AT COLLEGE, ALASKA. Ecology 46(1 & 2):206-207.

554. Herreid, Clyde F. and Stephen Kinney. 1967. TEMPERATURE AND DEVELOPMENT OF THE WOOD FROG, Rana sylvatica, IN ALASKA. Ecology 48(4):579-590.

555. Cope, E. D. 1893. A CONTRIBUTION TO THE HERPETOLOGY OF BRITISH COLUMBIA. Proceedings of the Academy of Natural Sciences of Philadelphia 44(Part I):181-184.

556. Martof, Bernard S. and Robert L. Humphries. 1959. GEOGRAPHIC VARIATION IN THE WOOD FROG, Rana sylvatica. American Midland Naturalist 61(2):350-389.

557. Woods, John G., James W. Mulchinock, Susan P. Wolff and Howard Coneybeare. 1980. ANIMALS AND PLANTS OBSERVED IN THE UPPER BEAVER VALLEY, GLACIER NATIONAL PARK. Unpublished Report, Parks Canada, Mount Revelstoke-Glacier National Parks, Revelstoke, British Columbia. 8 pages.

558. Burt, Charles E. 1935. A KEY TO THE LIZARDS OF THE UNITED STATES AND CANADA. Transactions of the Kansas Academy of Science 38:255-305.

559. Savage, Jay M. 1949. AN ILLUSTRATED KEY TO THE LIZARD, SNAKES AND TURTLES OF THE WESTERN UNITED STATES AND CANADA. Naturegraph Pocket Keys 2:1-32.

560. Allen, E. Ross and Wilfred T. Neill. 1950. HOW TO KEEP SNAKES, LIZARDS, TURTLES, ALLIGATORS, AND CROCODILES IN CAPTIVITY. Ross Allen's Reptile Institute Special Publication No. 1:1-24.

561. Tanner, Wilmer W. 1940. NOTES ON THE HERPETOLOGICAL SPECIMENS ADDED TO THE BRIGHAM YOUNG UNIVERSITY VERTEBRATE COLLECTION DURING 1939. Great Basin Naturalist 1(3 & 4):137-146.

562. Landesman, Richard. 1967. NEURAL-MESODERMAL INTERACTIONS SUBSEQUENT TO NEURAL INDUCTION IN Ambystoma. Developmental Biology 16(4):341-367.

563. Campbell, R. Wayne. 1979. REPORT ON VERTEBRATES OBSERVED ON BEAR FLATS ECOLOGICAL RESERVE, BRITISH COLUMBIA. Unpublished Report, British Columbia Provincial Museum, Vertebrate Zoology Division, Victoria. 2 pages.

564. Cook, Francis R. 1971. HERPTOFAUNA OF PACIFIC RIM NATIONAL PARK. Unpublished Report, Pacific Rim National Park, Ucluelet. 3 pages.

565. Savage, Jay M. 1958. THE IGUANID LIZARD GENERA Urosaurus AND Uta, WITH REMARKS ON RELATED GROUPS. Zoologica 43(2):41-54.

566. Nigrelli, Ross F. 1945. TRYPANOSOMES FROM NORTH AMERICAN AMPHIBIANS, WITH A DESCRIPTION OF Trypanosoma grylli NIGRELLI (1944) FROM Acris gryllus (LECONTE). Zoologica 30(5):47-56.

567. Test, Frederick Cleveland. 1896. A CONTRIBUTION OF THE KNOWLEDGE OF THE VARIATIONS OF THE TREE FROG Hyla regilla. Proceedings of the United States National Museum 21(1156):477-492.

568. Cope, E. D. 1889. SCIENTIFIC RESULTS OF EXPLORATIONS BY THE U.S. FISH COMMISSION STEAMER ALBATROSS. REPORT ON THE BATRACHIANS AND REPTILES COLLECTED IN 1887-'88. Proceedings of the United States National Museum 12(769):141-147.

569. Peters, James A. 1952. CATALOGUE OF TYPE SPECIMENS IN THE HERPETOLOGICAL COLLECTIONS OF THE UNIVERSITY OF MICHIGAN MUSEUM OF ZOOLOGY. Occasional Papers of the Museum of Zoology, University of Michigan No. 539:1-55.

570. Wynne-Edwards, V. C. 1952. FRESHWATER VERTEBRATES OF THE ARCTIC AND SUBARCTIC. Bulletin of the Fisheries Research Board of Canada No. 94:1-28.

571. Mason, Grant A., James L. Hall and Paul Gibbons Roofe. 1965. THE STRUCTURE AND INNERVATION OF THE VENOM GLANDS IN THE TAIL OF THE SALAM-ANDERS (Ambystoma). University of Kansas Science Bulletin 45(7):557-586.

572. National Research Council, Institute of Laboratory Animal Resources, Sub-committee on Amphibian Standards. 1974. AMPHIBIANS: GUIDELINES FOR THE BREEDING, CARE, AND MANAGE-MENT OF LABORATORY ANIMALS. National Academy of Sciences, Washington, District of Columbia. 153 pages.

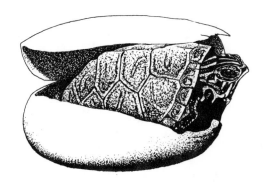

573. Gregory, Patrick T. 1978. REPORT ON RESEARCH ON ECOLOGY OF SNAKES AND FROGS IN PROVINCIAL PARKS. Unpublished Report, British Columbia Parks Branch, Victoria. 5 pages.

574. Zug, George R. 1971. THE DISTRIBUTION AND PATTERNS OF THE MAJOR ARTERIES OF THE IGUANIDS AND COMMENTS ON THE INTERGENERIC RELATIONSHIPS OF IGUANIDS (REPTILIA: LACERTILIA). Smithsonian Contributions to Zoology 83:1-23.

575. Zug, George R. 1978. ANURAN LOCOMOTION - STRUCTURE AND FUNCTION, 2: JUMPING PERFORMANCE OF SEMIAQUATIC, TERRESTRIAL, AND ARBOREAL FROGS. Smithsonian Contributions to Zoology 276:1-31.

576. Anonymous. 1967. ADDITIONS TO THE FLORA & FAUNA, SHUSWAP, 1967. Unpublished Report, British Columbia Parks Branch, Victoria. 2 pages.

577.   Green, David. 1975. REPTILES AND AMPHIBIANS OF SHUSWAP AREA 1975. Unpublished Report, British Columbia Parks Branch, Victoria. 3 pages.

578.   Noble, G. K. and A. Schmidt. 1937. THE STRUCTURE AND FUNCTION OF THE FACIAL AND LABIAL PITS OF SNAKES. Proceedings of the American Philosophical Society 77(3):263-288.

579.   Macartney, James Malcolm. 1979. DIFFERENTIAL SUSCEPTIBILITY OF THREE SPECIES OF GARTER SNAKE TO AMPHIBIAN SKIN SECRETIONS. B.Sc. Thesis, University of Victoria, Department of Biology, British Columbia. 94 pages.

580.   Dethlefsen, Edwin S. 1948. A SUBTERRANEAN NEST OF THE PACIFIC GIANT SALAMANDER, Dicamptodon ensatus (ESCHSCHOLTZ). Wasmann Collector 7(3):81-84.

581.   Kessel, Edward L. 1954. TRANSPORTATION OF AN EGG CLUSTER BY A FEMALE OF Ensatina eschscholtzi GRAY (CAUDATA: PLETHODONTIDAE). Wasman Journal of Biology 12(2):133-134.

582.   Kessel, Edward L. and Berta B. Kessel. 1944. METAMORPHOSIS OF THE PACIFIC GIANT SALAMANDER Dicamptodon ensatus (ESCHSCHOLTZ). Wasmann Collector 6(2):38-48.

583.   Kessel, Edward L. and Berta B. Kessel. 1943. THE RATE OF GROWTH OF THE OLDER LARVAE OF THE PACIFIC GIANT SALAMANDER, Dicamptodon ensatus (ESCHSCHOLTZ). Wasmann Collector 5(4):141-142.

584.   Kessel, Edward L. and Berta B. Kessel. 1943. THE RATE OF GROWTH OF THE YOUNG LARVAE OF THE PACIFIC GIANT SALAMANDER, Dicamptodon ensatus (ESCHSCHOLTZ). Wasmann Collector 5(3):108-111.

585.   Banta, Benjamin H. 1962. PRELIMINARY REMARKS UPON ZOOGEOGRAPHY OF THE LIZARDS INHABITING THE GREAT BASIN ON THE WESTERN UNITED STATES. Wasmann Journal of Biology 20(2):253-287.

586.   Coss, Richard G. and Donald H. Owings. 1978. SNAKE-DIRECTED BEHAVIOR BY SNAKE NAIVE AND EXPERIENCED CALIFORNIA GROUND SQUIRRELS IN A SIMULATED BURROW. Zeitschrift Fur Tierpsychologie 48(4):421-435.

587.   Taylor, Edward H. 1935. A TAXONOMIC STUDY OF THE COSMOPOLITAN SCINCOID LIZARDS OF THE GENUS Eumeces WITH AN ACCOUNT OF THE DISTRIBUTION AND RELATIONSHIPS OF ITS SPECIES. Kansas University Science Bulletin 23:1-643.

588.   Brown, Walter C. and James R. Slater. 1939. THE AMPHIBIANS AND REPTILES OF THE ISLANDS OF THE STATE OF WASHINGTON. Occasional Papers, Department of Biology, College of Puget Sound 4:6-31.

589.   Booth, Ernest S. 1942. FIELD KEY TO THE AMPHIBIANS AND REPTILES OF THE NORTHWEST. Unpublished Report, Walla Walla College, Washington. 22 pages.

590.   Dice, Lee Raymond. 1916. DISTRIBUTION OF THE LAND VERTEBRATES OF SOUTH-EASTERN WASHINGTON. University of California Publications in Zoology 16(17):293-348.

591.   Ruthven, Alexander G. 1908. VARIATIONS AND GENETIC RELATIONSHIPS OF THE GARTER-SNAKES. United States National Museum Bulletin 61:1-201.

592. Hodge, Robert Parker. 1976. OFTEN SEEN...LITTLE UNDERSTOOD! Washington Wildlife 23(3):10-11.

593. Johnson, Murray L. 1939. Lampropeltis zonata (BLAINVILLE) IN WASHINGTON STATE. Occasional Papers, Department of Biology, College of Puget Sound 1:2-3.

594. Slater, James R. 1939. SOME SPECIES OF AMPHIBIANS NEW TO THE STATE OF WASHINGTON. Occasional Papers, Department of Biology, College of Puget Sound 2:4-5.

595. Slater, James R. 1939. Contia tenuis REDISCOVERED IN WASHINGTON. Occasional Papers, Department of Biology, College of Puget Sound 3:5.

596. Slater, James R. 1939. Clemmys marmorata IN THE STATE OF WASHINGTON. Occasional Papers, Department of Biology, College of Puget Sound 5:32.

597. Slater, James R. 1940. SALAMANDER RECORDS FROM BRITISH COLUMBIA. Occasional Papers, Department of Biology, College of Puget Sound 9:43-44.

598. Slater, James R. 1941. WESTERN STRIPED RACER IN WASHINGTON. Occasional Papers, Department of Biology, College of Puget Sound 12:74.

599. Flynt, Alexander W. 1962. Contia tenuis DISCOVERED EAST OF THE CASCADE MOUNTAINS. Occasional Papers, Department of Biology, University of Puget Sound 22:207.

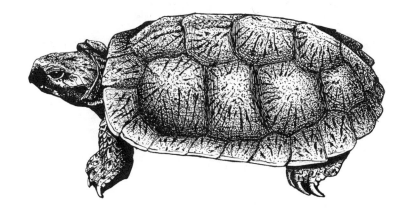

600. Metter, Dean E. 1962. Ascaphus truei STEJNEGER IN THE BLUE MOUNTAINS OF SOUTHEASTERN WASHINGTON. Occasional Papers, Department of Biology, University of Puget Sound 21:205-206.

601. Slater, James R. 1962. VARIATIONS AND NEW RANGE OF Clemmys marmorata marmorata. Occasional Papers, Department of Biology, University of Puget Sound 20:204-205.

602. Slater, James R. 1962. SOME FOOD OF SOME Ambystoma macrodactylum, BAIRD. Occasional Papers, Department of Biology, University of Puget Sound 19:203.

603. Slater, James R. 1964. A KEY TO THE ADULT AMPHIBIANS OF WASHINGTON STATE. Occasional Papers, Department of Biology, University of Puget Sound 25:235-236.

604. Slater, James R. 1964. COUNTY RECORDS OF AMPHIBIANS FOR WASHINGTON. Occasional Papers, Department of Biology, University of Puget Sound 26:237-242.

605. Slater, James R. 1963. A KEY TO THE ADULT REPTILES OF WASHINGTON STATE. Occasional Papers, Department of Biology, University of Puget Sound 23:209-211.

606. Slater, James R. 1963. DISTRIBUTION OF WASHINGTON REPTILES. Occasional Papers, Department of Biology, University of Puget Sound 24:212-232.

607. Slater, James R. and Walter C. Brown. 1941. ISLAND RECORDS OF AMPHIBIANS AND REPTILES FOR WASHINGTON. Occasional Papers, Department of Biology, College of Puget Sound 13:74-77.

608. Herreid, Clyde F. and Stephen Kinney. 1966. SURVIVAL OF ALASKAN WOODFROG (Rana sylvatica) LARVAE. Ecology 47(6):1039-1040.

609. Hodge, Robert Parker. 1972. THE WATERDOG, Ambystoma tigrinum, IN WASHINGTON STATE. Washington Wildlife 24(4):6-9.

610. British Columbia Fish and Wildlife Branch. 1979. PRELIMINARY REPTILE MANAGEMENT PLAN FOR BRITISH COLUMBIA. British Columbia Fish and Wildlife Branch Report, Victoria. 24 pages.

611. Hilton, William A. 1946. A PRELIMINARY STUDY OF SKELETONS OF AMBYLYSTOMIDAE. Journal of Entomology and Zoology 38(1):29-36.

612. Bishop, Sherman C. 1934. DESCRIPTION OF A NEW SALAMANDER FROM OREGON, WITH NOTES ON RELATED SPECIES. Proceedings of the Biological Society of Washington 47:169-172.

613. Schaub, David L. and John H. Larsen. 1978. THE REPRODUCTIVE ECOLOGY OF THE PACIFIC TREEFROG (Hyla regilla). Herpetologica 34(4):409-416.

614. Feder, Juliana H., Gloria Z. Wurst and David B. Wake. 1978. GENETIC VARIATION IN WESTERN SALAMANDERS OF THE GENUS Plethodon, AND THE STATUS OF Plethodon gordoni. Herpetologica 34(1):64-69.

615. Fowler, Henry W. and Emmett Reid Dunn. 1918. NOTES ON SALAMANDERS. Proceedings of the Academy of Natural Sciences of Philadelphia 69(Series 3):7-28.

616. Cope, E. D. 1867. A REVIEW OF THE SPECIES OF THE AMBLYSTOMIDAE. Proceedings of the Academy of Natural Sciences of Philadelphia 19(Series 2):166-211.

617. Parker, William S. and William S. Brown. 1973. SPECIES COMPOSITION AND POPULATION CHANGES IN TWO COMPLEXES OF SNAKE HIBERNACULA IN NORTHERN UTAH. Herpetologica 29(4):319-326.

618. Cope, E. D. 1869. A REVIEW OF THE SPECIES OF THE PLETHODONTIDAE AND DESMOGNATHIDAE. Proceedings of the Academy of Natural Sciences of Philadelphia 21(Series 2):93-118.

619. Brodie, Edmund D. 1968. OBSERVATIONS ON THE MENTAL HEDONIC GLAND-CLUSTERS OF WESTERN SALAMANDERS OF THE GENUS Plethodon. Herpetologica 24(3):248-250.

620. Emlen, Stephen T. 1968. A TECHNIQUE FOR MARKING ANURAN AMPHIBIANS FOR BEHAVIORAL STUDIES. Herpetologica 24(2):172-173.

621. Mahmoud, I. Y. 1968. NESTING BEHAVIOR IN THE WESTERN PAINTED TURTLE, Chrysemys picta bellii. Herpetologica 24(2):158-162.

622. Belton, John C. and Alfred Owczarzak. 1968. CELLULAR CHANGES ASSOCIATED WITH THE PRE-OVULATORY DEPOSITION AND STORAGE OF HEPATIC LIPIDS IN THE FROG Ascaphus truei. Herpetologica 24(2):113-127.

623. Post, Douglas D. and David Pettus. 1967. SYMPATRY OF TWO MEMBERS OF THE Rana pipiens COMPLEX IN COLORADO. Herpetologica 23(4):323.

624. Evans, Kenneth J. 1967. OBSERVATIONS ON THE DAILY EMERGENCE OF Coleonyx variegatus AND Uta stansburiana. Herpetologica 23(3):217-222.

625. Lambert, Lewis H. 1967. 'ANECTINE': A HERPETOLOGICAL KILLING AGENT. Herpetologica 23(2):135-136.

626. Wassersug, Richard J. 1973. ASPECTS OF SOCIAL BEHAVIOR IN ANURAN LARVAE. Pages 273-297 in J. L. Vial, Evolutionary Biology of Anurahs. University of Missouri Press, Columbia.

627. Dunn, E. R. 1926. THE STATUS OF Siredon gracilis BAIRD. Copeia 1926(155):135-136.

628. Maxson, Linda R., Richard Highton and David B. Wake. 1979. ALBUMIN EVOLUTION AND ITS PHYLOGENETIC IMPLICATIONS IN THE PLETHODONTID SALAMANDER GENERA Plethodon AND Ensatina. Copeia 1979(3):502-508.

629. Shinn, Elizabeth A. and Jim W. Dole. 1979. LIPID COMPONENTS OF PREY ODORS ELICIT FEEDING RESPONSES IN WESTERN TOADS (Bufo boreas). Copeia 1979(2):275-278.

630. Shine, Richard. 1979. SEXUAL SELECTION AND SEXUAL DIMORPHISM IN THE AMPHIBIA. Copeia 1979(2):297-306.

631. Case, Susan M. 1979. OBSERVATIONS ON SOME CRANIAL FORAMINA IN THE RANIDAE. Copeia 1979(2):346-348.

632. Goldberg, Stephen R. and William S. Parker. 1975. SEASONAL TESTICULAR HISTOLOGY OF THE COLUBRID SNAKES, Masticophis taeniatus AND Pituophis melanoleucus. Herpetologica 31(3):317-322.

633. Kauffeld, Carl F. 1937. THE STATUS OF THE LEOPARD FROGS, Rana brachycephala AND Rana pipiens. Herpetologica 1(3):84-87.

634. Wade, Keith. 1960. REPORT ON THE REPTILES AND AMPHIBIANS OF WELLS GRAY PARK - MAY AND JUNE, 1960. Unpublished Report, British Columbia Parks Branch, Victoria. 7 pages.

635. Bechtel, M. Bernard and Elizabeth Bechtel. 1972. REPTILES, AMPHIBIANS AND THE LAW. Herpetological Review 4(4):133–136.

636. Dietz, Thomas Howard. 1965. ENVIRONMENTAL IONIC CONCENTRATIONS AND TRANSEPITHELIAL POTENTIALS OF THE LARVAL SALAMANDER Ambystoma tigrinum. M.Sc. Thesis, Washington State University, Department of Zoology, Pullman. 42 pages.

637. Brodie, Edmund D. 1970. WESTERN SALAMANDERS OF THE GENUS Plethodon: SYSTEMATICS AND GEOGRAPHIC VARIATION. Herpetologica 26(4):468–516.

K.TAYLOR

638. Bury, R. Bruce, Franklin Gress and George C. Gorman. 1970. KARYOTYPIC SURVEY OF SOME COLUBRID SNAKES FROM WESTERN NORTH AMERICA. Herpetologica 26(4):461–466.

639. McKenzie, Donald S. and Robert M. Storm. 1970. PATTERNS OF HABITAT SELECTION IN THE CLOUDED SALAMANDER, Aneides ferreus (COPE). Herpetologica 26(4):450–454.

640. Hazelwood, W. G. 1976. TWEEDSMUIR PARK INITIAL WILDLIFE & FISHERIES INVENTORY (AREAS A TO D). Unpublished Report, British Columbia Parks Branch, Victoria. 220 pages.

641. Cope, Edward D. 1875. CHECK-LIST OF NORTH AMERICAN BATRACHIA AND REPTILIA: WITH A SYSTEMATIC LIST OF THE HIGHER GROUPS, AND AN ESSAY ON GEOGRAPHICAL DISTRIBUTION BASED ON THE SPECIMENS CONTAINED IN THE U.S. NATIONAL MUSEUM. United States National Museum Bulletin Vol. 1, No. (1):1–104.

642. Hensley, Max. 1959. ALBINISM IN NORTH AMERICAN AMPHIBIANS AND REPTILES. Publications of the Museum Biological Series, Michigan State University 1(4):135–159.

643. Cope, E. D. 1869. A REVIEW OF THE SPECIES OF THE PLETHODONTIDAE AND DESMOGNATHIDAE. Proceedings of the Academy of Natural Sciences of Philadelphia 21(2):93–118.

644. Giguere, Louis. 1979. AN EXPERIMENTAL TEST OF DODSON'S HYPOTHESIS THAT Ambystoma (A SALAMANDER) AND Chaoborus (A PHANTOM MIDGE) HAVE COMPLEMENTARY FEEDING NICHES. Canadian Journal of Zoology 57(5):1091–1097.

645. Fowler, Henry W. and Emmett Reid Dunn. 1917. NOTES ON SALAMANDERS. Proceedings of the Academy of Natural Sciences of Philadelphia 69(Part 1):7-28.

646. Marx, Hymen. 1958. CATALOGUE OF TYPE SPECIMENS OF REPTILES AND AMPHIBIANS IN CHICAGO NATURAL HISTORY MUSEUM. Fieldiana: Zoology 36(4):409-496.

647. Schmidt, Karl P. 1953. A CHECK LIST OF NORTH AMERICAN AMPHIBIANS AND REPTILES, SIXTH EDITION. American Society of Icthyologists and Herpetologists. 280 pages.

648. Hanlin, Hugh G., Joseph J. Beatty and Sue W. Hanlin. 1979. A NEST SITE OF THE WESTERN RED-BACKED SALAMANDER Plethodon vehiculum (COOPER). Journal of Herpetology 13(2):214-216.

649. Klauber, L. M. 1943. TAIL-LENGTH DIFFERENCES IN SNAKES WITH NOTES ON SEXUAL DIMORPHISM AND THE COEFFICIENT OF DIVERGENCE AND A GRAPHIC METHOD OF SHOWING RELATIONSHIPS. Bulletin of the Zoological Society of San Diego No. 18:1-76.

650. Stickel, William H. 1952. VENOMOUS SNAKES OF THE UNITED STATES AND TREATMENT OF THEIR BITES. United States Department of the Interior Fish and Wildlife Service Wildlife Leaflet 339:1-29.

651. Stickel, William H. 1953. CONTROL OF SNAKES. United States Department of the Interior Fish and Wildlife Service Wildlife Leaflet 345:1-8

652. Arnold, Stevan J. and Richard J. Wassersug. 1978. DIFFERENTIAL PREDATION ON METAMORPHIC ANURANS BY GARTER SNAKES (Thamnophis): SOCIAL BEHAVIOR AS A POSSIBLE DEFENSE. Ecology 59(5):1014-1022.

653. Snyder, Richard C. 1963. Ambystoma gracile. Catalogue of American Amphibians and Reptiles: 6.1-6.2.

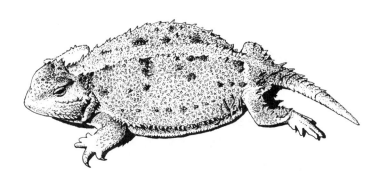

654. Gehlbach, Frederick R. 1967. Ambystoma tigrinum. Catalogue of American Amphibians and Reptiles: 52.1-52.4.

655. Green, David M. 1978. NORTHERN LEOPARD FROGS AND BULLFROGS ON VANCOUVER ISLAND. Canadian Field-Naturalist 92(1):78-79.

656. Anonymous. 1943. POISONOUS SNAKES OF THE UNITED STATES. United States Department of the Interior Fish and Wildlife Service Wildlife Leaflet 233:1-17.

657. Anonymous. 1936. POISONOUS SNAKES OF THE UNITED STATES. United States Department of Agriculture Bureau of Biological Survey Wildlife Research and Management Leaflet BS-70:1-19.

658. Licht, Lawrence E. 1971. BREEDING HABITS AND EMBRYONIC THERMAL REQUIREMENTS OF THE FROGS, Rana aurora aurora AND Rana pretiosa pretiosa, IN THE PACIFIC NORTHWEST. Ecology 52(1):116-124.

659. Patch, Clyde L. 1925. THE FROG EATS THE BIRD. Canadian Field-Naturalist 39(6):150.

660. Stull, Olive Griffith. 1940. VARIATIONS AND RELATIONSHIPS IN THE SNAKES OF THE GENUS Pituophis. United States National Museum Bulletin 175:1-225.

661. Logier, E. B. S. and G. C. Toner. 1961. CHECK LIST OF THE AMPHIBIANS AND REPTILES OF CANADA AND ALASKA. Life Sciences Division, Royal Ontario Museum, Contribution 53:1-92.

662. Jewett, Tim and Greg Brown. 1968. Crotalus viridus oregonus HOLBROOK. THE NORTHERN PACIFIC RATTLESNAKE. Unpublished Report, Whitman College, Washington. 104 pages.

663. Aughey, Samuel. 1873. THE RATTLE OF THE RATTLESNAKE. American Naturalist 7(1):85-86.

664. Stephenson, N. G. 1951. OBSERVATIONS ON THE DEVELOPMENT OF THE AMPHICOELOUS FROGS, Leiopelma AND Ascaphus. Journal of the Linnean Society of London, Zoology 42(283):18-31.

665. Whitney, Carl L. and John R. Krebbs. 1975. MATE SELECTION IN PACIFIC TREE FROGS. Nature 255(5506):325-326.

666. Karstad, Lars. 1961. REPTILES AS POSSIBLE RESERVOIR HOSTS FOR EASTERN ENCEPHALITIS VIRUS. Transactions of the North American Wildlife and Natural Resources Conference 26:186-202.

667. Switak, K. H. 1967. NOTES ON ALBINO REPTILES AND AMPHIBIANS AT STEINHART AQUARIUM. International Zoo Yearbook 7:228.

668. Honegger, Rene E. 1979. MARKING AMPHIBIANS AND REPTILES FOR FUTURE IDENTIFICATION. International Zoo Yearbook 19:14-22.

669. Nace, George W. 1977. BREEDING AMPHIBIANS IN CAPTIVITY. International Zoo Yearbook 17:44-50.

670. Laszlo, Jozsef. 1975. PROBING AS A PRACTICAL METHOD OF SEX RECOGNITION IN SS SNAKES. International Zoo Yearbook 15:178-179.

671. Ball, David J. 1974. HANDLING AND RESTRAINT OF REPTILES. International Zoo Yearbook 14:138-140.

672. Conant, R. 1971. REPTILE AND AMPHIBIAN MANAGEMENT PRACTICES AT PHILADELPHIA ZOO. International Zoo Yearbook 11:224-230.

673. Dietz, Thomas H. and Edmund D. Brodie. 1969. BLOOD ION CONCENTRATIONS AS A FUNCTION OF DEVELOPMENTAL STAGE IN THE GOPHER SNAKE, Pituophis melanoleucus catenifer. Comparative Biochemistry and Physiology 30(4):673-678.

674. Brown, Herbert A. 1975. TEMPERATURE AND DEVELOPMENT OF THE TAILED FROG, Ascaphus truei. Comparative Biochemistry and Physiology 50A(2A):397-405.

675. Ruben, John A. 1979. BLOOD PHYSIOLOGY DURING ACTIVITY IN THE SNAKES Masticophis flagellum (COLUBRIDAE) AND Crotalus viridis (CROTALIDAE). Comparative Biochemistry and Physiology 64A(4):577-580.

676. Hodge, Robert Parker. 1971. HERPETOLOGY NORTH OF 60°. Beaver 1971(302:1):36-38.

677. Githens, Thomas S. 1935. STUDIES ON THE VENOMS OF NORTH AMERICAN PIT VIPERS. Journal of Immunology 29(2):165-173.

678. Bragg, Arthur N. 1961. A THEORY OF THE ORIGIN OF SPADE-FOOTED TOADS DEDUCED PRINCIPALLY BY A STUDY OF THEIR HABITS. Animal Behavior 9(3):178-186.

679. Wiens, John A. 1972. ANURAN HABITAT SELECTION: EARLY EXPERIENCE AND SUBSTRATE SELECTION IN Rana cascadae TADPOLES. Animal Behavior 20(2):218-220.

680. Wells, Kentwood D. 1977. THE SOCIAL BEHAVIOUR OF ANURAN AMPHIBIANS. Animal Behavior 25(3):666-693.

681. Anonymous. 1895. SNAKES IN OREGON. Science N.S.2(48):730-731.

682. Diller, J. S. 1907. A SALAMANDER-SNAKE FIGHT. Science N.S.26(678):907-908.

683. Snyder, Gregory K. and Wesley W. Weathers. 1975. TEMPERATURE ADAPTATIONS IN AMPHIBIANS. American Naturalist 109(965):93-101.

684. Bogert, Charles M. 1958. SOUNDS OF NORTH AMERICAN FROGS: THE BIOLOGICAL SIGNIFICANCE OF VOICE IN FROGS. Folkways Records & Service Corporation, New York. 18 pages.

685. Anonymous. 1943. POISONOUS SNAKES OF THE UNITED STATES. United States Department of the Interior Fish and Wildlife Service Wildlife Leaflet 233:1-17.

686. Martin, Wm. F. and R. B. Huey. 1971. THE FUNCTION OF THE EPIGLOTTIS IN SOUND PRODUCTION (HISSING) OF Pituophis melanoleucus. Copeia 1971(4):752-754.

687. Harlan, Richard. 1826. GENERA OF NORTH AMERICAN REPTILIA, AND A SYNOPSIS OF THE SPECIES. Journal of the Academy of Natural Sciences of Philadelphia 5(Part 2):317-372.

688. Bishop, Sherman C. 1941. NOTES ON SALAMANDERS WITH DESCRIPTIONS OF SEVERAL NEW FORMS. Occasional Papers of the Museum of Zoology University of Michigan No. 451:1-21.

689. Hallowell, Edw. 1858. ON THE CADUCIBRANCHIATE URODELE BATRACHIANS. Journal of the Academy of Natural Sciences of Philadelphia 3(Second Series, Part 4, Article 21):337-366.

690. Baird, Spencer F. 1850. REVISION OF THE NORTH AMERICAN TAILED-BATRACHIA, WITH DESCRIPTIONS OF NEW GENERA AND SPECIES. Journal of the Academy of Natural Sciences of Philadelphia 1(New Series, Part 5):281-294.

691. Dodson, Stanley I. and Virginia E. Dodson. 1971. THE DIET OF _Ambystoma tigrinum_ LARVAE FROM WESTERN COLORADO. _Copeia_ 1971(4):614-624.

692. Shinn, Elizabeth A. and Jim W. Dole. 1979. EVIDENCE FOR A ROLE FOR OLFACTORY CUES IN THE FEEDING RESPONSE OF WESTERN TOADS, _Bufo boreas_. _Copeia_ 1979(1):163-165.

693. Martin, Kathy. 1979. COMMON GARTER SNAKE PREDATION ON ROBIN NESTLINGS. _Canadian Field-Naturalist_ 93(1):70-71.

694. Allen, Bennet M. 1938. THE ENDOCRINE CONTROL OF AMPHIBIAN METAMORPHOSIS. _Biological Reviews of the Cambridge Philosophical Society_ 13(1):1-19.

695. Anderson, J. R. 1901. RATTLESNAKES AND SCORPIONS. _Ottawa Naturalist_ 15(7):162-163.

696. Ortenburger, Arthur Irving. 1928. THE WHIP SNAKES AND RACERS: GENERA _Masticophis_ AND _Coluber_. _Memoirs of the University of Michigan Museums_ 1:1-247.

697. Pace, Ann E. 1974. SYSTEMATIC AND BIOLOGICAL STUDIES OF THE LEOPARD FROGS (_Rana pipiens_ COMPLEX) OF THE UNITED STATES. _Miscellaneous Publications, Museum of Zoology, University of Michigan_, No. 148:1-140.

698. Nussbaum, Ronald A. 1976. GEOGRAPHIC VARIATION AND SYSTEMATICS OF SALAMANDERS OF THE GENUS _Dicamptodon_ STRAUCH (AMBYSTOMATIDAE). _Miscellaneous Publications, Museum of Zoology, University of Michigan_, No. 149:1-94.

699. Tinkle, Donald W. 1967. THE LIFE AND DEMOGRAPHY OF THE SIDE-BLOTCHED LIZARD, _Uta stansburiana_. _Miscellaneous Publications, Museum of Zoology, University of Michigan_, No. 132:1-182.

700. Taylor, J. Mary. 1979. AMPHIBIANS, REPTILES AND MAMMALS OF BRITISH COLUMBIA. _Department of Zoology, University of British Columbia_, Vancouver. 144 pages.

701. Bragg, Arthur N. 1936. THE ECOLOGICAL DISTRIBUTION OF SOME NORTH AMERICAN ANURA. _American Naturalist_ 70(730):459-466.

702. Brown, Vinson. 1974. REPTILES AND AMPHIBIANS OF THE WEST. _Naturegraph Publishers Inc._, Healdsburg, California. 79 pages.

703. Welch, Paul S. and Eugene S. McCartney. 1925. A KEY TO THE SNAKES OF THE UNITED STATES, CANADA AND LOWER CALIFORNIA. _Papers of the Michigan Academy of Science Arts and Letters_ 4(2):1-63.

704. Hilton, William A. 1948. THE INTERNAL EAR OF SALAMANDERS. _Journal of Entomology and Zoology_ 40(4):95-99.

705. Hilton, William A. 1948. THE CARPUS AND TARSUS OF SALAMANDERS. _Journal of Entomology and Zoology_ 40(1):1-13.

706. Wake, David B. 1965. _Aneides ferreus_. _Catalogue of American Amphibians and Reptiles_: 16.1-16.2.

707. Slater, James R. 1955. DISTRIBUTION OF WASHINGTON AMPHIBIANS. Occasional Papers, Department of Biology, College of Puget Sound No. 16:120-154.

708. Awbrey, Frank T. 1978. SOCIAL INTERACTION AMONG CHORUSING PACIFIC TREE FROGS, Hyla regilla. Copeia 1978(2):208-214.

709. Guerra, Ladislao A. 1976. COLOR PRESERVATION IN SALAMANDERS. Herpetological Review 7(4):170-171.

710. Duellman, William E. 1979. THE NUMBER OF AMPHIBIANS AND REPTILES. Herpetological Review 10(3):83-84.

711. Ferguson, Denzel E. 1963. Ambystoma macrodactylum. Catalogue of American Amphibians and Reptiles: 4.1-4.2.

712. Anderson, James D. 1968. Rhyacotriton AND R. olympicus. Catalogue of American Amphibians and Reptiles: 68.1-68.2.

713. Tihen, Joseph A. 1969. Ambystoma. Catalogue of American Amphibians and Reptiles: 75.1-75.4.

714. Anderson, James D. 1969. Dicamptodon AND D. ensatus. Catalogue of American Amphibians and Reptiles: 76:1-76.2.

715. Storm, Robert M. and Edmund D. Brodie. 1970. Plethodon dunni. Catalogue of American Amphibians and Reptiles: 82.1-82.2.

716. Storm, Robert M. and Edmund D. Brodie. 1970. Plethodon vehiculum. Catalogue of American Amphibians and Reptiles: 83.1-83.2.

717. Brodie, Edmund D. and Robert M. Storm. 1970. Plethodon vandykei. Catalogue of American Amphibians and Reptiles: 91.1-91.2.

718. Brodie, Edmund D. and Robert M. Storm. 1971. Plethodon elongatus. Catalogue of American Amphibians and Reptiles: 102.1-102.2.

719. Wake, David B. 1974. Aneides. Catalogue of American Amphibians and Reptiles: 157.1-157.2.

720. Altig, Ronald and Philip C. Dumas. 1972. Rana aurora. Catalogue of American Amphibians and Reptiles: 160.1-160.4.

721. Metter, Dean E. 1968. Ascaphus AND A. truei. Catalogue of American Amphibians and Reptiles:69.1-69.2

722. Martof, Bernard S. 1970. Rana sylvatica. Catalogue of American Amphibians and Reptiles: 86.1-86.4.

723. Altig, Ronald and Philip C. Dumas. 1971. Rana cascadae. Catalogue of American Amphibians and Reptiles: 105.1-105.2.

724. Turner, Frederick B. and Philip C. Dumas. 1972. Rana pretiosa. Catalogue of American Amphibians and Reptiles: 119.1-119.4.

725. Bury, R. Bruce. 1970. Clemmys marmorata. Catalogue of American Amphibians and Reptiles: 100.1-100.3.

726. Ernst, Carl H. 1971. <u>Chrysemys picta</u>. Catalogue of American Amphibians and Reptiles: 106.1–106.4.

727. Bury, R. Bruce and Carl H. Ernst. 1977. <u>Clemmys</u>. Catalogue of American Amphibians and Reptiles: 203.1–203.2.

728. Blaney, Richard M. 1973. <u>Lampropeltis</u>. Catalogue of American Amphibians and Reptiles: 150.1–150.2.

729. Zweifel, Richard G. 1974. <u>Lampropeltis zonata</u>. Catalogue of American Amphibians and Reptiles: 174.1–174.4.

730. Stewart, Glenn R. 1977. <u>Charina, C. bottae</u>. Catalogue of American Amphibians and Reptiles: 205.1–205.2.

731. Wilson, Larry David. 1978. <u>Coluber constrictor</u>. Catalogue of American Amphibians and Reptiles: 218.1–218.4.

732. Kirk, James L. 1979. <u>Thamnophis ordinoides</u>. Catalogue of American Amphibians and Reptiles: 233.1–233.2.

733. Lais, P. Mike. 1976. <u>Gerrhonotus coeruleus</u>. Catalogue of American Amphibians and Reptiles: 178.1–178.4.

734. Lais, P. Mike. 1976. <u>Gerrhonotus multicarinatus</u>. Catalogue of American Amphibians and Reptiles: 187.1–187.4.

735. Gaudin, Anthony J. 1965. LARVAL DEVELOPMENT OF THE TREE FROGS <u>Hyla regilla</u> AND <u>Hyla californiae</u>. Herpetologica 21(2):117–130.

736. Etheridge, Richard. 1965. THE ABDOMINAL SKELETON OF LIZARDS IN THE FAMILY IGUANIDAE. <u>Herpetologica</u> 21(3):161–168.

737. Mueller, Charles F. and Robert E. Moore. 1969. GROWTH OF THE SAGEBRUSH LIZARD, <u>Sceloporous graciosus</u>, IN YELLOWSTONE NATIONAL PARK. <u>Herpetologica</u> 25(1):35–38.

738. Licht, Lawrence E. 1969. OBSERVATIONS ON THE COURTSHIP BEHAVIOR OF <u>Ambystoma gracile</u>. Herpetologica 25(1):49–52.

739. Houck, W. J. 1969. ALBINO <u>Aneides ferreus</u>. Herpetologica 25(1):54.

740. Altig, Ronald. 1969. NOTES ON THE ONTOGENY OF THE OSSEOUS CRANIUM OF <u>Ascaphus truei</u>. Herpetologica 25(1):59–62.

741. Noble, G. K. and E. R. Mason. 1933. EXPERIMENTS ON THE BROODING HABITS OF THE LIZARDS <u>Eumeces</u> AND <u>Ophisaurus</u>. <u>American Museum Novitates</u> No. 619:1–29.

742. Johnson, Clifford Ray. 1965. THE DIET OF THE PACIFIC FENCE LIZARD, <u>Sceloporus occidentalis occidentalis</u> (BAIRD AND GIRARD), FROM NORTHERN CALIFORNIA. <u>Herpetologica</u> 21(2):114–117.

743. Klauber, Laurence M. 1943. THE SUBSPECIES OF THE RUBBER SNAKE, <u>Charina</u>. <u>Transactions of the San Diego Society of Natural History</u> 10(7):83–90.

744. Hilton, William A. 1950. THE DEVELOPMENT OF THE CHONDOCRANIUM IN <u>Ambystoma</u> (PRELIMINARY REMARKS). <u>Journal of Entomology and Zoology</u> 42(1):2–4.

745. Bryant, H. C. 1925. THE EGGS OF THE WESTERN YELLOW-BELLIED RACER. Journal of Entomology and Zoology 17(1):9-10.

746. Hilton, William A. 1945. THE SKELETON OF BATRACHOCEPS. Journal of Entomology and Zoology 37(1):8-17.

747. Stewart, Glenn R. 1965. THERMAL ECOLOGY OF THE GARTER SNAKES Thamnophis sirtalis concinnus (HALLOWELL) AND Thamnophis ordinoides (BAIRD AND GIRARD). Herpetologica 21(2):81-102.

748. Wortham, J. W. Edward, Ronald A. Brandon and Jan Martan. 1977. COMPARATIVE MORPHOLOGY OF SOME PLETHODONTID SALAMANDER SPERMATOZOA. Copeia 1977(4):666-680.

749. Hirth, Harold F. 1966. WEIGHT CHANGES AND MORTALITY OF THREE SPECIES OF SNAKES DURING HIBERNATION. Herpetologica 22(1):8-12.

750. Lynn, W. Gardner, Sister Mary Cyrilla O'Brien and Rev. Peter Herhenreader. 1966. THYROID MORPHOLOGY IN LIZARDS OF THE FAMILIES IGUANIDAE AND AGAMIDAE. Herpetologica 22(2):90-93.

751. Peterson, Ernest A. 1966. HEARING IN THE LIZARD: SOME COMMENTS ON THE AUDITORY CAPACITIES OF A NONMAMMALIAN EAR. Herpetologica 22(3):161-171.

752. Cunningham, John D. 1966. ADDITIONAL OBSERVATIONS ON THE BODY TEMPERATURES OF REPTILES. Herpetologica 22(3):184-189.

753. Landreth, Hobart F. and Denzel E. Ferguson. 1967. MOVEMENTS AND ORIENTATION OF THE TAILED FROG, Ascaphus truei. Herpetologica 23(2):81-93.

754. Licht, Lawrence E. 1967. INITIAL APPEARANCE OF THE PAROTID GLAND IN THREE SPECIES OF TOADS (GENUS Bufo). Herpetologica 23(2):115-118.

755. Foster, Woodbridge A. 1967. CHORUS STRUCTURE AND VOCAL RESPONSE IN THE PACIFIC TREE FROG, Hyla regilla. Herpetologica 23(2):100-104.

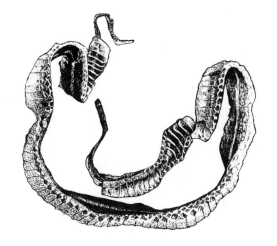

756. Howse, Harold D., Victor J. Ferrans and Richard G. Hibbs. 1969. OBSERV- ATIONS ON THE FINE STRUCTURE OF THE VENTRICULAR MYOCARDIUM OF A SALAMANDER, Ambystoma maculatum SHAW. Herpetologica 25(2):75-85.

757. Wernz, James G. and Robert M. Storm. 1969. PRE-HATCHING STAGES OF THE TAILED FROG, Ascaphus truei STEJNEGER. Herpetologica 25(2):86- 93.

758. Brodie, Edmund D. and Linda S. Gibson. 1969. DEFENSIVE BEHAVIOR AND SKIN GLANDS OF THE NORTHWESTERN SALAMANDER, Ambystoma gracile. Herpetologica 25(3):187-194.

759. Brodie, Edmund D., Ronald A. Nussbaum and Robert M. Storm. 1969. AN EGG-LAYING AGGREGATION OF FIVE SPECIES OF OREGON REPTILES. Herpetologica 25(3):223-227.

760. Nussbaum, Ronald A. 1969. NESTS AND EGGS OF THE PACIFIC GIANT SALAMANDER, Dicamptodon ensatus (ESCHSCHOLTZ). Herpetologica 25(4):257-262.

761. Nussbaum, Ronald A. 1969. A NEST SITE OF THE OLYMPIC SALAMANDER, Rhyacotriton olympicus (GAIGE). Herpetologica 25(4):277-278.

762. Hutchison, Victor H. and Michael R. Ferrance. 1970. THERMAL TOLERANCES OF *Rana pipiens* ACCLIMATED TO DAILY TEMPERATURE CYCLES. Herpetologica 26(1):1-8.

763. Marcellini, Dale and James P. Mackey. 1970. HABITAT PREFERENCES OF THE LIZARDS, *Sceloporus occidentalis* AND *S. graciosus* (LACTERTILIA, IGUANIDAE). Herpetologica 26(1):51-56.

764. Mueller, Charles F. 1970. TEMPERATURE ACCLIMATION IN TWO SPECIES OF *Sceloporus*. Herpetologica 26(1):83-85.

765. Altig, Ronald. 1970. A KEY TO THE TADPOLES OF CONTINENTAL UNITED STATES AND CANADA. Herpetologica 26(2):180-207.

766. Campbell, James B. 1970. HIBERNACULA OF A POPULATION OF *Bufo boreas boreas* IN THE COLORADO FRONT RANGE. Herpetologica 26(2):278-282.

767. Briggs, Jeffrey L. and Robert M. Storm. 1970. GROWTH AND POPULATION STRUCTURE OF THE CASCADE FROG, *Rana cascadae* SLATER. Herpetologica 26(3):283-300.

768. Funkhouser, Anne and Susan Ann Foster. 1970. OXYGEN UPTAKE AND THYROID ACTIVITY IN *Hyla regilla* TADPOLES. Herpetologica 26(3):366-371.

769. Haertel, John D. and Robert M. Storm. 1970. EXPERIMENTAL HYBRIDIZATION BETWEEN *Rana pretiosa* AND *Rana cascadae*. Herpetologica 26(4):436-444.

770. Runyan, Craig S. 1977. A SLUG IN THE WINTER DIET OF THE NORTHWESTERN SALAMANDER. Discovery 6(2):43.

771. Yarrow, H. C. 1882. CHECK LIST OF NORTH AMERICAN REPTILIA AND BATRACHIA, WITH CATALOGUE OF SPECIMENS IN THE U.S. NATIONAL MUSEUM. United States National Museum Bulletin No. 24:1-249.

772. Bennett, Albert F. and Paul Licht. 1972. ANAEROBIC METABOLISM DURING ACTIVITY IN LIZARDS. Journal of Comparative Physiology 81(3):277-288.

773. Jones, David R. and Tariq Mustafa. 1973. THE LACTACID OXYGEN DEBT IN FROGS AFTER ONE HOUR'S APNOEA IN AIR. Journal of Comparative Physiology 85(1):15-24.

774. Bennett, Albert F. and Paul Licht. 1974. ANAEROBIC METABOLISM DURING ACTIVITY IN AMPHIBIANS. Comparative Biochemical Physiology 48A(2A):319-327.

775. Shaler, N. S. 1872. THE RATTLESNAKE AND NATURAL SELECTION. American Naturalist 6(1):32-37.

776. Ballou, W. H. 1880. VICTIMIZING RATTLESNAKES. American Naturalist 14(7):523.

777. Henderson, J. G. 1872. USE OF THE RATTLES OF THE RATTLESNAKE. American Naturalist 6(5):260-263.

778. Cope, E. D. 1896. THE GEOGRAPHICAL DISTRIBUTION OF BATRACHIA AND REPTILIA IN NORTH AMERICA. American Naturalist 30(359):886-902; 30(360):1003-1026.

779. Taylor, W. Edgar. 1895. PRELIMINARY NOTES ON THE OSTEOLOGY OF NORTH AMERICAN CROTALIDAE. American Naturalist 29(339):281-285.

780. Cope, E. D. 1896. SYNONYMIC LIST OF THE NORTH AMERICAN SPECIES OF Bufo AND Rana, WITH DESCRIPTIONS OF SOME NEW SPECIES OF BATRACHIA, FROM SPECIMENS IN THE NATIONAL MUSEUM. Proceedings of the American Philosophical Society 23(124):514-526.

781. Cope, E. D. 1887. THE HYOID STRUCTURE IN THE AMBLYSTOMID SALAMANDERS. American Naturalist 21(1):87-88.

782. Martin, Robert F. 1973. OSTEOLOGY OF NORTH AMERICAN Bufo: THE americanus, cognatus, AND boreas SPECIES GROUPS. Herpetologica 29(4):375-387.

783. Goldberg, Stephen R. 1973. OVARIAN CYCLE OF THE WESTERN FENCE LIZARD, Sceloporus occidentalis. Herpetologica 29(3):284-289.

784. Gaudin, Anthony J. 1973. THE DEVELOPMENT OF THE SKULL IN THE PACIFIC TREE FROG, Hyla regilla. Herpetologica 29(3):205-218.

785. Gradwell, Norman. 1973. ON THE FUNCTIONAL MORPHOLOGY OF SUCTION AND GILL IRRIGATION IN THE TADPOLE OF Ascaphus, AND NOTES ON HIBERNATION. Herpetologica 29(1):84-93.

786. Pendlebury, George B. 1972. TAGGING AND REMOTE IDENTIFICATION OF RATTLESNAKES. Herpetologica 28(4):349-350.

787. Sivula, Janice C., Michael C. Mix and Donald S. McKenzie. 1972. OXYGEN CONSUMPTION OF Bufo boreas boreas TADPOLES DURING VARIOUS DEVELOPMENTAL STAGES OF METAMORPHOSIS. Herpetologica 28(4):309-313.

788. Purdue, James R. and Charles C. Carpenter. 1972. A COMPARATIVE STUDY OF THE DISPLAY MOTION IN THE IGUANID GENERA Sceloporus, Uta AND Urosaurus. Herpetologica 28(2):137-141.

789. Anderson, James D. 1972. EMBRYONIC TEMPERATURE TOLERANCE AND RATE OF DEVELOPMENT IN SOME SALAMANDERS OF THE GENUS Ambystoma. Herpetologica 28(2):126-130.

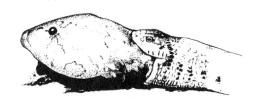

790. Liu, Ch'eng Chao. 1935. TYPES OF VOCAL SAC IN THE SALIENTIA. Proceedings of the Boston Society of Natural History 41(3):19-40.

791. Carr, A. F. 1942. NOTES ON SEA TURTLES. Proceedings of the New England Zoological Club 21:1-16.

792. Ryder, Glen R. 1973. FEEDING HABITS OF THE SCREECH OWL NEAR VANCOUVER, BRITISH COLUMBIA. Vancouver Natural History Society Discovery (New Series) 2(2):51-52.

793. Storm, Robert M. 1947. EGGS AND YOUNG OF Aneides ferreus. Herpetologica 4(2):60-62.

794. Burkholder, Gary L. and Wilmer W. Tanner. 1974. A NEW GLAND IN Sceloporus graciosus MALES (SAURIA: IGUANIDAE). Herpetologica 30(4):368-371.

795. Herzog, Harold A. and Gordon M. Burghardt. 1974. PREY MOVEMENT AND PREDATORY BEHAVIOR OF JUVENILE WESTERN YELLOW-BELLIED RACERS, Coluber constrictor mormon. Herpetologica 30(3):285-289.

796. Hoyer, Richard F. 1974. DESCRIPTION OF A RUBBER BOA (<u>Charina</u> <u>bottae</u>) POPULATION FROM WESTERN OREGON. <u>Herpetologica</u> 30(3):275-283.

797. Altig, Ronald and J. Padgett Kelly. 1974. INDICES OF FEEDING IN ANURAN TADPOLES AS INDICATED BY GUT CHARACTERISTICS. <u>Herpetologica</u> 30(2):200-203.

798. Seale, Dianne and Martin Boraas. 1974. A PERMANENT MARK FOR AMPHIBIAN LARVAE. <u>Herpetologica</u> 30(2):160-162.

799. Gregory, Patrick T. 1979. PREDATOR AVOIDANCE BEHAVIOR OF THE RED-LEGGED FROG (<u>Rana</u> <u>aurora</u>). <u>Herpetologica</u> 35(2):175-184.

800. McKenzie, Donald S. and Robert M. Storm. 1971. ONTOGENETIC COLOR PATTERNS OF THE CLOUDED SALAMANDER, <u>Aneides</u> <u>ferreus</u> (COPE). <u>Herpetologica</u> 27(2):142-147.

801. Bider, J. R. and W. Hoek. 1971. AN EFFICIENT AND APPARENTLY UN-BIASED SAMPLING TECHNIQUE FOR POPULATION STUDIES OF PAINTED TURTLES. <u>Herpetologica</u> 27(4):481-484.

802. Nussbaum, Ronald A. and Edmund D. Brodie. 1971. THE TAXONOMIC STATUS OF THE ROUGH-SKINNED NEWT, <u>Taricha</u> <u>granulosa</u> (SKIL-TON), IN THE ROCKY MOUNTAINS. <u>Herpetologica</u> 27(3):260-270.

803. Grass, Al. 1970. AN UNUSUAL GARTER SNAKE MORTALITY. <u>Vancouver Natural History Society Discovery</u> No. 147:10.

804. Cope, Edward Drinker. 1900. THE CROCODILIANS, LIZARDS, AND SNAKES OF NORTH AMERICA. <u>Report of the United States National Museum</u> 1898:153-1270.

805. Noble, G. K. 1925. THE EVOLUTION AND DISPERSAL OF THE FROGS. <u>American Naturalist</u> 59(662):265-271.

806. Campbell, Wayne. 1969. BURNABY LAKE WILDLIFE - HABITAT OR EPITAPH? <u>Bulletin of the Vancouver Natural History Society</u> No. 144:12-13; No. 145:20.

807. Brodie, Edmund D. 1968. A CASE OF INTERBREEDING BETWEEN <u>Bufo</u> <u>boreas</u> AND <u>Rana</u> <u>cascadae</u>. <u>Herpetologica</u> 24(1):86.

808. Ruthven, Alexander G. 1912. DIRECTIONS FOR COLLECTING AND PRESERVING SPECIMENS OF REPTILES AND AMPHIBIANS FOR MUSEUM PURPOSES. <u>Annual Report of the Michigan Academy of Science</u> 14:165-177.

809. Savage, Jay M. 1973. THE GEOGRAPHIC DISTRIBUTION OF FROGS: PATTERNS AND PREDICTIONS. Pages 351-445, <u>in</u> J. L. Vial, Evolutionary Biology of the Anurans. <u>University of Missouri Press</u>, Columbia.

810. Woolery, Donald L. 1971. EVAPORATIVE WATER LOSS IN TWO NORTHWEST SNAKE: <u>Pituophis</u> <u>catenifer</u> AND <u>Crotalus</u> <u>viridis</u>. M.Sc. Thesis, <u>Department of Biology, Central Washington University</u>, Ellensburg. 23 pages.

811. Haneline, Patricia G. and Anders G. J. Rhodin. 1976. SKELETAL PREPARATIONS OF HERPETOLOGICAL SPECIMENS. <u>Herpetological Review</u> 7(4):169-170.

812. Cope, E. D. 1886. AN ANALYTICAL TABLE OF THE GENERA OF SNAKES. Proceedings of the American Philosophical Society 23(124):479-499.

813. Green, D. 1968. INTERMEDIATE TRIP TO WIDGEON VALLEY. Bulletin of the Vancouver Natural History Society No. 140:11.

814. Vitt, Laurie Joseph. 1968. REPRODUCTIVE BIOLOGY OF THE ANGUID LIZARD Gerrhonotus coeruleus principis. M.Sc. Thesis, Department of Biology, Western Washington University, Bellingham. 62 pages.

815. Orchard, Stan A. 1978. AMPHIBIANS OF BRITISH COLUMBIA. Unpublished Report, British Columbia Fish and Wildlife Branch, Victoria. 92 pages.

816. Orchard, Stan A. 1978. REPTILES OF BRITISH COLUMBIA. Unpublished Report, British Columbia Fish and Wildlife Branch, Victoria. 72 pages.

817. Thomas, Robert A. 1977. SELECTED BIBLIOGRAPHY OF CERTAIN VERTEBRATE TECHNIQUES. United States Department of the Interior Bureau of Land Management Technical Note 306:1-88.

818. Metcalf, Maynard M. 1923. THE ORIGIN AND DISTRIBUTION OF THE ANURA. American Naturalist 57(652):385-411.

819. Woods, John G. 1978. THE WESTERN TOAD: A COLD-BLOODED MOUNTAINEER. Unpublished Report, Parks Canada, Mount Revelstoke National Park, British Columbia. 3 pages.

820. Woods, John G. 1977. THE 'GATORS' OF MOUNT REVELSTOKE. Unpublished Report, Parks Canada, Mount Revelstoke National Park, British Columbia. 3 pages.

821. Dyrness, C. T., Jerry F. Franklin, Chris Maser, Stanton A. Cook, James D. Hall and Glenda Faxon. 1975. RESEARCH NATURAL AREA NEEDS IN THE PACIFIC NORTHWEST - A CONTRIBUTION TO LAND-USE PLANNING. United States Department of Agriculture Forest Service General Technical Report PNW 38:1-231.

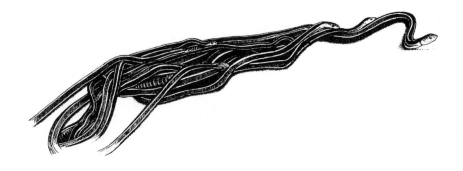

822. Bernard, Stephen and Kenneth F. Brown. 1977. DISTRIBUTION OF MAMMALS, REPTILES AND AMPHIBIANS BY BLM PHYSIOGRAPHIC REGIONS AND A. W. KUCHLER'S ASSOCIATIONS FOR THE ELEVEN WESTERN STATES. United States Department of the Interior Bureau of Land Management Technical Note, Denver, Colorado. 169 pages.

823. Cope, E. D. 1894. THE CLASSIFICATION OF SNAKES. American Naturalist 28(334):831-844.

824. Lockington, W. N. 1884. REVIEW OF THE PROGRESS OF NORTH AMERICAN BATRACHOLOGY IN THE YEARS 1880-1883. American Naturalist 18(2):149-154.

825. Brons, H. A. 1882. NOTES ON THE HABITS OF SOME WESTERN SNAKES. American Naturalist 16(7):564-567.

826. Smith, Vivien. 1955. REPORTS OF MEETINGS - CULTUS LAKE. Bulletin of the Vancouver Natural History Society 95:3-4.

827. White, Charles A. 1884. ON THE CHARACTER AND FUNCTION OF THE EPIGLOTTIS IN THE BULL-SNAKE (Pityophis). American Naturalist 18(1):19-21.

828. Jamieson, E. W., A. A. Heusner and R. Arbogast. 1977. OXYGEN CONSUMPTION OF Sceloporus occidentalis FROM THREE DIFFERENT ELEVATIONS. Comparative Biochemistry and Physiology 56A(1A):73-79.

829. Derickson, W. Kenneth. 1974. LIPID DEPOSITION AND UTILIZATION IN THE SAGEBRUSH LIZARD, Sceloporus graciosus: ITS SIGNIFICANCE FOR REPRODUCTION AND MAINTENANCE. Comparative Biochemistry and Physiology 49A(2A):267-272.

830. Moore, Frank L., Richard L. Seide, Jennifer L. Specker and Lloyd Swanson. 1978. EFFECTS OF PROLACTIN AND METHALLIBURE ON SECOND METAMORPHOSIS AND PLASMA ANDROGENS IN MALE NEWTS, Taricha granulosa. Comparative Biochemistry and Physiology 61A(3):419-422.

831. Claussen, Dennis L. 1973. THE THERMAL RELATIONS OF THE TAILED FROG, Ascaphus truei, AND THE PACIFIC TREEFROG, Hyla regilla. Comparative Biochemistry and Physiology 44A(1A):137-153.

832. Claussen, Dennis L. 1973. THE WATER RELATIONS OF THE TAILED FROG, Ascaphus truei, AND THE PACIFIC TREEFROG, Hyla regilla. Comparative Biochemistry and Physiology 44A(1A):155-171.

833. Lillywhite, Harvey B. 1971. TEMPERATURE SELECTION BY THE BULLFROG, Rana catesbeiana. Comparative Biochemistry and Physiology 40A(1A):213-227.

834. Kerstetter, Theodore H. and Leonard B. Kirschner. 1971. THE ROLE OF THE HYPOTHALAMO-NEUROHYPOPHYSIAL SYSTEM IN MAINTAINING HYDROMINERAL BALANCE IN LARVAL SALAMANDERS (Ambystoma tigrinium). Comparative Biochemistry and Physiology 40A(2A):373-384.

835. Klicka, John and I. Y. Mahmoud. 1971. A COMPARATIVE STUDY OF RESPIRATORY PIGMENT CONCENTRATIONS IN SIX SPECIES OF TURTLES. Comparative Biochemistry and Physiology 38A(1A):53-58.

836. Brown, Herbert A. 1975. EMBRYONIC TEMPERATURE ADAPTATIONS OF THE PACIFIC TREEFROG, Hyla regilla. Comparative Biochemistry and Physiology 51A(4A):863-873.

837. Bennett, Albert F. and Paul Licht. 1973. RELATIVE CONTRIBUTIONS OF ANAEROBIC AND AEROBIC ENERGY PRODUCTION DURING ACTIVITY IN AMPHIBIA. Journal of Comparative Physiology 87(4):351-360.

838. Lillywhite, Harvey B. 1971. THERMAL MODULATION OF CUTANEOUS MUCUS DISCHARGE AS A DETERMINANT OF EVAPORATIVE WATER LOSS IN THE FROG, Rana catesbeiana. Zeitschrift fur Vergleichende Physiologie 73(1):84-104.

839. Humphrey, D. G. 1958. NEW CHROMOSOME NUMBER FOR THE ORDER CAUDATA. <u>Science</u> 128(3319):304.

840. Juelson, Thomas C., Steven J. Sweeney, Keith W. Kurko, Leo J. Salo and William A. Bradbury. 1980. SNOHOMISH MEDIATED PLAN WILDLIFE STUDY. Unpublished Report, <u>Washington Department of Game</u>, Seattle. 199 pages.

841. Smith, Hobart M. 1978. A GUIDE TO FIELD IDENTIFICATION AMPHIBIANS OF NORTH AMERICA. <u>Western Publishing Company Inc.</u>, Racine, Wisconsin. 160 pages.

842. Van Denburgh, John. 1898. HERPETOLOGICAL NOTES. <u>Proceedings of the American Philosophical Society</u> 37(157):139-141.

843. Schultz, Richard H. 1978. EFFECTS OF TEMPERATURE AND PHOTOPERIOD ON IN VITRO METABOLIC RATE OF LIVER HOMOGENATES FROM <u>Thamnophis elegans</u>. M.Sc. Thesis, <u>Central Washington University</u>, <u>Department of Biology</u>, Ellensburg. 44 pages.

844. Anonymous. 1965. NOTES ON GARTER SNAKE AND ALLIGATOR LIZARD HABITATS IN MANNING PARK, BRITISH COLUMBIA. Unpublished Report, <u>British Columbia Provincial Museum Vertebrate Zoology Division</u>, Victoria. 2 pages.

845. Kullman, Cal. 1976. GARTER SNAKE CAPTURES, JUNE 16 - AUGUST 18, 1976, COMOX BURN. Unpublished Report, <u>British Columbia Provincial Museum Vertebrate Zoology Division</u>, Victoria. 1 page.

846. Hard, Robert Paul. 1970. INTRACELLULAR MOVEMENTS IN THE EOSINOPHILIC LEUCOCYTES OF <u>Taricha granulosa</u>. M.Sc. Thesis, <u>University of Washington</u>, <u>Department of Zoology</u>, Seattle. 60 pages.

847. Kardong, Kenneth Victor. 1968. THE COMPARATIVE MORPHOLOGY OF THE RESPIRATORY SYSTEM AND ASSOCIATED MUSCULATURE OF <u>Charina bottae</u>, <u>Elaphe obsoleta</u>, <u>Quadrivittata</u>, AND <u>Crotalus viridis oreganus</u>. M.Sc. Thesis, <u>University of Washington</u>, <u>Department of Zoology</u>, Seattle. 80 pages.

848. Hebard, William Bartlett. 1949. STATUS, RELATIONSHIPS AND VARIATION IN THE GARTER SNAKES, GENUS <u>Thamnophis</u>, OF THE PUGET SOUND REGION OF WASHINGTON STATE. M.Sc. Thesis, <u>University of Washington</u>, <u>Department of Zoology</u>, Seattle. 82 pages.

849. Dawe, Neil K. 1980. FLORA AND FAUNA OF THE MARSHALL-STEVENSON UNIT, QUALICUM NATIONAL WILDLIFE AREA (UPDATE TO JUNE, 1979). Unpublished Report, <u>Canadian Wildlife Service</u>, Qualicum Beach, British Columbia. 149 pages.

850. Dawe, Neil K. and Sylvia D. Lang. 1980. FLORA AND FAUNA OF THE NANOOSE UNIT, QUALICUM NATIONAL WILDLIFE AREA. Unpublished Report, <u>Canadian Wildlife Service</u>, Qualicum Beach, British Columbia. 117 pages.

851. Green, David M. and R. Wayne Campbell. 1980. THE AMPHIBIANS OF BRITISH COLUMBIA. Unpublished Report, <u>British Columbia Provincial Museum, Vertebrate Zoology Division</u>, Victoria. 105 pages.

852. Gregory, Patrick T. and R. Wayne Campbell. 1980. THE REPTILES OF BRITISH COLUMBIA. Unpublished Report, <u>British Columbia Provincial Museum, Vertebrate Zoology Division</u>, Victoria. 101 pages.

853. Dawe, Neil K. and Stephen P. Wetmore. 1980. THE CLUXEWE RIVER ESTUARY: AN AQUISITION PROPOSAL. Unpublished Report, Canadian Wildlife Service, Qualicum Beach, British Columbia. 21 pages.

854. Alvarado, Ronald Herbert. 1962. OSMOTIC AND IONIC REGULATION IN Ambystoma tigrinum. Ph.D. Thesis, Washington State University, Department of Zoology, Pullman. 131 pages.

855. Antonelli, Arthur L. 1969. FOOD HABITS OF Dicamptodon ensatus AND ASSOCIATED FISH SPECIES OF MARATTA CREEK, WASHINGTON. M.Sc. Thesis, Central Washington University, Department of Biology, Ellensburg. 55 pages.

856. Beirne, Maryann B. 1979. AN ELECTRO-PHORETIC SURVEY OF THE SERUM PROTEIN PATTERNS OF THE AMBYSTOMATID SALAMANDERS OF THE COASTAL PACIFIC NORTHWEST. M.Sc. Thesis, Western Washington University, Department of Biology, Bellingham. 35 pages.

857. Bradford, Jack. 1968. THE EFFECT OF FOLLICLE-STIMULATING HORMONE AND TESTOSTERONE PROPIONATE ON THE REPRODUCTION OF THE BULL SNAKES, Pituophis melanoleucus catenifer AND Pituophis melanoleucus affinis; ACCOMPANIED WITH ANALYSIS OF CHANGES IN BLOOD PROTEIN CONSTITUENTS FOLLOWING STIMULATION. M.Sc. Thesis, Central Washington University, Department of Biology, Ellensburg. 35 pages.

858. Byrne, James J. 1971. ACTIVE PERIOD CHANGES IN LIVER AND MUSCLE GYCOGEN, TISSUE LIPID, AND BLOOD GLUCOSE IN A NATURALLY OCCURRING POPULATION OF Rana catesbeiana. M.Sc. Thesis, Eastern Washington State College, Department of Biology, Cheney. 54 pages.

859. Cahall, Anna Marie, Char Eberhardt, Nikki Ellman, Andy Keller and Karen Von Der Linn. 1979. DESCRIPTIVE ECOLOGY OF A DIVERSE LOWLAND HABITAT ON ELD INLET, THURSTON COUNTY, WASHINGTON. Evergreen State College Report, Olympia. 30 pages.

860. Creso, Irene Owens. 1949. A COMPARATIVE STUDY OF THE GROSS ANATOMY OF THE CIRCULATORY SYSTEMS OF THE SALIENTIA OF THE NORTHWEST. M.Sc. Thesis, University of Puget Sound, Department of Biology, Tacoma. 111 pages.

861. Etheridge, Jack, Deanna Frost, Melany Harris and Tyra Lindquist. 1977. DESCRIPTIVE ECOLOGY OF A SMALL BEAVER POND AND SURROUNDING FOREST, THURSTON COUNTY, WASHINGTON. Evergreen State College Report, Olympia. 27 pages.

862. Engel, Steve, Dave Simpson and Tim Wyatt. 1978. A PHOTO-ECO PRESENTATION OF THE McLANE CREEK BEAVER POND. Evergreen State College Report, Olympia. 79 pages.

863. Dunlap, Donald G. 1955. THE COMPARATIVE MYOLOGY OF THE PELVIC APPENDAGE IN THE SALIENTIA. Ph.D. Thesis, Washington State University, Department of Zoology, Pullman. 283 pages.

864. Fish, Joseph Leroy. 1972. GROWTH AND SURVIVAL OF ANURAN TADPOLES (Bufo boreas AND Rana aurora) IN RELATION TO ACUTE GAMMA RADIATION, WATER TEMPERATURE, AND POPULATION DENSITY. Ph.D. Thesis, Washington State University, Department of Zoology, Pullman. 91 pages.

865. Fors, Susan Robin. 1979. A VEGETATIONAL ANALYSIS AND PARTIAL BIOTIC SURVEY OF THE CARLISLE BOG. M.Sc. Thesis, University of Puget Sound, Department of Biology, Tacoma. 163 pages.

866. Hardin, Edith. 1929. A BIOLOGICAL STUDY OF THE AUSTIN PASS REGION OF MOUNT BAKER. M.Sc. Thesis, Washington State University, Department of Zoology, Pullman. 77 pages.

867. Herbig, Raymond J. 1975. ADAPTIVE STRATEGIES OF Hyla regilla AND Rana aurora IN A TEMPORARY POND. Master Natural Sciences Thesis, Pacific Lutheran University, Tacoma. 40 pages.

868. Holmes, Charles Oliver. 1969. A BIOLOGICAL INVESTIGATION ON Plethodon larselli. M.Sc. Thesis, Central Washington University, Department of Biology, Ellensburg. 45 pages.

869. Hillman, Peter Eric. 1974. SIMULATION AND MODELING OF TRANSIENT THERMAL RESPONSES OF THE WESTERN FENCE LIZARD, Sceloporus occidentalis. Ph.D. Thesis, Washington State University, Department of Zoology, Pullman. 120 pages.

870. Beery, Don. 1971. A BOA CONSTRICTOR IN THE NORTHWEST. Pacific Search 5(10):23.

871. Hodge, Robert. 1971. RANA RAPPING. Pacific Search 5(10):13.

872. Kerstetter, Theodore Harvey. 1969. A STUDY OF THE ENDOCRINE CONTROL OF IONIC AND OSMOTIC REGULATION IN Ambystoma tigrinum. Ph.D. Thesis, Washington State University, Department of Zoology, Pullman. 101 pages.

873. Klotz, Sally A., Sarah J. Madsen, Pamela A. Miller and Daphne F. Smith. 1978. A SURVEY OF TERRESTRIAL ORGANISMS ON THE NISQUALLY RIVER DELTA, WASHINGTON. Evergreen State College Report, Olympia. 166 pages.

874. Korsmo, Paul S. 1973. THE EFFECT OF THERMAL ACCLIMATION ON THE WHOLE BODY OXYGEN CONSUMPTION OF THE NORTHERN ALLIGATOR LIZARD, Gerrhonotus coeruleus principis. M.Sc. Thesis, Western Washington University, Department of Biology, Bellingham. 55 pages.

875. Loeb, Timothy G. 1979. GEOGRAPHIC VARIATION AND TAXONOMIC RELATIONSHIPS OF PACIFIC NORTHWEST GARTER SNAKES. M.Sc. Thesis, Central Washington University, Department of Biology, Ellensburg. 113 pages.

876. Metter, Dean Edward. 1960. THE DISTRIBUTION OF AMPHIBIANS IN EASTERN WASHINGTON. M.Sc. Thesis, Washington State University, Department of Zoology, Pullman. 89 pages.

877. Mullen, Terry L. 1971. THE MICROCLIMATE, ION AND WATER BALANCE OF LARVAL AND ADULT Ascaphus truei STEJNEGER. M.Sc. Thesis, Central Washington University, Department of Biology, Ellensburg. 106 pages.

878. Olson, Richard Lee. 1977. THE HELMINTH PARASITES OF Thamnophis sirtalis (L.) AND Thamnophis elegans (BAIRD AND GIRARD) FROM TURNBULL NATIONAL WILDLIFE REFUGE, WASHINGTON. M.Sc. Thesis, Eastern Washington State College, Department of Biology, Cheney. 52 pages.

4

879. Perry, Alfred E. 1974. A SURVEY OF TERRESTRIAL VERTEBRATE FAUNA OF THE TOUCHET RIVER DRAINAGE, WASHINGTON. Unpublished Report, Walla Walla College, College Place, Washington. 107 pages. (A Report to the U.S. Department of the Interior, Bureau of Reclamation, Boise, Idaho.)

880. Peters, Ralph I. 1975. AMINO ACID UPTAKE AND LEARNING IN MYELENCEPHALIC Rana pipiens. Ph.D. Thesis, Washington State University, Department of Zoology, Pullman. 73 pages.

881. Petterson, Cynthia M. 1978. OBSERVATIONS OF BASKING IN THE PAINTED TURTLE, Chrysemys picta belli (GRAY). Unpublished Report, Washington Department of Game, Olympia. 10 pages.

882. Sorenson, Dwight C. 1968. A SURVEY TO DETERMINE THE IDENTITY AND SPECIFICITY OF INTESTINAL PLATYHELMINTH PARASITES IN AMPHIBIANS OF NORTH WHIDBEY ISLAND, ISLAND COUNTY, WASHINGTON. M.Ed. Thesis, Western Washington University, Department of Education, Bellingham. 16 pages.

883. Stewart, Doris Mae. 1949. SKELETAL STRUCTURES OF THE GENUS Rana OF THE PACIFIC STATES. M.Sc. Thesis, University of Puget Sound, Department of Biology, Tacoma. 42 pages.

884. Thompson, Georgeanna B. 1977. A NATURAL HISTORY AND INVENTORY OF A SALTWATER, FRESHWATER, UPLAND ASSOCIATION ON THE KITSAP PENINSULA IN THE STATE OF WASHINGTON. M.Sc. Thesis, University of Puget Sound, Department of Biology, Tacoma. 97 pages.

885. Wickham, Marvin Gary. 1972. MORPHOGENESIS OF AMPHIBIAN SKIN: THE LATERAL LINE SENSORY SYSTEMS OF Ambystoma macrodactylum BAIRD AND Dicamptodon ensatus ESCHSCHOLTZ. Ph.D. Thesis, Washington State University, Department of Zoology, Pullman. 208 pages.

886. Wake, David B. 1963. COMPARATIVE OSTEOLOGY OF THE PLETHODONTID SALAMANDER GENUS Aneides. Journal of Morphology 113(1):77-118.

887. Larsen, John H. 1969. ULTRASTRUCTURAL STUDY ON CELL-VIRUS RELATIONSHIPS IN THE TYROID OF A SALAMANDER (Ambystoma macrodactylum BAIRD). Zeitschrift fur Zellforschung und Mikroskopische Anatomie 95:511-519.

888. Lewke, Robert E. 1974. FREEZE-BRANDING AS A METHOD OF MARKING SNAKES. Copeia 1974(4):997-1000.

889. Efford, Ian E. and Kanji Tsumura. 1973. A COMPARISON OF THE FOOD OF SALAMANDERS AND FISH IN MARION LAKE, BRITISH COLUMBIA. Transactions of the American Fisheries Society 102(1):33-47.

890. Kruse, Kipp C. and Michael G. Francis. 1977. A PREDATION DETERRENT IN LARVAE OF THE BULLFROG, Rana catesbeiana. Transactions of the American Fisheries Society 106(3):248-252.

891. Miller, Malcolm R. 1978. FURTHER SCANNING ELECTRON MICROSCOPE STUDIES OF LIZARD AUDITORY PAPILLAE. Journal of Morphology 156(3):381-418.

892. Bleakney, Sherman. 1958. POSTGLACIAL DISPERSAL OF THE TURTLE Chrysemys picta. Herpetologica 14(2):101-104.

893. Legler, John M. 1954. NESTING HABITS OF THE WESTERN PAINTED TURTLE, Chrysemys picta bellii (GRAY). Herpetologica 10(3):137-144.

894. Pimentel, Richard A. 1959. POSITIVE EMBRYO-MATERNAL SIZE CORRELATION IN THE NORTHERN ALLIGATOR LIZARD, Gerrhonotus coeruleus principis. Herpetologica 15(1):6-8.

895. Turner, Frederick B., Philip A. Medica and Bruce W. Kowalewsky. 1976. ENERGY UTILIZATION BY A DESERT LIZARD (Uta stansburiana). Desert Biome Monograph No. 1:1-57.

896. Gantert, Robert. 1974. ABOUT POISONOUS SNAKES - NOT FOR CHILDREN ONLY. Pacific Search 8(4):26.

897. Worthington, Richard D. and David B. Wake. 1971. LARVAL MORPHOLOGY AND ONTOGENY OF THE AMBYSTOM-ATID SALAMANDER, Rhyacotriton olympicus. American Midland Naturalist 85(2):349-365.

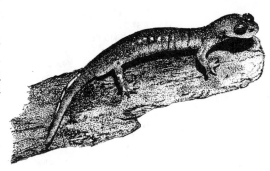

898. Lombard, Eric and David B. Wake. 1977. TONGUE EVOLUTION IN THE LUNGLESS SALAMANDERS, FAMILY PLETHODONTIDAE. II. FUNCTION AND EVOLUTIONARY DIVERSITY. Journal of Morphology 153(1):39-77.

899. Ruben, John A. 1977. SOME CORRELATES OF CRANIAL AND CERVICAL MORPHOLOGY WITH PREDATORY MODES IN SNAKES. Journal of Morphology 152(1):89-99.

900. Larsen, John H. and Dan J. Guthrie. 1975. THE FEEDING SYSTEM OF TERRESTRIAL SALAMANDERS (Ambystoma tigrinum melanostictum BAIRD). Journal of Morphology 147(2):137-154.

901. Wassersug, Richard J. and Karen Rosenberg. 1979. SURFACE ANATOMY OF BRANCHIAL FOOD TRAPS OF TADPOLES: A COMPARATIVE STUDY. Journal of Morphology 159(3):393-426.

902. Burrage, Bryan R. 1966. OBSERVATIONS ON THE MACRONYSSID MITE (ORDER ACARINA), Ophionyssus natricis (GERVAIS), ON THE TWO IGUANID LIZARDS, Uta stansburiana hesperis AND Sceloporus occidentalis occidentalis. British Journal of Herpetology 3(11):275-278.

903. Elkan, E. 1968. THE "TAILED" FROG, Ascaphus truei. British Journal of Herpetology 4(2):42.

904. Ernst, Carl H. 1971. OBSERVATIONS ON THE EGG AND HATCHLING OF THE AMERICAN TURTLE, Chrysemys picta. British Journal of Herpetology 4(9):224-228.

905. White, N. 1956. THE KEEPING OF AMPHIBIA. British Journal of Herpetology 2(2):30-33.

906. Elkan, E. 1957. ON KEEPING AMPHIBIANS. British Journal of Herpetology 2(4):75-77.

907. Gemmell, D. J. 1970. SOME OBSERVATIONS ON THE NESTING OF THE WESTERN PAINTED TURTLE, Chrysemys picta belli, IN NORTHERN MINNESOTA. Canadian Field-Naturalist 84(4):308-309.

908. Wassersug, Richard J. and David G. Sperry. 1977. THE RELATIONSHIP OF LOCOMOTION TO DIFFERENTIAL PREDATION ON Pseudacris triseriata (ANURA: HYLIDAE). Ecology 58:830-839.

909. Allan, Douglas M. 1973. SOME RELATIONSHIPS OF VOCALIZATION TO BEHAVIOR IN THE PACIFIC TREEFROG, Hyla regilla. Herpetologica 29(4):366-371.

910. Aven, Edward L. and David A. Langebartel. 1977. THE CRANIAL NERVES OF THE COLUBRID SNAKES Elaphe AND Thamnophis. Journal of Morphology 154(1):205-222.

911. Edwards, James L. 1976. SPINAL NERVES AND THEIR BEARING ON SALAMANDER PHYLOGENY. Journal of Morphology 148(3):305-328.

912. Hailman, Jack P. 1976. OIL DROPLETS IN THE EYES OF ADULT ANURAN AMPHIBIANS: A COMPARATIVE STUDY. Journal of Morphology 148(4):453-468.

913. Ernst, Carl H. and Evelyn M. Ernst. 1980. RELATIONSHIPS BETWEEN NORTH AMERICAN TURTLES OF THE Chrysemys COMPLEX AS INDICATED BY THEIR ENDOPARASITIC HELMINTHS. Proceedings of the Biological Society of Washington 93(2):339-345.

914. Fellers, Gary M. 1979. AGGRESSION, TERRITORIALITY, AND MATING BEHAVIOUR IN NORTH AMERICAN TREE FROGS. Animal Behaviour 27(1):107-119.

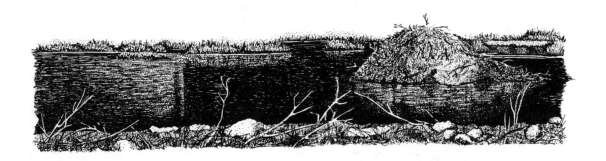

915. Carey, Cynthia. 1979. AEROBIC AND ANAEROBIC ENERGY EXPENDITURE DURING REST AND ACTIVITY IN MONTANE Bufo b. boreas AND Rana pipiens. Oecologia 39(2):213-228.

916. Berry, James F. and Richard Shine. 1980. SEXUAL SIZE DIMORPHISM AND SEXUAL SELECTION IN TURTLES (ORDER TESTUDINES). Oecologia 44(2):185-191.

917. Adler, Kraig. 1979. A BRIEF HISTORY OF HERPETOLOGY IN NORTH AMERICA BEFORE 1900. Society for the Study of Amphibians and Reptiles Herpetological Circular No. 8:1-40.

918. Christiansen, James L. and Edward O. Moll. 1973. LATITUDINAL REPRODUCTIVE VARIATION WITHIN A SINGLE SUBSPECIES OF PAINTED TURTLE, Chrysemys picta bellii. Herpetologica 29(2):152-163.

919. Rie, Ivo P. 1973. APPLICATION OF DRUGS TO THE SKIN OF SALAMANDERS. Herpetologica 29(1):55-59.

920. Ferguson, Gary W. 1973. CHARACTER DISPLACEMENT OF THE PUSH-UP DISPLAYS OF TWO PARTIALLY-SYMPATRIC SPECIES OF SPINY LIZARDS, Sceloporus (SAURIA:IGUANIDAE). Herpetologica 29(3):281-284.

921. Vitt, Laurie J. 1973. REPRODUCTIVE BIOLOGY OF THE ANGUID LIZARD, Gerrhonotus coeruleus principis. Herpetologica 29(2):176-184.

922. Tobiason, Fred L. 1974. SHY BOA OF THE NORTHWEST. Pacific Search 8(5):39.

923. Hillman, Stanley S. and Philip C. Withers. 1979. AN ANALYSIS OF RESPIRATORY SURFACE AREA AS A LIMIT TO ACTIVITY METABOLISM IN ANURANS. Canadian Journal of Zoology 57(11):2100-2105.

924. Dole, Jim W. 1972. EVIDENCE OF CELESTIAL ORIENTATION IN NEWLY-METAMORPHOSED Rana pipiens. Herpetologica 28(3):273-276.

925. Dole, Jim W. 1972. THE ROLE OF OLFACTION AND AUDITION IN THE ORIENTATION OF LEOPARD FROGS, Rana pipiens. Herpetologica 28(3):258-260.

926. Deyrup, Mark. 1975. THE TOADWATCHER'S YEAR. Pacific Search 9(9):6-7.

927. Hodge, Robert Parker. 1973. A YEAR IN THE LIFE OF A BOG. Pacific Search 8(3):4-5.

928. Beecher, Kit. 1970. KNOW YOUR PACIFIC RATTLER (THERE'S ONLY ONE). Pacific Search 5(2):5.

929. Lande, Susan Pritchard and Sheldon I. Guttman. 1973. THE EFFECTS OF COPPER SULFATE ON THE GROWTH AND MORTALITY RATE OF Rana pipiens TADPOLES. Herpetologica 29(1):22-27.

930. Clark, William H. 1973. AUTUMNAL DIET OF THE SAN JOAQUIN FENCE LIZARD, Sceloporus occidentalis biseriatus HALLOWELL, IN WEST-CENTRAL NEVADA. Herpetologica 29(1):73-75.

931. Whitney, Carl L. 1980. THE ROLE OF THE "ENCOUNTER" CALL IN SPACING OF PACIFIC TREE FROGS, Hyla regilla. Canadian Journal of Zoology 58(1):75-78.

932. Gregory, Patrick T. and A. G. Duncan McIntosh. 1980. THERMAL NICHE OVERLAP IN GARTER SNAKES (Thamnophis) ON VANCOUVER ISLAND. Canadian Journal of Zoology 58(3):351-355.

933. Smith, Arnold J. M. 1968. FRIENDS IN THE GARDEN: GARTER SNAKES IN THE NORTHWEST. Pacific Search 2(6):5-6.

934. Green, David M. 1979. TREEFROG TOE PADS: COMPARATIVE SURFACE MORPHOLOGY USING SCANNING ELECTRON MICROSCOPY. Canadian Journal of Zoology 57(10):2033-2046.

935. Seidel, Michael E. and Robert G. Lindeborg. 1973. LAGS IN METABOLIC RESPONSE TO TEMPERATURE OF TWO GARTER SNAKES, Thamnophis elegans AND Thamnophis radix. Herpetologica 29(4):358-360.

936. Anonymous. 1967. FANGS HELP RATTLESNAKE CONQUER ITS WEAK VENOM. Pacific Search 2(1):2.

937. Ferguson, Denzel. 1971. A NORTHWEST ORIGINAL - THE TAILED FROG. Pacific Search 5(10):5-6.

938. Kermode, Francis. 1927. ACCESSIONS. Pages 38-39 in Report of the Provincial Museum of Natural History for the Year 1926. Provincial Museum of Natural History, Victoria, British Columbia.

939. Davis, John. 1980. THE TIMES OF MATING AND OVIPOSITION OF THE WESTERN FENCE LIZARD, Sceloporus occidentalis occidentalis. Journal of Herpetology 14(1):102.

940. Snow, Jonathan E. 1980. SECOND CLUTCH LAYING BY PAINTED TURTLES. Copeia 1980(3):534-536.

941. Waldschmidt, Steve. 1980. ORIENTATION TO THE SUN BY THE IGUANID LIZARDS Uta stansburiana AND Sceloporus undulatus: HOURLY AND MONTHLY VARIATIONS. Copeia 1980(3):458-462.

942. Johnston, J. A. and B. J. Parker. 1980. AN EFFECTIVE METHOD OF PRESERVING LARGE REPTILES. Herpetological Review 11(3):77-78.

943. Dodd, C. 1980. MONEY FOR RESEARCH IN FEDERAL ENDANGERED SPECIES PROGRAM. Herpetological Review 11(3):70-72.

944. Shadduck, John A. and James B. Murphy. 1979. SUGGESTIONS FOR THE POST MORTEM EXAMINATION OF REPTILES. Herpetological Review 10(4):113-115.

945. Ryan, Michael J. 1980. THE REPRODUCTIVE BEHAVIOR OF THE BULLFROG (Rana catesbeiana). Copeia 1980(1):108-114.

946. Vitt, Laurie J. 1977. OBSERVATIONS ON CLUTCH AND EGG SIZE AND EVIDENCE FOR MULTIPLE CLUTCHES IN SOME LIZARDS OF SOUTHWESTERN UNITED STATES. Herpetologica 33(3):333-338.

947. Holman, J. Alan. 1977. COMMENTS ON TURTLES OF THE GENUS Chrysemys GRAY. Herpetologica 33(3):274-276.

948. Funkhouser, Anne. 1977. PLASMA OSMOLARITY OF Rana catesbeiana AND Scaphiopus hammondi TADPOLES. Herpetologica 33(3):272-274.

949. Gregory, Patrick T., J. Malcolm McCartney and Donald H. Rivard. 1980. SMALL MAMMAL PREDATION AND PREY HANDLING BEHAVIOR BY THE GARTER SNAKE Thamnophis elegans. Herpetologica 36(1):87-93.

950. Wright, Debra L., Kenneth V. Kardong and David L. Bentley. 1979. THE FUNCTIONAL ANATOMY OF THE TEETH OF THE WESTERN TERRESTRIAL GARTER SNAKE, Thamophis elegans. Herpetologica 35(3):223-228.

951. Wake, David B. 1980. EVIDENCE OF HETEROCHRONIC EVOLUTION: A NASAL BONE IN THE OLYMPIC SALAMANDER, Rhyacotriton olympicus. Journal of Herpetology 14(3):292-295.

952. Kephart, Donald G. 1980. INEXPENSIVE TELEMETRY TECHNIQUES FOR REPTILES. Journal of Herpetology 14(3):285-290.

953. Claessen, Hugo. 1979. REPRODUCTION EGGS: FACTORS ASSOCIATED WITH INCUBATION AND HATCHING AND SUGGESTION FOR LABORATORY REARING. Journal of Herpetology 13(4):472-475.

954. Sellers, Jeffrey C., Stanley E. Trauth and Laurence C. Wit. 1980. A METHOD OF CAUDAL BLOOD COLLECTION IN LIZARDS. Journal of Herpetology 14(2):183-185.

955. Aldridge, Robert D. 1979. FEMALE REPRODUCTIVE CYCLES OF THE SNAKES Arizona elegans AND Crotalus viridis. Herpetologica 35(3):256-261.

956. Lindquist, Sarah B. and Marilyn D. Bachmann. 1980. FEEDING BEHAVIOR OF THE TIGER SALAMANDER, Ambystoma tigrinum. Herpetologica 36(2):144-158.

957. Stewart, James R. 1979. THE BALANCE BETWEEN NUMBER AND SIZE OF YOUNG IN THE LIVE BEARING LIZARD Gerrhonotus coeruleus. Herpetologica 35(4):342-350.

958. Jameson, E. W., Jr., A. A. Heusner and Donna Lem. 1980. SEASONAL, SEXUAL AND ALTITUDINAL VARIATIONS IN STOMACH CONTENT AND INGESTED FAT IN Sceloporus occidentalis. Journal of Herpetology 14(3):255-261.

959. Nietfeldt, Joseph W., Steven M. Jones, Dale L. Droge and Royce E. Ballinger. 1980. RATE OF THERMAL ACCLIMATION IN LARVAL Ambystoma tigrinum. Journal of Herpetology 14(3):209-211.

960. Gray, Randall L. and Dennis C. Stroud. 1980. A WINTER AGGREGATION OF THE WESTERN FENCE LIZARD, Sceloporus occidentalis. Journal of Herpetology 14(1):103.

961. Huey, Raymond B. 1980. SPRING VELOCITY OF TADPOLES (Bufo boreas) THROUGH METAMORPHOSIS. Copeia 1980(3):537-540.

962. Vogt, Richard C. 1980. NEW METHODS FOR TRAPPING AQUATIC TURTLES. Copeia 1980(2):368-371.

963. Bury, R. Bruce, C. Kenneth Dodd, Jr. and Gary M. Fellers. 1980. CONSERVATION OF THE AMPHIBIA OF THE UNITED STATES. United States Department of the Interior Fish and Wildlife Service Resource Publication No. 134:1-34.

964. Hall, Russell J. 1980. EFFECTS OF ENVIRONMENTAL CONTAMINANTS ON REPTILES: A REVIEW. United States Department of the Interior Fish and Wildlife Service Special Scientific Report - Wildlife No. 228:1-12.

965. Alvarado, Ronald H. and Leonard B. Kirschner. 1963. OSMOTIC AND IONIC REGULATION IN Ambystoma tigrinum. Comparative Biochemistry and Physiology 10(1):55-67.

966. Anderson, William J. 1971. SUMMER REPORT - ALICE LAKE PROVINCIAL PARK, 1971. Unpublished Report, British Columbia Parks Branch, Victoria. 21 pages.

967. Logier, E. B. S. and G. C. Toner. 1942. AMPHIBIANS AND REPTILES OF CANADA. Canadian Field-Naturalist 56(2):15-16.

968. Kermode, Francis. 1931. ACCESSIONS. Pages 17-23 in Report of the Provincial Museum of Natural History for the Year 1930. Provincial Museum of Natural History, Victoria, British Columbia.

969. Lehman, Grace C. 1978. THE EFFECTS OF FOUR ARTHROPOD DIETS ON THE BODY AND ORGAN WEIGHTS OF THE LEOPARD FROG, Rana pipiens, DURING VITELLO-GENESIS. Growth 42(4):505-518.

970. Andre, John B. and James A. MacMahon. 1980. REPRODUCTION IN THREE SYMPATRIC LIZARD SPECIES FROM WEST-CENTRAL UTAH. Great Basin Naturalist 40(1):68–72.

971. DeJongh, H. J. and Carl Gans. 1969. ON THE MECHANISM OF RESPIRATION IN THE BULLFROG, Rana catesbeiana: A REASSESSMENT. Journal of Morphology 127(3):259–290.

972. Huey, Raymond B. 1979. THE COMPLEAT DICTIONARY OF ZOOLOGY: I. VERNACULAR NAMES IN HERPETOLOGY. Quarterly Review of Biology 54(3):301–307.

973. Rossman, Douglas A. 1979. MORPHOLOGICAL EVIDENCE FOR TAXONOMIC PARTITIONING OF THE Thamnophis elegans COMPLEX (SERPENTES, COLUBRIDAE). Occasional Papers of the Museum of Zoology Louisiana State University No. 55:1–12.

974. Lawson, Robin and Herbert C. Dessauer. 1979. BIOCHEMICAL GENETICS AND SYSTEMATICS OF GARTER SNAKES OF THE Thamnophis elegans - couchii - ordinoides COMPLEX. Occasional Papers of the Museum of Zoology Louisiana State University No. 56:1–24.

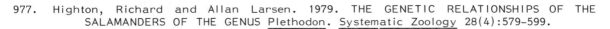

975. Frazzetta, T. H. 1962. A FUNCTIONAL CONSIDERATION OF CRANIAL KINESIS IN LIZARDS. Journal of Morphology 111(3):287–319.

976. Parsons, Thomas S. and Ernest E. Williams. 1962. THE TEETH OF THE AMPHIBIA AND THEIR RELATION TO AMPHIBIAN PYLOGENY. Journal of Morphology 110(3):375–389.

977. Highton, Richard and Allan Larsen. 1979. THE GENETIC RELATIONSHIPS OF THE SALAMANDERS OF THE GENUS Plethodon. Systematic Zoology 28(4):579–599.

978. Wilhoft, D. C. and W. B. Quay. 1961. TESTICULAR HISTOLOGY AND SEASONAL CHANGES IN THE LIZARD, Sceloporus occidentalis. Journal of Morphology 108(1):95–106.

979. Eaton, Theodore H., Jr. 1936. THE MYOLOGY OF SALAMANDERS WITH PARTICULAR REFERENCE TO Dicamptodon ensatus (ESCHSCHOLTZ). Journal of Morphology 60(1):31–75.

980. Vaslit, Frank H. 1890. RATTLESNAKE ANTIDOTES. Zoe 1(8):221.

981. Eaton, Theodore H., Jr. 1937. THE GULARIS MUSCLE IN URODELA. Journal of Morphology 60(2):317–324.

982. Lash, Ruth. 1980. FROM SEINING TO SALAMANDERS. Victoria Naturalist 36(6):104–105.

983. Merrell, David J. 1977. LIFE HISTORY OF THE LEOPARD FROG, Rana pipiens, IN MINNESOTA. Occasional Papers of the Bell Museum of Natural History No. 15:1–23.

984. Duvall, David and David O. Norris. 1980. STIMULATION OF TERRESTRIAL-SUBSTRATE PREFERENCES AND LOCOMOTOR ACTIVITY IN NEWLY TRANSFORMED TIGER SALAMANDERS (Ambystoma tigrinum) BY EXOGENOUS OR ENDOGENOUS THYROXINE. Animal Behaviour 28(1):116–123.

985. Winokur, Robert M. and John M. Legler. 1975. CHELONIAN MENTAL GLANDS. Journal of Morphology 147(3):275–292.

986. Howard, James H. and Richard L. Wallace. 1980. EFFECTS OF ALTITUDE ON SELECTED BLOOD PARAMETERS IN POPULATIONS OF THE SALAMANDER Ambystoma macrodactylum. Comparative Biochemistry and Physiology 65A(2):243-245.

987. Heath, Alan G. 1980. CARDIAC RESPONSES OF LARVAL AND ADULT TIGER SALAMANDERS TO SUBMERGENCE AND EMERGENCE. Comparative Biochemistry and Physiology 65A(4):439-444.

988. Reinking, Larry N., Charles H. Daugherty and Lynn B. Daugherty. 1980. PLASMA ALDOSTERONE CONCENTRATIONS IN WILD AND CAPTIVE WESTERN SPOTTED FROGS (Rana pretiosa). Comparative Biochemistry and Physiology 65A(4):517-518.

989. Winokur, Robert M. and John M. Legler. 1974. ROSTRAL PORES IN TURTLES. Journal of Morphology 143(1):107-120.

990. Mahmoud, I. Y., George L. Hess and John Klicka. 1973. NORMAL EMBRYONIC STAGES OF THE WESTERN PAINTED TURTLE, Chrysemys picta bellii. Journal of Morphology 141(3):269-280.

991. Rosenberg, Herbert I. 1973. FUNCTIONAL ANATOMY OF PULMONARY VENTILATION IN THE GARTER SNAKE, Thamnophis elegans. Journal of Morphology 140(2):171-184.

992. Ritland, Richard M. 1955. STUDIES ON THE POST-CRANIAL MORPHOLOGY OF Ascaphus truei. I. SKELETON AND SPINAL NERVES. Journal of Morphology 97(1):119-177.

993. Anderson, Craig Thornton. 1965. A SURVEY OF THE GENERAL ECOLOGY OF SELECTED HABITATS ON HARSTINE ISLAND. M.Sc. Thesis, University of Puget Sound, Department of Biology, Tacoma. 140 pages.

994. Cooke, Cedric Vincent. 1949. A COMPARISON OF THE SKELETAL STRUCTURE OF SOME SALAMANDERS OF WASHINGTON. M.Sc. Thesis, University of Puget Sound, Department of Biology, Tacoma. 69 pages.

995. Brown, Walter Creighton. 1938. THE DISTRIBUTION OF AMPHIBIANS AND REPTILES ON THE ISLANDS OF PUGET SOUND, ADMIRALITY INLET, AND WASHINGTON SOUND. M.A. Thesis, University of Puget Sound, Department of Biology, Tacoma. 57 pages.

996. McDiarmid, Roy W. 1980. U.S. NATIONAL MUSEUM SPECIMENS OF REPTILES AND AMPHIBIANS FROM THE UNITED STATES FOR THE STATE OF WASHINGTON. Unpublished Report, United States National Museum, Washington, D.C. 55 pages.

997. Robinson, Douglas A. 1976. A SURVEY OF THE AMPHIBIANS AND REPTILES OF WHITMAN COUNTY, WASHINGTON AND LATAH COUNTY, IDAHO. Unpublished Report, Washington Department of Game, Olympia. 62 pages.

998. Pauley, Gilbert B. and Douglas L. Robberson. 1966. A PAINTED TURTLE (Chrysemys picta) WITH ULCERS IN THE STOMACH AND DUODENUM. Northwest Science 40(2):79-82.

999.   Dronen, Norman Obert. 1970. THE LIFE HISTORY OF A SPECIES OF Cephalogonimus (TREMATODA: CEPHALOGONIMIDAE) FROM Ambystoma tigrinum (GREEN) OF EASTERN WASHINGTON. M.Sc. Thesis, Eastern Washington State College, Department of Biology, Cheney. 50 pages.

1000.   Slater, James R. and C. Frank Brockman. 1936. AMPHIBIANS OF MT. RAINIER NATIONAL PARK. Mt. Rainier National Park Nature Notes 14(4):113-138.

1001.   Bury, R. B., J. H. Wolfheim and R. A. Luckenbach. 1979. RESTORATION OF MEDICAL LAKE: RESPONSES OF WILDLIFE. Unpublished Report, Washington Department of Game, Olympia. 6 pages.

1002.   Guthrie, Dan James. 1975. THE MECHANICS AND IMPLICATIONS OF FEEDING IN TRANSFORMED AMBYSTOMATID SALAMANDERS. Ph.D. Thesis, Washington State University, Department of Zoology, Pullman. 134 pages.

1003.   Putnam, Phillips Griswold. 1931. LIFE HISTORY AND HABITS OF THE Ascaphus truei. M.Sc. Thesis, Washington State University, Department of Zoology, Pullman. 47 pages.

1004.   Myhrman, Herman M. 1934. THE NATURE AND EXTENT OF THE BIDDER'S ORGAN IN Bufo boreas AND ALLIED ANIMALS. M.A. Thesis, University of Puget Sound, Department of Biology, Tacoma. 54 pages.

1005.   Nussbaum, Ronald A. 1968. GEOGRAPHIC VARIATION IN Dicamptodon ensatus (ESCHSCHOLTZ) WITH NOTES ON LIFE HISTORY AND ZOOGEOGRAPHY. M.Sc. Thesis, Central Washington University, Department of Biology, Ellensburg. 74 pages.

1006.   Stewart, Glenn R. and Ronald S. Daniel. 1973. SCANNING ELECTRON MICROSCOPY OF SCALES FROM DIFFERENT BODY REGIONS OF THREE LIZARD SPECIES. Journal of Morphology 139(4):377-388.

1007.   Wassersug, Richard. 1972. THE MECHANISM OF ULTRAPLANKTONIC ENTRAPMENT IN ANURAN LARVAE. Journal of Morphology 137(3):279-288.

1008.   Worthington, Richard D. and David B. Wake. 1972. PATTERNS OF REGIONAL VARIATION IN THE VERTEBRAL COLUMN OF TERRESTRIAL SALAMANDERS. Journal of Morphology 137(3):257-278.

1009.   Cuellar, Orlando. 1970. EGG TRANSPORT IN LIZARDS. Journal of Morphology 130(2):129-136.

1010.   Samollow, Paul B. 1980. SELECTIVE MORTALITY AND REPRODUCTION IN A NATURAL POPULATION OF Bufo boreas. Evolution 34(1):18-39.

1011.   Collins, James P. 1979. INTRAPOPULATION VARIATION IN THE BODY SIZE AT METAMORPHOSIS AND TIMING OF METAMORPHOSIS IN THE BULLFROG, Rana catesbeiana. Ecology 60(4):738-749.

1012.   Feder, Juliana. 1979. NATURAL HYBRIDIZATION AND GENETIC DIVERGENCE BETWEEN THE TOADS Bufo boreas AND Bufo punctatus. Evolution 33(4):1089-1097.

1013.   Sage, Richard D. and Robert K. Selander. 1979. HYBRIDIZATION BETWEEN SPECIES OF THE Rana pipiens COMPLEX IN CENTRAL TEXAS. Evolution 33(4):1069-1088.

1014. Heckel, David G. and Jonathan Roughgarden. 1979. A TECHNIQUE FOR ESTIMATING THE SIZE OF LIZARD POPULATIONS. Ecology 60(5):966-975.

1015. Jessup, David A. 1980. FIBROSING ADENOCARCINOMA OF THE INTESTINE OF A GOPHER SNAKE (Pituophis melanoleucus). Journal of Wildlife Diseases 16(3):419-421.

1016. Bledsoe, Bob. 1979. SPOROGONY OF Sarcocystis idahoensis IN THE GOPHER SNAKE, Pituophis melanoleucus (DAUDIN). Journal of Parasitology 65(6):875-879.

1017. McLain, Robert Baird. 1971. CONTRIBUTIONS TO NORTH AMERICAN HERPETOLOGY: CRITICAL NOTES ON A COLLECTION OF REPTILES FROM THE WESTERN COAST OF THE UNITED STATES. Society for the Study of Amphibians and Reptiles Facsimile Reprints in Herpetology, Athens, Ohio. 13 pages.

1018. Ritland, Richard M. 1955. STUDIES ON THE POST-CRANIAL MORPHOLOGY OF Ascaphus truei. II. MYOLOGY. Journal of Morphology 97(2):215-282.

1019. Gove, Doris. 1979. A COMPARATIVE STUDY OF SNAKE AND LIZARD TONGUE-FLICKING, WITH AN EVOLUTIONARY HYPOTHESIS. Zeitschrift fur Tierpsychologie 51(1):58-76.

1020. Steinwascher, Kurt. 1979. COMPETITIVE INTERACTIONS AMONG TADPOLES: RESPONSES TO RESOURCE LEVEL. Ecology 60(6):1172-1183.

1021. Northcutt, R. Glenn and G. James Royce. 1975. OLFACTORY BULB PROJECTIONS IN THE BULLFROG, Rana catesbeiana. Journal of Morphology 145(3):251-268.

1022. Gilchrist, Cathy. 1980. WILDLIFE AND AQUATIC RESOURCES OF THE ISLANDS TRUST AREA - B.C. Islands Trust Report, Victoria. 118 pages.

1023. Meade, Shawna. 1973. ANNUAL REPORT 1973 - GOLDEN EARS PARK. Unpublished Report, British Columbia Parks Branch, Victoria. 21 pages.

1024. Dow, Douglas D. 1963. A NATURAL HISTORY OF THE SOUTHERN PORTION OF GARIBALDI PROVINCIAL PARK. Unpublished Report, British Columbia Parks Branch, Victoria. 95 pages.

1025. Dobie, J. Frank. 1965. RATTLESNAKES. Little, Brown and Company, Boston. 201 pages.

1026. Smith, Hobart M. 1953. SNAKES AS PETS. All-Pets Books, Inc., Fond du Lac, Wisconsin. 50 pages.

1027. Bowman, Irene. 1978. STATUS OF HERPTILES IN CANADA. Unpublished Report, Ontario Ministry of Natural Resources, Ottawa. 166 pages.

1028. Burt, Charles E. 1935. A KEY TO THE LIZARDS OF THE UNITED STATES AND CANADA. Transactions of the Kansas Academy of Science 38:255-305.

1029. Froom, Barbara. 1976. THE TURTLES OF CANADA. McClelland and Stewart Limited, Toronto, Canada. 120 pages.

1030. Fitch, Henry S. 1970. REPRODUCTIVE CYCLES OF LIZARDS AND SNAKES. University of Kansas Museum of Natural History Miscellaneous Publication No. 52:1-247.

1031. Morris, Percy A. 1974. AN INTRODUCTION TO THE REPTILES AND AMPHIBIANS OF THE UNITED STATES. Dover Publications, Inc., New York. 253 pages.

1032. Frazer, J. F. D. 1973. AMPHIBIANS. Wykeham Publications (London) Ltd., England. 122 pages.

1033. Peterson, Phil H. 1973. MOUNTAIN OF FROGS. Pacific Search 7(7):18.

1034. O'Farrell, Thomas P. 1973. PROJECT ALE - A NATURAL DESERT COMMUNITY. Pacific Search 7(9):3-9.

1035. Osmond-Jones, E. J., M. Sather, W. G. Hazelwood and B. Ford. 1977. WILDLIFE AND FISHERIES INVENTORY OF SPATSIZI WILDERNESS AND TATLATUI PROVINCIAL PARKS BRITISH COLUMBIA. British Columbia Parks Branch Report, Victoria. 292 pages.

1036. Gorham, Stanley W. 1974. CHECKLIST OF WORLD AMPHIBIANS UP TO JANUARY 1, 1970. New Brunswick Museum, Saint John. 172 pages.

1037. Gloyd, Howard K. 1938. SNAKE POISON-ING IN THE UNITED STATES: A REVIEW OF PRESENT KNOWLEDGE. Bulletin of the Jackson Park Branch of the Chicago Medical Society 15(7):1-8.

1038. Strong, Kenneth V. 1974. GUIDE TO THE REPTILES OF BRITISH COLUMBIA. Unpublished Manuscript, British Columbia Provincial Museum Vertebrate Zoology Division, Victoria. 74 pages.

1039. Wright, Anna Allen and Albert Hazen Wright. 1933. HANDBOOK OF FROGS AND TOADS - THE FROGS AND TOADS OF THE UNITED STATES AND CANADA. Comstock Publishing Company, Inc., New York. 231 pages.

1040. Barker, Will. 1964. FAMILIAR REPTILES AND AMPHIBIANS OF AMERICA. Harper and Row Publishers, New York. 220 pages.

1041. Cochran, Doris M. and Coleman J. Goin. 1970. THE NEW FIELD BOOK OF REPTILES AND AMPHIBIANS. C. P. Putnam's Sons, New York. 359 pages.

1042. Anonymous. 1947. ANTIVENIN (NORTH AMERICAN ANTISNAKE-BITE SERUM). John Wyeth and Brother, Ltd., Walkerville, Ontario. 16 pages.

1043. British Columbia Fish and Wildlife Branch. 1980. PRELIMINARY AMPHIBIAN MANAGEMENT PLAN FOR BRITISH COLUMBIA. British Columbia Ministry of Environment, Fish and Wildlife Branch, Victoria. 29 pages.

1044. Allen, Anne L., Stephen C. Samis and Elizabeth A. Stanlake. 1977. URBAN WILDLIFE IN VANCOUVER AND VICTORIA, BRITISH COLUMBIA. Unpublished Report, British Columbia Fish and Wildlife Branch, Victoria. 76 pages.

1045. Joslin, Paul. 1980. PERIPHERAL SPECIES. Pages 243-245. In Richard Stace-Smith, Lois Johns and Paul Joslin (Editors), Proceedings of the Symposium on Threatened and Endangered Species and Habitats in British Columbia and the Yukon. British Columbia Ministry of Environment, Fish and Wildlife Branch, Victoria.

1046. Orchard, S. A. 1980. THE STATUS OF REPTILES IN BRITISH COLUMBIA. Pages 152-159. In Richard Stace-Smith, Lois Johns and Paul Joslin (Editors), Proceedings of the Symposium on Threatened and Endangered Species and Habitats in British Columbia and the Yukon. British Columbia Ministry of Environment, Fish and Wildlife Branch, Victoria.

1047. MacIntyre, D. H. and R. V. Palermo. 1980. THE CURRENT STATUS OF THE AMPHIBIA IN BRITISH COLUMBIA. Pages 146-151. In Richard Stace-Smith, Lois Johns and Paul Joslin (Editors), Proceedings of the Symposium on Threatened and Endangered Species and Habitats in British Columbia and the Yukon. British Columbia Ministry of Environment, Fish and Wildlife Branch, Victoria.

1048. Scudder, G. G. E. 1980. THE OSOYOOS-ARID BIOTIC AREA. Pages 49-55. In Richard Stace-Smith, Lois Johns and Paul Joslin (Editors), Proceedings of the Symposium on Threatened and Endangered Species and Habitats in British Columbia and the Yukon. British Columbia Ministry of Environment, Fish and Wildlife Branch, Victoria.

1049. Gregory, Patrick T. 1977. RARE AND THREATENED SNAKE SPECIES IN CANADA. Pages 122-126. In Theodore Mosquin and Cecile Suchal (Editors), Proceedings of the Symposium on Canada's Threatened Species and Habitats. Canadian Nature Federation, Ottawa, Ontario.

1050. Cook, Francis R. 1977. REVIEW OF THE CANADIAN HERPETOLOGICAL SCENE. In Theodore Mosquin and Cecile Suchal (Editors), Proceedings of the Symposium on Canada's Threatened Species and Habitats. Canadian Nature Federation, Ottawa, Ontario.

1051. Milsom, William Kenneth. 1978. PULMONARY RECEPTORS AND THEIR ROLE IN THE CONTROL OF BREATHING IN TURTLES. Ph.D. Thesis, University of British Columbia, Department of Zoology, Vancouver. 127 pages.

1052. Van Eeden, J. A. 1951. THE DEVELOPMENT OF THE CHONDROCRANIUM OF Ascaphus truei stejneger WITH SPECIAL REFERENCE TO THE RELATIONS OF THE PALATOQUADRATE TO THE NEUROCRANIUM. Acta Zoologica 32:41-173.

1053. Dawe, Neil K. 1976. FLORA AND FAUNA OF THE MARSHALL-STEVENSON WILDLIFE AREA. Unpublished Report, Canadian Wildlife Service, Qualicum Beach, British Columbia. 201 pages.

1054. Guillette, Louis J., Jr., Richard E. Jones, Kevin T. Fitzgerald and Hobart M. Smith. 1980. EVOLUTION OF VIVIPARITY IN THE LIZARD GENUS Sceloporus. Herpetologica 36(3):201-215.

1055. Smith, Hobart M. and Anthony J. Kohler. 1977. A SURVEY OF HERPETOLOGICAL INTRODUCTIONS IN THE UNITED STATES AND CANADA. Transactions of the Kansas Academy of Science 80(1 & 2):1-24.

1056. Cook, Francis R. 1980. CHECKLIST OF AMPHIBIANS AND REPTILES OF CANADA. Canadian Amphibian and Reptile Conservation Society Newsletter 18(2):1-6.

1057. Harless, Marion and Henry Morlock, editors. 1979. TURTLES - PERSPECTIVES AND RESEARCH. John Wiley and Sons, New York. 695 pages.

1058. Wright, Albert Hazen and Anna Allen Wright. 1957. HANDBOOK OF SNAKES OF THE UNITED STATES AND CANADA. (VOLUMES I AND II) Comstock Publishing Associates, Ithaca, New York. 1105 pages.

1059. Schueler, Frederick W., Francis R. Cook and Donald H. Rivard. 1980. BRITISH COLUMBIA DISTRIBUTION DATA FROM THE HERPETOLOGY COLLECTION OF THE NATIONAL MUSEUMS OF CANADA. Unpublished Report, National Museums of Canada, Herpetology Section, Ottawa, Ontario. 6 pages.

1060. Anonymous. 1943. POISONOUS SNAKES OF THE UNITED STATES. United States Department of the Interior Fish and Wildlife Service Wildlife Leaflet No. 233, Chicago. 17 pages.

1061. Swarth, Harry S. 1936. ORIGINS OF THE FAUNA OF THE SITKAN DISTRICT, ALASKA. Proceedings of the California Academy of Sciences 23(3):59-78.

1062. Larsen, John H., Jr., Paul C. Schroeder and Allen E. Waldo. 1977. STRUCTURE AND FUNCTION OF THE AMPHIBIAN FOLLICULAR EPITHELIUM DURING OVULATION. Cell and Tissue Research 181:505-518.

1063. Green, David. 1970. LET IT GO! Vancouver Natural History Society Discovery 148:6.

1064. Gans, Carl, H. J. de Jongh and J. Farber. 1969. BULLFROG (Rana catesbeiana) VENTILATION: HOW DOES THE FROG BREATHE? Science 163:1223-1225.

1065. Stelmock, James J. and Alton S. Harestad. 1979. FOOD HABITS AND LIFE HISTORY OF THE CLOUDED SALAMANDER (Aneides ferreus) ON NORTHERN VANCOUVER ISLAND, BRITISH COLUMBIA. Syesis 12:71-75.

1066. Cook, Francis R. 1977. ENDANGERED WILDLIFE - REPTILES AND AMPHIBIANS. Pages 10-15. In Endangered Wildlife in Canada. Canadian Wildlife Federation, Ottawa, Ontario.

1067. Howard, Chris. 1977. GENERAL NOTES ON VIVARIUM TEMPERATURE CONTROL. Herptile 2(3):2-3.

1068. Griffin, John. 1977. THE IMPORTANCE OF TEMPERATURE IN AMPHIBIAN HUSBANDRY. Herptile 2(3):6-8.

1069. Bury, R. Bruce and Roger A. Luckenbach. 1976. INTRODUCED AMPHIBIANS AND REPTILES IN CALIFORNIA. Biological Conservation 10:1-14.

1070. Madison, Harold L. 1934. TURTLE SHIELDS. Cleveland Museum of Natural History Zoological Series No. 1, Cleveland, Ohio. 4 pages.

1071. Boyd, Claude E. and C. Phillip Goodyear. 1971. THE PROTEIN CONTENT OF SOME COMMON REPTILES AND AMPHIBIANS. Herpetologica 27(3):317-320.

1072. Weary, G. C. 1969. AN IMPROVED METHOD OF MARKING SNAKES. Copeia 1969(4):854-855.

1073. Spellerberg, Ian F. 1977. REPTILE BODY TEMPERATURES. Herptile 2(3):8-37.

1074. Riches, Robert J. 1977. SOME ECONOMY MEASURES IN HEATING. Herptile 2(3):38-41.

1075. Storer, Tracy I. 1933. FROGS AND THEIR COMMERCIAL USE. California Fish and Game 19(3):203-213.

1076. Slater, James R. 1962. REESTABLISHMENT OF RANGE EXTENSION OF Dicamptodon ensatus. Occasional Papers Department of Biology University of Puget Sound No. 18:201-202.

1077. Green, David M., Charles H. Daugherty and James P. Bogart. 1980. KARYOLOGY AND SYSTEMATIC RELATIONSHIPS OF THE TAILED FROG, Ascaphus truei. Herpetologica 36(4):346-352.

1078. Runyan, Craig S. 1978. PITT WILDLIFE MANAGEMENT AREA WILDLIFE INVENTORY REPORT. Unpublished Report, British Columbia Fish and Wildlife Branch, Vancouver. 102 pages.

1079. Reid, D. B. 1977. HEATING SYSTEMS OF A LARGE PUBLIC DISPLAY AND OF A SMALL PRIVATE COLLECTION - A PERSONAL COMPARISON. Herptile 2(3):46-49.

1080. Millichamp, N. J. 1977. MAINTENANCE OF TEMPERATURE REQUIREMENTS OF REPTILES. Herptile 2(3):49-53.

1081. Anonymous. 1977. ENDANGERED WILDLIFE IN CANADA - VERTEBRATES: REPTILES AND AMPHIBIANS. Pages 24E-24F, In Wildlife Report: The Canadian Scene. Canadian Wildlife Federation, Ottawa, Ontario.

1082. Campbell, R. Wayne. 1979. CHECK-LIST OF AMPHIBIANS AND REPTILES OF BRITISH COLUMBIA. Unpublished Report, British Columbia Provincial Museum, Vertebrate Zoology Division, Victoria. 5 pages.

1083. Stanwell-Fletcher, John F. and Theodora C. Stanwell-Fletcher. 1940. NATURALISTS IN THE WILDS OF BRITISH COLUMBIA. Scientific Monthly 50:1-44.

1084. Hassell, Sharon. 1972. GOLDEN EARS PROVINCIAL PARK: NATURALIST'S REPORT, 1972. Unpublished Report, British Columbia Parks Branch, Victoria. 27 pages.

1085. Bopp, Teresita E. 1971. 1971 NATURALIST PROGRAM IN GARIBALDI PARK. Unpublished Report, British Columbia Parks Branch, Victoria. 12 pages.

1086. Gregory, Patrick T. 1978. FEEDING HABITS AND DIET OVERLAP OF THREE SPECIES OF GARTER SNAKES (Thamnophis) ON VANCOUVER ISLAND. Canadian Journal of Zoology 56(9):1967-1974.

1087. Ernst, Carl H. and Roger W. Barbour. 1972. TURTLES OF THE UNITED STATES. University of Kentucky Press, Lexington. 347 pages.

1088. Goin, Coleman J., Olive B. Goin and George R. Zug. 1962. INTRODUCTION TO HERPETOLOGY. W. H. Freeman and Company, San Francisco, California. 378 pages.

1089. Cope, E. D. 1889. THE BATRACHIA OF NORTH AMERICA. United States National Museum Bulletin No. 34:1-525.

1090. Mayhew, Wilbur W. 1968. BIOLOGY OF DESERT AMPHIBIANS AND REPTILES. Pages 195-356 in G. W. Brown, editor. Desert Biology. Academic Press, New York.

1091. Leviton, Alan E. 1979. REPTILES AND AMPHIBIANS OF NORTH AMERICA. Doubleday and Company, Inc., New York. 250 pages.

1092. Fitch, Henry S. 1970. REPRODUCTIVE CYCLES IN LIZARDS AND SNAKES. University of Kansas Museum of Natural History Miscellaneous Publication No. 52:1-247.

1093. Campbell, R. Wayne. 1973. HIGHWAY CASUALTIES TO VERTEBRATES RECORDED ACROSS SOUTHERN BRITISH COLUMBIA, MID-SEPTEMBER 1973. Unpublished Report, British Columbia Provincial Museum, Vertebrate Zoology Division, Victoria. 9 pages.

1094. Gilboa, Itzchak. 1975. KARYOTYPES OF AMPHIBIANS AND REPTILES: A BIBLIOGRAPHIC REVIEW. Pages 91-156 in Herndon G. Dowling, editor. 1974 Yearbook of Herpetology, Volume 1. Herpetological Information Search Systems Publications in Herpetology No. 8, New York. 256 pages.

1095. Dowling, Herndon G. 1975. HERPETOLOGICAL PHENOLOGY. Pages 35-40 in Herndon G. Dowling, editor. 1974 Yearbook of Herpetology, Volume 1. Herpetological Information Search Systems Publications in Herpetology No. 8, New York. 256 pages.

1096. Dowling, Herndon G. 1975. HERPETOLOGICAL TAXONOMY. Pages 157-158 in Herndon G. Dowling, editor. 1974 Yearbook of Herpetology, Volume 1. Herpetological Information Search Systems Publications in Herpetology No. 8, New York. 256 pages.

1097. Dowling, Herndon G. 1975. A CLASSIFICATION OF AMPHIBIANS. Pages 159-161 in Herndon G. Dowling, editor. 1974 Yearbook of Herpetology, Volume 1. Herpetological Information Search Systems Publications in Herpetology No. 8, New York. 256 pages.

1098. Behler, John L. and F. Wayne King. 1979. THE AUDUBON SOCIETY FIELD GUIDE TO NORTH AMERICAN REPTILES AND AMPHIBIANS. Alfred A. Knopf, Inc., New York. 719 pages.

1099. Anderson, Rudolph Martin. 1960. METHODS OF COLLECTING AND PRESERVING VERTEBRATE ANIMALS. National Museum of Canada Bulletin No. 69, Ottawa. 164 pages.

1100. Milstead, William W., editor. 1967. LIZARD ECOLOGY A SYMPOSIUM. University of Missouri Press, Columbia. 300 pages.

1101. Dowling, Herndon G. 1975. A CLASSIFIC-ATION OF REPTILES. Pages 163-166 in Herndon G. Dowling, editor. 1974 Yearbook of Herpetology, Volume 1. Herpetological Information Search Systems Publications in Herpetology No. 8, New York. 256 pages.

1102. Boulenger, G. A. 1920. A MONOGRAPH OF THE AMERICAN FROGS OF THE GENUS Rana. Proceedings of the American Academy of Arts and Sciences 55(9):413-480.

1103. Dowling, Herndon G. 1975. A CLASSIFICATION OF SNAKES. Pages 167-170 in Herndon G. Dowling, editor. 1974 Yearbook of Herpetology, Volume 1. Herpetological Information Search Systems Publications in Herpetology No. 8, New York. 256 pages.

1104. Cowles, Raymond Bridgman and Charles Mitchill Bogert. 1944. A PRELIMINARY STUDY OF THE THERMAL REQUIREMENTS OF DESERT REPTILES. Bulletin of the American Museum of Natural History 83(5):261-296.

1105. Peters, James A. 1964. A DICTIONARY OF HERPETOLOGY: A BRIEF AND MEANINGFUL DEFINITION OF WORDS AND TERMS USED IN HERPETOLOGY. Hafner Publishing Company, New York. 426 pages.

1106. Dowling, Herndon G. 1975. A CLASSIFICATION AND CHECKLIST OF THE SPECIES OF AMPHIBIANS AND REPTILES FOUND IN THE UNITED STATES AND CANADA. Pages 175-189 in Herndon G. Dowling, editor. 1974 Yearbook of Herpetology, Volume 1. Herpetological Information Search Systems Publications in Herpetology No. 8, New York. 256 pages.

1107. Gilboa, I., H. G. Dowling and T. C. Majupuria. 1973. A BIBLIOGRAPHY ON THE REPRODUCTIVE SYSTEM OF REPTILES, 1822-1972. Herpetological Information Search Systems Publications in Herpetology No. 5:1-34.

1108. Boulenger, G. A. 1897. A REVISION OF THE LIZARDS OF THE GENUS Sceloporus. Proceedings of the Zoological Society of London 1897(III):474-522.

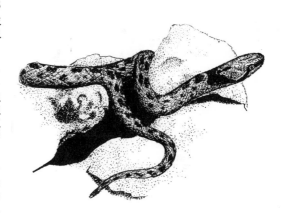

1109. Howie, Rick and David Stirling. 1981. SKAGIT VALLEY FIELD TRIP. Unpublished Report, British Columbia Ministry of Lands, Parks and Housing, Parks and Outdoor Recreation Division, Victoria. 8 pages.

1110. Campbell, R. Wayne. 1979. CHECKLIST OF BRITISH COLUMBIA AMPHIBIANS AND REPTILES. Unpublished Report, British Columbia Provincial Museum, Vertebrate Zoology Division, Victoria. 4 pages.

1111. Bandy, P. J. 1952. REPORT ON THE BIOLOGICAL INVESTIGATIONS CARRIED OUT IN E. C. MANNING PARK, BRITISH COLUMBIA, DURING THE SUMMER OF 1952. Unpublished Report, British Columbia Forest Service, Victoria. 193 pages.

1112. Liner, Ernest A. 1978. A HERPETOLOGICAL COOKBOOK: HOW TO COOK AMPHIBIANS AND REPTILES. Ernest A. Liner Publication, 310 Malibou Boulevard, Houma, Louisiana, 70360. 60 pages.

1113. Dowling, Herndon G. 1975. THE NEARCTIC SNAKE FAUNA. Pages 191-202 in Herndon G. Dowling, editor. 1974 Yearbook of Herpetology, Volume 1. Herpetological Information Search Systems Publications in Herpetology No. 8, New York. 256 pages.

1114. Gilboa, I. and H. G. Dowling. 1972. A BIBLIOGRAPHY ON THE LONGEVITY OF AMPHIBIANS AND REPTILES, 1882-1971. Herpetological Information Search Systems Publications in Herpetology No. 3:1-6.

1115. Jacobs, George J. 1978. DICTIONARY OF VERTEBRATE ZOOLOGY: RUSSIAN-ENGLISH: ENGLISH-RUSSIAN. Smithsonian Institution Press, Washington, D.C. 48 pages.

1116. Murphy, James B. 1975. A BRIEF OUTLINE OF SUGGESTED TREATMENTS FOR DISEASES OF CAPTIVE REPTILES. Society for the Study of Amphibians and Reptiles Herpetological Circular No. 4:1-13.

1117.   Dowling, Herndon G. 1975. SNAKE VENOMS AND VENOMOUS SNAKES. Pages 203–212 in Herndon G. Dowling, editor. 1974 Yearbook of Herpetology, Volume 1. Herpetological Information Search Systems Publications in Herpetology No. 8, New York. 256 pages.

1118.   Bowler, J. Kevin. 1977. LONGEVITY OF REPTILES AND AMPHIBIANS IN NORTH AMERICAN COLLECTIONS. Society for the Study of Amphibians and Reptiles Herpetological Circular No. 6:1–32.

1119.   Orchard, Stan A. 1978. MINIMUM STANDARDS FOR MAINTAINING AMPHIBIAN AND REPTILES IN CAPTIVITY. Unpublished Report, British Columbia Fish and Wildlife Branch, Victoria. 21 pages.

1120.   Dowling, Herndon G. and Sherman A. Minton. 1975. SNAKEBITE. Pages 213–218 in Herndon G. Dowling, editor. 1974 Yearbook of Herpetology, Volume 1. Herpetological Information Search Systems Publications in Herpetology No. 8, New York. 256 pages.

1121.   Meyer, Gene R. 1975. EVALUATION OF SNAKEBITE FIRST–AID KITS IN THE UNITED STATES. Pages 219–224 in Herndon G. Dowling, editor. 1974. Yearbook of Herpetology, Volume 1. Herpetological Information Search Systems Publications in Herpetology No. 8, New York. 256 pages.

1122.   Boulenger, G. A. 1887. ON THE AFFINITY OF THE NORTH–AMERICAN LIZARD FAUNA. Annals and Magazine of Natural History (Series 5) 20(119):345–346.

1123.   Hall, E. Raymond. 1962. COLLECTING AND PREPARING STUDY SPECIMENS OF VERTEBRATES. University of Kansas Museum of Natural History, Miscellaneous Publication No. 30, Lawrence. 46 pages.

1124.   Osgood, Wilfred H. 1901. NATURAL HISTORY OF THE QUEEN CHARLOTTE ISLANDS, BRITISH COLUMBIA. United States Department of Agriculture Division of Biological Survey North American Fauna No. 21, Washington, D.C. 50 pages.

1125.   Boulenger, G. A. 1919. SYNOPSIS OF THE AMERICAN SPECIES OF Rana. Annals and Magazine of Natural History (Series 9) III(16):408–416.

1126.   Boulenger, G. A. 1891. NOTES ON AMERICAN BATRACHIANS. Annals and Magazine of Natural History (Series 6) VIII(48):453–457.

1127.   Bogart, James P. 1972. KARYOTYPES. Pages 171–195 in W. Frank Blair, editor, Evolution in the Genus Bufo. University of Texas Press, Austin.

1128.   Boulenger, G. A. 1888. NOTE ON THE CLASSIFICATION OF THE RANIDAE. Proceedings of the Zoological Society of London 1888(II):204–206.

1129.   Blair, W. Frank. 1972. EVIDENCE FROM HYBRIDIZATION. Pages 196–232 in W. Frank Blair, editor, Evolution in the Genus Bufo. University of Texas Press, Austin.

1130.   Low, Bobbi S. 1972. EVIDENCE FROM PAROTID–GLAND SECRETIONS. Pages 244–264 in W. Frank Blair, editor, Evolution in the Genus Bufo. University of Texas Press, Austin.

1131.   Guttman, Sheldon I. 1972. BLOOD PROTEINS. Pages 265–278 in W. Frank Blair, editor, Evolution in the Genus Bufo. University of Texas Press, Austin.

1132. Cei, Jose M., Vittorio Erspamer and M. Roseghini. 1972. BIOGENIC AMINES. Pages 233-243 in W. Frank Blair, editor, Evolution in the Genus Bufo. University of Texas Press, Austin.

1133. Dowling, Herndon G. and William E. Duellman. 1978. SYSTEMATIC HERPETOLOGY: A SYNOPSIS OF FAMILIES AND HIGHER CATEGORIES. Herpetological Information Search Systems Publications in Herpetology No. 7:1.1-118.3.

1134. Campbell, R. Wayne. 1970. AMPHIBIANS AND REPTILES OF BURNABY LAKE, BRITISH COLUMBIA. Unpublished Report, University of British Columbia, Department of Zoology, Vancouver. 3 pages.

1135. Cohen, Nicholas. 1968. A METHOD FOR MASS REARING Ambystoma tigrinum DURING AND AFTER METAMORPHOSIS IN A LABORATORY ENVIRONMENT. Herpetologica 24(1):86-87.

1136. Scott, A. Floyd and James L. Dobie. 1980. AN IMPROVED DESIGN FOR A THREAD TRAILING DEVICE USED TO STUDY TERRESTRIAL MOVEMENTS OF TURTLES. Herpetological Review 11(4):106-107.

1137. Berger, T. 1980. FEDERAL CONTROLLED SPECIES. Herpetological Review 11(4):105.

1138. Burgess, T. E. 1966. WILDLIFE OF BURNABY LAKE. Pages 1-39 (Appendix VI) in The Development of Burnaby Lake, A report to the Corporation of the District of Burnaby prepared jointly by Associated Engineering Services Ltd. and Swan Wooster Engineering Co. Ltd., Vancouver, British Columbia.

1139. Fannin, John. 1898. A PRELIMINARY CATALOGUE OF THE COLLECTIONS OF NATURAL HISTORY AND ETHNOLOGY IN THE PROVINCIAL MUSEUM, VICTORIA, BRITISH COLUMBIA. British Columbia Provincial Museum, Victoria. 196 pages.

1140. Carl, G. C. and C. J. Guiguet. 1957. ALIEN ANIMALS IN BRITISH COLUMBIA. British Columbia Provincial Museum Handbook No. 14, Victoria. 103 pages.

1141. Blair, W. Frank. 1972. Bufo OF NORTH AND CENTRAL AMERICA. Pages 93-101 in W. Frank Blair, editor, Evolution in the Genus Bufo. University of Texas Press, Austin.

1142. Campbell, Craig. 1976. CANADA'S THREATENED TURTLES. Page 132, In Theodore Mosquin and Cecile Suchal, editors, Proceedings of the Symposium on Canada's Threatened Species and Habitats. Canadian Nature Federation, Special Publication No. 6, Ottawa.

1143. Martin, William F. 1972. EVOLUTION OF VOCALIZATION IN THE GENUS Bufo. Pages 279-309, in W. Frank Blair, editor. Evolution in the Genus Bufo. University of Texas Press, Austin.

1144. Feuer, Robert C. 1980. UNDERWATER TRAPS FOR AQUATIC TURTLES. Herpetological Review 11(4):107-108.

1145. Kirk, James L. 1979. Thamnophis ordinoides. Catalogue of American Amphibians and Reptiles 233.1-233.2.

1146. Fitch, Henry S. 1980. Thamnophis sirtalis. Catalogue of American Amphibians and Reptiles 270.1-270.4.

1147. Pritchard, Peter C. 1980. Dermochelys coriacea. Catalogue of American Amphibians and Reptiles 238.1–238.4.

1148. Hirth, Harold F. 1980. Chelonia. Catalogue of American Amphibians and Reptiles 248.1–248.2.

1149. Hirth, Harold F. 1980. Chelonia mydas. Catalogue of American Amphibians and Reptiles 249.1–249.4.

1150. Pisani, George R. 1973. A GUIDE TO PRESERVATION TECHNIQUES FOR AMPHIBIANS AND REPTILES. Society for the Study of Amphibians and Reptiles Herpetological Circular No. 1:1–22.

1151. Ferner, John W. 1979. A REVIEW OF MARKING TECHNIQUES FOR AMPHIBIANS AND REPTILES. Society for the Study of Amphibians and Reptiles Herpetological Circular No. 9:1–41.

1152. Stebbins, Robert C. 1954. AMPHIBIANS AND REPTILES OF WESTERN NORTH AMERICA. McGraw-Hill Book Company, Inc., New York. 536 pages.

1153. Lord, John Keast. 1866. THE NATURALIST IN VANCOUVER ISLAND AND BRITISH COLUMBIA. Richard Bently Publishers, London, England. 733 pages.

1154. Holbrook, John Edwards. 1976. NORTH AMERICAN HERPETOLOGY. Society for the Study of Amphibians and Reptiles Facsimile Reprints in Herpetology. 732 pages.

1155. Jenks, Bruce Griffin. 1976. THE CONTROL OF SYNTHESIS AND RELEASE OF MELANOCYTE STIMULATING HORMONE IN THE PITUITARY GLAND OF AMPHIBIA. Ph.D. Thesis, Simon Fraser University, Department of Biological Sciences, Burnaby, British Columbia. 80 pages.

1156. Eagleson, Gerald Wayne. 1977. THE POSSIBLE CAUSES OF "METAMORPHIC FAILURE" IN THE URODELE AMPHIBIAN, Ambystoma gracile (BAIRD). Ph.D. Thesis, Simon Fraser University, Department of Biological Sciences, Burnaby, British Columbia. 149 pages.

All 51 species are listed alphabetically by their scientific name. The authority and common name are also included. These follow the Society for the Study of Amphibians and Reptiles publication Standard Common and Current Scientific Names for North American Amphibians and Reptiles issued in 1978 (see reference number 93). A complete list of the species of salamanders, frogs and toads, turtles, lizards and snakes is found on page 2.

Some duplication in references will appear for some species, especially where single records have occurred and have been cited (sometimes with additional information) in several sources.

Sub-species are not considered.

Ambystoma gracile (Baird)
NORTHWESTERN SALAMANDER

2, 4, 9, 12, 13, 22, 27, 28, 34, 42, 45, 60, 64, 69, 70, 71, 72, 75, 78, 79, 83, 93, 95, 97, 98, 99, 100, 101, 103, 105, 108, 116, 117, 125, 128, 136, 142, 151, 157, 178, 182, 205, 222, 227, 230, 242, 246, 247, 248, 251, 254, 257, 259, 262, 270, 277, 297, 298, 299, 311, 313, 314, 319, 321, 351, 353, 354, 355, 360, 362, 364, 369, 421, 427, 428, 429, 436, 456, 474, 475, 491, 505, 514, 528, 533, 538, 550, 562, 564, 579, 588, 589, 592, 603, 604, 607, 616, 627, 641, 644, 647, 653, 661, 700, 702, 707, 713, 738, 758, 770, 771, 780, 781, 789, 815, 839, 840, 849, 851, 856, 865, 876, 884, 889, 911, 927, 967, 993, 995, 996, 1000, 1022, 1036, 1041, 1043, 1047, 1053, 1056, 1078, 1082, 1091, 1094, 1098, 1106, 1110, 1134, 1152, 1155, 1156

Ambystoma macrodactylum Baird
LONG-TOED SALAMANDER

5, 9, 11, 13, 24, 28, 42, 45, 64, 70, 72, 79, 80, 83, 88, 93, 98, 103, 114, 127, 133, 136, 157, 175, 178, 183, 187, 204, 205, 242, 252, 257, 270, 297, 298, 299, 313, 314, 319, 321, 336, 351, 353, 355, 357, 364, 366, 367, 370, 374, 386, 401, 421, 427, 428, 429, 436, 450, 456, 474, 475, 500, 503, 504, 512, 519, 538, 555, 573, 577, 588, 589, 592, 602, 603, 607, 615, 616, 634, 641, 645, 647, 661, 689, 690, 700, 702, 707, 711, 713, 771, 781, 815, 839, 849, 851, 865, 866, 873, 876, 879, 885, 887, 911, 927, 938, 967, 986, 994, 995, 996, 997, 1000, 1004, 1008, 1035, 1036, 1041, 1043, 1047, 1056, 1059, 1082, 1083, 1089, 1091, 1094, 1098, 1106, 1110, 1111, 1134, 1138, 1139, 1152

Ambystoma tigrinum (Green)
TIGER SALAMANDER

9, 13, 28, 64, 72, 81, 83, 93, 131, 178, 205, 287, 297, 298, 299, 313, 351, 364, 399, 421, 428, 429, 437, 446, 456,

Ambystoma tigrinum (Green)
TIGER SALAMANDER (cont'd)

459, 474, 475, 491, 500, 571, 572, 588, 589, 590, 592, 603, 604, 609, 611, 636, 647, 654, 661, 684, 691, 694, 700, 702, 704, 707, 713, 744, 781, 789, 815, 817, 822, 834, 839, 851, 854, 872, 876, 900, 956, 959, 965, 967, 984, 987, 996, 997, 999, 1001, 1002, 1031, 1036, 1040, 1041, 1043, 1047, 1055, 1056, 1069, 1071, 1082, 1089, 1091, 1094, 1095, 1098, 1106, 1110, 1118, 1135, 1152, 1154

Aneides ferreus Cope
CLOUDED SALAMANDER

9, 12, 13, 41, 42, 50, 64, 72, 77, 83, 93, 169, 178, 223, 224, 242, 245, 295, 297, 298, 299, 313, 314, 319, 351, 353, 258, 374, 375, 379, 436, 442, 462, 474, 475, 505, 514, 564, 573, 588, 589, 618, 639, 643, 647, 661, 700, 702, 706, 719, 739, 748, 771, 793, 800, 815, 849, 851, 886, 911, 938, 967, 968, 1027, 1036, 1041, 1043, 1047, 1056, 1059, 1065, 1082, 1091, 1094, 1098, 1106, 1110, 1152

Ascaphus truei Stejneger
TAILED FROG

1, 2, 9, 12, 13, 16, 26, 29, 63, 64, 66, 83, 93, 113, 118, 119, 124, 125, 128, 178, 181, 188, 192, 194, 198, 200, 205, 249, 267, 268, 286, 298, 299, 312, 313, 319, 340, 351, 364, 367, 402, 405, 407, 408, 421, 427, 428, 429, 431, 436, 470, 472, 474, 475, 487, 491, 528, 546, 575, 588, 589, 592, 600, 603, 604, 622, 626, 630, 647, 661, 664, 668, 674, 680, 684, 700, 702, 707, 721, 740, 753, 757, 765, 785, 790, 797, 805, 813, 815, 817, 821, 822, 831, 832, 840, 851, 860, 863, 865, 866, 876, 877, 879, 901, 903, 912, 937, 967, 976, 992, 996, 1000, 1003, 1004, 1005, 1007, 1018, 1027, 1036, 1039, 1041, 1043, 1047, 1050, 1052, 1056, 1059, 1066, 1077, 1082, 1084, 1091, 1098, 1106, 1110, 1152

Bufo boreas Baird and Girard
WESTERN TOAD

3, 5, 9, 13, 29, 35, 46, 63, 64, 72, 73, 77, 78, 79, 80, 83, 84, 93, 98, 102, 103, 107, 110, 114, 127, 128, 149, 157, 163, 178, 204, 205, 215, 228, 238, 241, 242, 253, 257, 267, 268, 276, 277, 280, 286, 293, 298, 299, 305, 313, 314, 319, 337, 344, 351, 353, 354, 355, 363, 366, 367, 368, 369, 370, 371, 379, 383, 384, 385, 386, 387, 412, 418, 421, 427, 428, 429, 436, 472, 474, 475, 491, 501, 503, 504, 505, 506, 507, 508, 511, 513, 514, 517, 519, 520, 521, 522, 523, 525, 526, 527, 547, 550, 551, 555, 564, 573, 575, 577, 579, 588, 589, 590, 592, 594, 603, 604, 607, 626, 629, 634, 640, 641, 647, 652, 659, 661, 680, 684, 692, 700, 701, 702, 707, 765, 766, 771, 774, 780, 782, 787, 790, 807, 815, 819, 837, 840, 842, 849, 851, 860, 863, 864, 865, 871, 876, 879, 882, 912, 915, 923, 926, 938, 961, 967, 968, 995, 996, 997, 1000, 1004, 1010, 1012, 1022, 1024, 1033, 1035, 1036, 1039, 1041, 1043, 1047, 1056, 1059, 1061, 1063, 1078, 1082, 1083, 1084, 1085, 1089, 1090, 1091, 1093, 1094, 1098, 1106, 1110, 1111, 1118, 1124, 1127, 1129, 1130, 1131, 1132, 1134, 1138, 1139, 1141, 1143, 1152, 1153

Bufo woodhousei Girard
WOODHOUSE'S TOAD

63, 83, 92, 93, 178, 267, 268, 276, 286, 298, 299, 305, 313, 319, 351, 421, 428, 429, 474, 475, 588, 589, 592, 594, 603, 604, 625, 647, 668, 680, 684, 702, 707, 754, 765, 780, 782, 790, 797, 821, 822, 876, 912, 997, 1036, 1041, 1090, 1091, 1098, 1106, 1129, 1143, 1152

Charina bottae (Blainville)
RUBBER BOA

9, 14, 64, 72, 83, 91, 93, 127, 141, 144, 148, 161, 166, 178, 179, 195, 209, 242, 269, 289, 296, 298, 300, 302, 308, 313, 348, 349, 367, 421, 425, 428, 429, 436, 463, 473, 474, 475, 476, 481, 482, 497, 503, 509, 510, 511, 512, 519, 522, 524, 544, 573, 577, 588, 589, 590, 599, 605, 606, 607, 610, 641, 647, 649, 661, 700, 702, 703, 730, 743, 771, 796, 804, 816, 822, 847, 852, 870, 879, 922, 938, 967, 996, 997, 1026, 1038, 1041, 1046, 1049, 1056, 1058, 1082, 1091, 1092, 1094, 1098, 1106, 1110, 1118, 1152

Chelonia mydas (Linnaeus)
GREEN TURTLE

14, 58, 62, 83, 93, 111, 178, 313, 350, 356, 605, 606, 610, 635, 661, 668, 700, 791, 816, 852, 1029, 1031, 1038, 1040, 1041, 1046, 1056, 1057, 1082, 1087, 1091, 1094, 1098, 1106, 1110,

Chelonia mydas (Linnaeus)
GREEN TURTLE (cont'd)

1112, 1137, 1148, 1149, 1152, 1154

Chelydra serpentina Linnaeus
SNAPPING TURTLE

93, 156, 1041, 1091, 1098, 1106, 1152

Chrysemys picta (Sneider)
PAINTED TURTLE

9, 10, 14, 18, 20, 43, 62, 64, 72, 82, 83, 93, 107, 111, 114, 122, 127, 141, 144, 178, 186, 233, 235, 237, 240, 242, 287, 294, 296, 298, 313, 349, 350, 383, 415, 421, 425, 428, 429, 473, 474, 475, 480, 503, 507, 509, 510, 511, 512, 513, 519, 524, 525, 577, 588, 589, 590, 596, 599, 605, 606, 610, 621, 625, 635, 647, 661, 700, 702, 726, 771, 801, 816, 822, 835, 852, 879, 881, 892, 893, 904, 907, 913, 916, 918, 940, 947, 962, 964, 967, 985, 989, 990, 996, 997, 998, 999, 1001, 1029, 1031, 1038, 1040, 1041, 1044, 1046, 1051, 1056, 1057, 1063, 1070, 1073, 1082, 1087, 1091, 1094, 1098, 1106, 1110, 1118, 1134, 1152, 1154

Clemmys marmorata (Baird and Girard)
WESTERN POND TURTLE

2, 9, 10, 14, 18, 20, 62, 64, 72, 83, 92, 93, 111, 120, 141, 144, 178, 237, 242, 296, 298, 313, 320, 349, 350, 421, 425, 428, 429, 436, 473, 474, 475, 491, 537, 588, 589, 596, 599, 601, 605, 606, 610, 635, 641, 647, 661, 700, 702, 725, 727, 806, 816, 821, 822, 852, 967, 985, 989, 996, 1029, 1038, 1040, 1041, 1045, 1046, 1050, 1056, 1057, 1082, 1087, 1091, 1094, 1098, 1106, 1110, 1134, 1138, 1139, 1142, 1152

Coluber constrictor Linnaeus
RACER

9, 14, 64, 72, 83, 93, 114, 127, 132, 141, 144, 149, 154, 178, 195, 242, 269, 296, 298, 300, 302, 303, 313, 348, 349, 421, 425, 428, 429, 436, 474, 475, 476, 481, 482, 484, 491, 497, 522, 524, 573, 577, 588, 589, 590, 605, 606, 610, 617, 625, 638, 641, 647, 649, 661, 666, 668, 687, 696, 700, 702, 703, 731, 745, 749, 759, 771, 795, 804, 816, 822, 825, 852, 879, 967, 996, 997, 1019, 1030, 1031, 1038, 1040, 1041, 1046, 1049, 1056, 1058, 1073, 1082, 1091, 1092, 1094, 1098, 1106, 1110, 1152, 1154

Contia tenuis (Baird and Girard)
SHARPTAIL SNAKE

2, 8, 14, 67, 83, 92, 93, 141, 144, 178, 195, 236, 269, 296, 298, 300, 302, 313, 348, 349, 350, 380, 421, 425, 428, 429, 436, 473, 474, 475, 476, 481, 482, 497, 536, 589, 595, 599, 605, 606, 610,

Contia tenuis (Baird and Girard)
SHARPTAIL SNAKE (cont'd)

638, 641, 661, 700, 702, 703, 759, 816,
821, 822, 852, 1022, 1026, 1038, 1041,
1046, 1050, 1058, 1066, 1082, 1091,
1098, 1106, 1110, 1152

Crotalus viridis Rafinesque
WESTERN RATTLESNAKE

9, 14, 64, 72, 83, 93, 109, 114,
127, 141, 144, 150, 163, 178, 195, 242,
269, 296, 298, 300, 301, 302, 313, 348,
349, 350, 421, 424, 428, 429, 434, 435,
436, 473, 474, 475, 476, 477, 478, 479,
481, 482, 484, 485, 488, 492, 493, 494,
495, 496, 497, 499, 502, 522, 555, 573,
578, 586, 588, 589, 590, 605, 606, 610,
617, 641, 647, 649, 650, 656, 657, 661,
662, 663, 667, 668, 675, 677, 685, 695,
700, 702, 703, 749, 771, 776, 779, 786,
804, 810, 816, 822, 825, 847, 852, 879,
888, 896, 899, 928, 936, 955, 967, 980,
996, 997, 1025, 1030, 1034, 1037, 1038,
1041, 1042, 1046, 1049, 1056, 1058,
1060, 1082, 1091, 1092, 1093, 1094,
1098, 1104, 1106, 1110, 1117, 1118,
1152, 1153, 1154

Dermochelys coriacea (Linnaeus)
LEATHERBACK

9, 14, 33, 51, 62, 64, 72, 76, 83,
93, 111, 178, 237, 313, 350, 356, 588,
610, 647, 661, 700, 816, 822, 852, 942,
967, 1029, 1031, 1038, 1040, 1041,
1046, 1053, 1056, 1057, 1082, 1087,
1091, 1098, 1106, 1110, 1137, 1147,
1152, 1154

Diadophis punctatus Linnaeus
RINGNECK SNAKE

83, 92, 93, 127, 137, 141, 144,
178, 269, 287, 298, 300, 313, 348, 349,
350, 421, 428, 429, 436, 473, 474, 475,
456, 481, 482, 484, 486, 588, 605, 606,
638, 647, 668, 702, 703, 752, 759, 821,
822, 997, 1019, 1026, 1030, 1031, 1040,
1041, 1049, 1058, 1091, 1092, 1094,
1098, 1106, 1152, 1154

Dicamptodon copei Nussbaum
COPE'S GIANT SALAMANDER

93, 159, 201, 549, 698, 996, 1036,
1041, 1091, 1098, 1106, 1152

Dicamptodon ensatus (Eschscholtz)
PACIFIC GIANT SALAMANDER

2, 9, 13, 28, 64, 68, 72, 83, 93,
121, 123, 126, 127, 128, 130, 142, 159,
160, 178, 187, 201, 202, 205, 242, 245,
279, 297, 298, 299, 313, 319, 336, 351,
353, 362, 364, 395, 421, 427, 428, 429,
436, 450, 456, 474, 475, 500, 538, 580,
582, 583, 584, 588, 589, 592, 603, 604,
611, 641, 647, 661, 684, 698, 700, 702,

Dicamptodon ensatus (Eschscholtz)
PACIFIC GIANT SALAMANDER (cont'd)

707, 714, 760, 815, 822, 839, 840, 851,
855, 856, 876, 885, 967, 976, 979, 981,
994, 996, 1000, 1002, 1005, 1036, 1041,
1043, 1047, 1050, 1056, 1066, 1076,
1082, 1091, 1094, 1098, 1106, 1110, 1152

Ensatina eschscholtzi Gray
ENSATINA

12, 13, 19, 28, 30, 41, 42, 64, 72,
83, 93, 168, 178, 205, 206, 242, 245,
278, 295, 297, 298, 299, 313, 319, 331,
334, 336, 339, 351, 353, 364, 375, 421,
427, 428, 429, 436, 444, 462, 474, 475,
505, 573, 581, 588, 589, 592, 597, 603,
604, 607, 628, 641, 647, 661, 700, 702,
707, 748, 815, 826, 849, 851, 865, 886,
927, 967, 993, 994, 995, 996, 1000,
1004, 1027, 1036, 1041, 1043, 1047,
1056, 1082, 1091, 1098, 1106, 1110,
1118, 1134, 1138, 1152

Eumeces skiltonianus (Baird and
Girard) WESTERN SKINK

9, 14, 15, 59, 64, 72, 83, 93, 127,
141, 144, 163, 178, 213, 292, 296, 298,
313, 329, 349, 352, 404, 421, 428, 429,
436, 465, 473, 474, 475, 503, 585, 587,
588, 589, 605, 606, 610, 647, 661, 700,
702, 741, 752, 804, 816, 822, 852, 879,
954, 967, 997, 1028, 1038, 1041, 1046,
1048, 1056, 1082, 1091, 1092, 1098,
1106, 1110, 1122, 1152

Gerrhonotus coeruleus (Wiegmann)
NORTHERN ALLIGATOR LIZARD

9, 14, 41, 47, 59, 64, 72, 83, 93,
106, 141, 144, 145, 166, 178, 216, 218,
242, 243, 263, 266, 296, 298, 309, 345,
349, 357, 367, 368, 381, 391, 404, 421,
425, 426, 428, 429, 436, 473, 474, 475,
491, 498, 503, 505, 506, 507, 508, 511,
514, 518, 519, 522, 524, 525, 568, 573,
577, 588, 589, 599, 605, 606, 607, 610,
634, 641, 647, 661, 700, 702, 733, 771,
804, 814, 816, 820, 822, 840, 844, 849,
852, 865, 874, 884, 894, 921, 938, 954,
957, 967, 975, 995, 996, 997, 1017,
1022, 1024, 1028, 1030, 1031, 1038,
1040, 1041, 1046, 1056, 1059, 1073,
1082, 1084, 1091, 1092, 1098, 1106,
1110, 1111, 1122, 1139, 1152, 1153

Gerrhonotus multicarinatus (Blainville)
SOUTHERN ALLIGATOR LIZARD

59, 74, 83, 85, 92, 93, 129, 141,
144, 150, 178, 263, 266, 296, 298, 313,
345, 347, 349, 404, 421, 426, 428, 429,
467, 474, 475, 498, 585, 588, 589, 605,
606, 641, 647, 702, 734, 751, 759, 804,
821, 822, 891, 954, 996, 1006, 1019,
1028, 1030, 1040, 1041, 1073, 1091,
1092, 1098, 1100, 1106, 1118, 1152

Hyla regilla Baird and Girard
PACIFIC TREEFROG

6, 9, 13, 25, 41, 53, 63, 64, 72,
74, 78, 79, 83, 93, 98, 103, 114, 127,
133, 155, 163, 176, 177, 178, 180, 193,
205, 228, 229, 238, 242, 253, 257, 260,
267, 277, 286, 298, 299, 306, 311, 313,
316, 317, 318, 319, 323, 324, 325, 327,
328, 330, 346, 351, 353, 355, 357, 359,
367, 368, 374, 375, 378, 379, 382, 385,
386, 387, 392, 414, 421, 427, 428, 429,
432, 433, 436, 451, 461, 469, 472, 474,
475, 487, 491, 501, 503, 505, 506, 507,
511, 514, 516, 519, 522, 525, 528, 532,
555, 564, 567, 573, 575, 577, 579, 588,
589, 590, 592, 603, 604, 607, 613, 626,
630, 634, 641, 647, 652, 661, 665, 680,
683, 684, 700, 701, 702, 707, 708, 735,
755, 765, 768, 771, 774, 784, 790, 792,
815, 822, 824, 831, 832, 836, 837, 840,
849, 850, 859, 860, 861, 862, 863, 865,
867, 871, 873, 876, 879, 882, 884, 901,
909, 912, 914, 927, 931, 934, 967, 968,
993, 995, 996, 997, 1000, 1004, 1022,
1024, 1036, 1039, 1040, 1041, 1043,
1044, 1047, 1053, 1056, 1059, 1062,
1078, 1082, 1084, 1089, 1090, 1091,
1094, 1098, 1106, 1109, 1110, 1111,
1134, 1138, 1139, 1152, 1155

Hypsiglena torquata (Gunther)
NIGHT SNAKE

83, 92, 93, 139, 141, 144, 147,
166, 178, 211, 269, 298, 300, 313, 348,
349, 350, 420, 421, 428, 429, 436, 474,
475, 476, 481, 482, 589, 605, 606, 647,
649, 668, 702, 752, 821, 822, 1026,
1041, 1058, 1091, 1098, 1106, 1152

Lampropeltis zonata Blainville
CALIFORNIA MOUNTAIN KINGSNAKE

83, 92, 93, 144, 147, 178, 269,
298, 300, 313, 349, 350, 421, 428, 429,
436, 458, 464, 474, 475, 476, 481, 482,
588, 589, 593, 606, 647, 702, 703, 728,
729, 752, 821, 822, 1041, 1058, 1091,
1092, 1098, 1106, 1118, 1152

Masticophis taeniatus Hallowell
STRIPED WHIPSNAKE

83, 92, 93, 144, 174, 178, 195,
269, 298, 300, 313, 349, 350, 421, 428,
429, 436, 474, 475, 476, 481, 482, 598,
605, 606, 617, 632, 647, 649, 668, 702,
703, 749, 804, 821, 822, 1026, 1041,
1058, 1091, 1092, 1094, 1098, 1106, 1152

Phrynosoma douglassi (Bell)
SHORT-HORNED LIZARD

2, 9, 14, 59, 64, 72, 83, 90, 93,
127, 141, 144, 178, 196, 242, 296, 298,
338, 345, 349, 421, 428, 429, 436, 457,
473, 474, 475, 491, 540, 574, 585, 588,
589, 590, 605, 606, 610, 641, 647, 661,
700, 702, 771, 804, 816, 822, 852, 879,

Phrynosoma douglassi (Bell)
SHORT-HORNED LIZARD (cont'd)

967, 975, 996, 997, 1028, 1031, 1038,
1040, 1041, 1046, 1048, 1050, 1056,
1066, 1081, 1082, 1091, 1092, 1098,
1106, 1110, 1118, 1122, 1139, 1152,
1153, 1154

Phrynosoma platyrhinos (Girard)
DESERT HORNED LIZARD

59, 93, 141, 144, 296, 421, 474,
475, 588, 589, 605, 606, 647, 771, 996,
1041, 1090, 1091, 1092, 1098, 1106, 1152

Pituophis melanoleucus Daudin
GOPHER SNAKE

2, 9, 14, 64, 72, 83, 93, 127, 141,
144, 163, 178, 195, 242, 269, 288, 296,
298, 300, 302, 313, 342, 343, 345, 349,
421, 425, 428, 429, 436, 474, 475, 476,
481, 482, 483, 484, 490, 491, 497, 522,
555, 573, 586, 588, 589, 590, 605, 606,
610, 617, 625, 632, 638, 641, 647, 649,
660, 661, 668, 673, 686, 695, 700, 702,
703, 752, 759, 771, 804, 810, 816, 822,
827, 852, 857, 879, 888, 964, 967, 996,
997, 1015, 1016, 1026, 1031, 1038,
1040, 1041, 1045, 1046, 1049, 1050,
1056, 1058, 1066, 1081, 1082, 1091,
1092, 1098, 1106, 1110, 1118, 1139,
1152, 1153, 1154

Plethodon dunni Bishop
DUNN'S SALAMANDER

83, 92, 93, 173, 178, 205, 278,
297, 298, 299, 313, 421, 428, 429, 436,
440, 453, 462, 475, 588, 589, 592, 603,
604, 612, 614, 619, 628, 637, 647, 702,
707, 715, 748, 821, 822, 886, 977, 994,
1036, 1041, 1091, 1098, 1106, 1152

Plethodon larselli Burns
LARCH MOUNTAIN SALAMANDER

83, 92, 93, 178, 185, 205, 278,
428, 429, 453, 462, 592, 603, 604, 619,
628, 637, 702, 707, 821, 822, 868, 886,
943, 963, 977, 1036, 1041, 1091, 1098,
1106, 1152

Plethodon vandykei Van Denburgh
VAN DYKE'S SALAMANDER

83, 93, 126, 169, 178, 185, 295,
297, 298, 299, 313, 351, 421, 427, 428,
429, 436, 453, 454, 462, 474, 475, 588,
589, 592, 603, 604, 619, 628, 637, 647,
702, 707, 717, 748, 822, 886, 977, 994,
996, 1000, 1036, 1041, 1091, 1098,
1106, 1152

Plethodon vehiculum Cooper
WESTERN REDBACK SALAMANDER

6, 9, 13, 19, 42, 50, 64, 72, 83,
93, 98, 125, 126, 128, 178, 242, 295,

Plethodon vehiculum Cooper
WESTERN REDBACK SALAMANDER
(cont'd)

297, 298, 299, 313, 351, 353, 357, 364,
368, 373, 374, 375, 393, 421, 427, 428,
429, 436, 444, 453, 462, 474, 475, 505,
538, 547, 564, 573, 579, 588, 589, 592,
597, 603, 604, 607, 612, 614, 616, 618,
619, 628, 637, 641, 643, 647, 648, 661,
700, 702, 707, 716, 748, 815, 822, 826,
851, 865, 868, 886, 911, 927, 967, 977,
982, 993, 994, 995, 996, 1000, 1027,
1036, 1040, 1041, 1043, 1047, 1056,
1082, 1091, 1098, 1106, 1110, 1118,
1134, 1138, 1152

Pseudacris triseriata (Wied)
STRIPED CHORUS FROG

9, 13, 35, 63, 64, 83, 84, 93, 157,
178, 267, 268, 286, 287, 299, 313, 315,
351, 403, 455, 474, 475, 529, 575, 647,
661, 676, 684, 700, 702, 765, 790, 797,
815, 851, 890, 908, 967, 1031, 1036,
1039, 1040, 1041, 1043, 1047, 1056,
1059, 1082, 1091, 1098, 1106, 1110, 1152

Rana aurora Baird and Girard
RED-LEGGED FROG

9, 13, 23, 36, 39, 44, 53, 54, 61,
63, 64, 69, 70, 71, 72, 78, 83, 93, 96,
97, 98, 101, 103, 105, 152, 153, 162,
178, 205, 210, 230, 238, 242, 257, 265,
267, 268, 272, 277, 286, 298, 299, 310,
311, 313, 319, 351, 353, 357, 359, 368,
374, 375, 378, 379, 380, 412, 421, 427,
428, 429, 436, 452, 472, 474, 475, 491,
503, 505, 506, 514, 528, 539, 547, 548,
555, 561, 564, 573, 575, 579, 588, 589,
592, 603, 604, 607, 626, 631, 647, 655,
658, 661, 679, 680, 694, 700, 702, 707,
720, 765, 771, 780, 790, 799, 815, 822,
840, 849, 851, 860, 861, 862, 864, 865,
867, 871, 873, 876, 882, 883, 884, 927,
938, 967, 968, 993, 995, 996, 1000,
1014, 1022, 1036, 1039, 1040, 1041,
1043, 1047, 1053, 1056, 1059, 1082,
1084, 1089, 1091, 1094, 1098, 1102,
1106, 1110, 1125, 1126, 1134, 1138,
1139, 1152

Rana cascadae Slater
CASCADES FROG

36, 63, 83, 178, 205, 267, 268,
270, 272, 298, 299, 313, 419, 421, 427,
428, 429, 436, 439, 491, 548, 588, 589,
592, 603, 604, 626, 631, 647, 679, 680,
702, 707, 723, 765, 767, 769, 807, 822,
851, 860, 876, 883, 996, 1036, 1040,
1041, 1091, 1094, 1098, 1106, 1152

Rana catesbeiana Shaw
BULLFROG

9, 13, 29, 36, 63, 83, 93, 103,
127, 156, 178, 197, 205, 232, 257, 267,

Rana catesbeiana Shaw
BULLFROG (cont'd)

268, 277, 286, 287, 298, 299, 313, 363,
390, 394, 417, 421, 427, 428, 429, 487,
514, 529, 548, 566, 572, 575, 588, 589,
592, 594, 603, 604, 607, 620, 626, 630,
631, 635, 642, 652, 655, 661, 668, 669,
680, 684, 694, 700, 701, 702, 707, 765,
774, 780, 790, 815, 822, 833, 838, 851,
858, 860, 863, 873, 876, 883, 890, 905,
912, 945, 967, 971, 976, 995, 997,
1011, 1021, 1027, 1031, 1036, 1039,
1040, 1041, 1043, 1047, 1055, 1056,
1059, 1064, 1075, 1078, 1082, 1084,
1089, 1091, 1094, 1095, 1098, 1102,
1106, 1110, 1112, 1118, 1125, 1134,
1138, 1140, 1152, 1154

Rana clamitans Latreille
GREEN FROG

12, 13, 29, 40, 63, 83, 93, 156,
178, 267, 268, 277, 286, 287, 298, 299,
363, 398, 428, 429, 487, 529, 566, 572,
575, 588, 589, 592, 594, 603, 604, 626,
661, 668, 680, 684, 694, 700, 701, 702,
707, 765, 780, 790, 815, 817, 821, 822,
851, 860, 912, 934, 967, 976, 1020,
1031, 1036, 1039, 1040, 1041, 1043,
1047, 1055, 1056, 1075, 1078, 1082,
1091, 1095, 1098, 1102, 1106, 1110,
1125, 1134, 1140, 1152, 1154

Rana pipiens Schreber
NORTHERN LEOPARD FROG

9, 12, 13, 36, 63, 64, 65, 72, 83,
90, 93, 178, 199, 231, 267, 268, 277,
286, 287, 298, 299, 319, 351, 359, 363,
421, 428, 429, 455, 460, 487, 514, 529,
566, 572, 575, 588, 589, 590, 592, 603,
604, 623, 625, 626, 631, 633, 647, 655,
661, 668, 669, 683, 684, 694, 697, 700,
701, 702, 707, 762, 765, 773, 774, 790,
797, 815, 822, 851, 863, 876, 879, 880,
883, 890, 901, 912, 915, 923, 924, 925,
929, 934, 967, 969, 976, 983, 1007,
1013, 1031, 1036, 1039, 1040, 1041,
1043, 1047, 1056, 1071, 1075, 1082,
1091, 1095, 1098, 1106, 1110, 1152, 1155

Rana pretiosa Baird and Girard
SPOTTED FROG

5, 9, 13, 29, 36, 54, 63, 64, 72,
80, 83, 84, 90, 93, 103, 107, 114, 115,
127, 128, 133, 149, 152, 157, 178, 204,
205, 214, 228, 242, 253, 257, 267, 268,
272, 273, 274, 286, 298, 299, 307, 310,
319, 344, 351, 353, 354, 366, 367, 370,
371, 383, 386, 387, 421, 427, 428, 429,
436, 459, 472, 474, 475, 491, 501, 504,
507, 513, 519, 520, 526, 547, 548, 550,
555, 577, 588, 589, 590, 592, 603, 604,
631, 634, 640, 641, 647, 658, 661, 680,
700, 702, 707, 724, 765, 769, 771, 780,
790, 815, 817, 822, 851, 860, 876, 879,
883, 938, 967, 976, 988, 996, 997, 999,

Rana pretiosa Baird and Girard
SPOTTED FROG (cont'd)

1000, 1001, 1004, 1027, 1035, 1036,
1039, 1041, 1043, 1047, 1056, 1059,
1061, 1082, 1083, 1089, 1091, 1094,
1098, 1102, 1106, 1110, 1111, 1125,
1126, 1139, 1152

Rana sylvatica Le Conte
WOOD FROG

5, 7, 9, 13, 21, 35, 36, 63, 64,
72, 73, 80, 83, 84, 86, 87, 89, 93,
120, 138, 157, 178, 212, 242, 267, 268,
286, 287, 299, 314, 351, 353, 366, 370,
371, 459, 472, 474, 475, 487, 491, 501,
534, 541, 542, 543, 550, 552, 553, 554,
556, 563, 570, 572, 575, 588, 608, 626,
631, 647, 661, 676, 680, 694, 700, 702,
722, 765, 780, 790, 815, 824, 851, 967,
976, 1031, 1035, 1036, 1039, 1040,
1041, 1043, 1047, 1056, 1059, 1082,
1083, 1089, 1091, 1094, 1095, 1098,
1102, 1106, 1110, 1125, 1126, 1152, 1154

Rhyacotriton olympicus (Gaige)
OLYMPIC SALAMANDER

83, 93, 126, 128, 130, 178, 187,
189, 200, 205, 247, 282, 297, 298, 299,
313, 321, 332, 351, 362, 364, 421, 428,
429, 436, 438, 444, 450, 456, 474, 475,
491, 545, 569, 588, 589, 592, 603, 604,
611, 647, 702, 704, 705, 707, 712, 761,
822, 839, 856, 897, 951, 994, 996,
1002, 1036, 1041, 1091, 1098, 1106,
1118, 1152

Scaphiopus intermontanus (Cope)
GREAT BASIN SPADEFOOT

6, 9, 13, 25, 63, 64, 72, 83, 93,
107, 127, 172, 178, 205, 208, 242, 267,
286, 298, 299, 313, 319, 351, 353, 359,
363, 421, 428, 429, 436, 472, 474, 475,
487, 555, 588, 589, 590, 592, 603, 604,
641, 647, 661, 678, 684, 700, 702, 707,
765, 790, 815, 822, 851, 863, 876, 879,
912, 948, 967, 996, 997, 1027, 1036,
1039, 1040, 1041, 1043, 1047, 1056,
1059, 1082, 1089, 1090, 1091, 1094,
1098, 1106, 1110, 1139, 1152

Sceloporus graciosus Baird and Girard
SAGEBRUSH LIZARD

59, 83, 93, 141, 144, 178, 191,
271, 296, 298, 326, 349, 389, 406, 421,
428, 429, 436, 466, 473, 474, 475, 585,
588, 590, 605, 606, 647, 702, 737, 750,
752, 763, 764, 788, 794, 804, 822, 828,
879, 920, 954, 996, 997, 1028, 1031,
1041, 1054, 1073, 1090, 1091, 1092,
1094, 1098, 1106, 1108, 1122, 1152, 1153

Sceloporus occidentalis Baird and
Girard WESTERN FENCE LIZARD

14, 55, 59, 72, 83, 93, 135, 141,
144, 149, 150, 178, 183, 191, 296, 298,
345, 347, 349, 388, 400, 406, 411, 413,
421, 425, 428, 429, 436, 468, 473, 474,
475, 585, 588, 589, 605, 606, 607, 647,
700, 702, 742, 752, 763, 764, 771, 783,
804, 822, 828, 869, 879, 891, 902, 930,
939, 946, 954, 958, 960, 967, 975, 978,
995, 996, 1006, 1028, 1030, 1041, 1073,
1082, 1090, 1091, 1092, 1094, 1098,
1100, 1106, 1108, 1110, 1152, 1153

Taricha granulosa (Skilton)
ROUGHSKIN NEWT

9, 13, 34, 38, 41, 42, 49, 52, 56,
57, 64, 69, 72, 78, 79, 83, 93, 97, 98,
103, 105, 128, 146, 151, 157, 158, 165,
178, 187, 190, 195, 205, 219, 220, 221,
225, 226, 227, 230, 242, 244, 245, 250,
251, 255, 256, 257, 258, 275, 281, 283,
297, 298, 299, 311, 313, 319, 335, 336,
344, 351, 353, 355, 357, 364, 368, 369,
373, 374, 421, 427, 428, 429, 436, 474,
475, 500, 505, 514, 516, 517, 530, 550,
555, 564, 573, 579, 588, 589, 592, 603,
604, 607, 641, 645, 647, 661, 668, 700,
702, 707, 771, 802, 815, 822, 830, 840,
846, 849, 851, 861, 862, 865, 873, 876,
884, 889, 911, 919, 927, 966, 968, 982,
993, 994, 995, 996, 1000, 1008, 1022,
1023, 1036, 1040, 1041, 1043, 1044,
1046, 1053, 1056, 1059, 1061, 1082,
1085, 1089, 1091, 1094, 1098, 1106,
1110, 1134, 1138, 1139, 1152, 1153

Thamnophis elegans Baird and Girard
WESTERN TERRESTRIAL GARTER SNAKE

9, 14, 31, 37, 41, 64, 72, 80, 83,
93, 104, 114, 127, 134, 141, 143, 144,
149, 157, 167, 170, 178, 195, 207, 234,
242, 261, 269, 291, 296, 298, 300, 302,
313, 322, 333, 341, 348, 349, 350, 357,
361, 367, 372, 374, 375, 376, 379, 381,
383, 421, 423, 425, 428, 429, 436, 441,
445, 447, 449, 471, 473, 474, 475, 476,
481, 482, 489, 491, 497, 505, 507, 509,
511, 514, 519, 521, 524, 531, 555, 573,
576, 577, 579, 588, 589, 590, 591, 605,
606, 607, 610, 634, 641, 646, 647, 649,
652, 661, 700, 702, 703, 752, 771, 799,
804, 816, 822, 843, 844, 848, 850, 852,
853, 861, 862, 875, 878, 879, 932, 933,
935, 949, 950, 967, 973, 974, 991, 996,
997, 1017, 1022, 1026, 1027, 1030,
1038, 1040, 1041, 1046, 1049, 1053,
1056, 1058, 1059, 1082, 1086, 1091,
1092, 1094, 1098, 1106, 1110, 1111,
1118, 1134, 1138, 1139, 1152, 1153

Thamnophis ordinoides Baird and Girard
NORTHWESTERN GARTER SNAKE

9, 14, 17, 32, 64, 72, 77, 83, 93,
104, 112, 115, 141, 143, 144, 167, 178,
195, 207, 210, 234, 239, 242, 261, 269,
285, 296, 298, 300, 302, 313, 322, 341,
349, 350, 357, 367, 368, 374, 375, 376,
377, 379, 381, 385, 409, 421, 422, 423,
425, 428, 429, 436, 445, 447, 448, 449,
471, 474, 475, 476, 481, 482, 489, 491,
497, 505, 506, 514, 547, 555, 561, 564,
573, 579, 588, 589, 591, 605, 606, 607,
610, 646, 647, 649, 661, 700, 702, 703,
732, 747, 804, 816, 822, 840, 844, 845,
848, 850, 861, 862, 865, 875, 884, 910,
932, 933, 938, 967, 968, 974, 995, 996,
1022, 1024, 1026, 1027, 1030, 1038,
1041, 1046, 1049, 1053, 1056, 1058,
1059, 1082, 1084, 1086, 1091, 1092,
1094, 1098, 1106, 1110, 1111, 1134,
1138, 1139, 1145, 1152

Thamnophis sirtalis Linnaeus
COMMON GARTER SNAKE

9, 14, 32, 35, 48, 64, 72, 73, 77,
78, 80, 83, 93, 103, 104, 105, 114,
115, 127, 140, 141, 144, 149, 153, 157,
171, 178, 184, 195, 204, 207, 234, 242,
257, 261, 264, 269, 284, 287, 290, 296,
298, 300, 302, 304, 311, 313, 341, 348,
349, 350, 357, 361, 368, 369, 370, 371,
374, 375, 376, 379, 381, 383, 384, 385,
386, 387, 397, 409, 410, 416, 421, 423,
425, 428, 429, 436, 445, 447, 471, 473,
474, 475, 476, 481, 482, 484, 489, 497,
501, 503, 505, 506, 507, 511, 514, 519,
524, 525, 531, 535, 547, 555, 564, 573,
577, 578, 579, 588, 589, 591, 605, 606,
607, 610, 634, 640, 641, 642, 647, 652,
661, 668, 681, 693, 700, 702, 703, 747,
771, 799, 803, 804, 816, 817, 822, 840,
844, 845, 848, 852, 859, 861, 862, 865,
875, 878, 879, 884, 908, 932, 933, 964,
967, 996, 997, 999, 1017, 1019, 1022,
1024, 1026, 1027, 1030, 1031, 1038,
1040, 1041, 1046, 1049, 1053, 1056,
1058, 1059, 1078, 1082, 1084, 1086,
1091, 1092, 1093, 1098, 1106, 1110,
1111, 1134, 1138, 1139, 1146, 1152,
1153, 1154

Uta stansburiana Baird and Girard
SIDE-BLOTCHED LIZARD

59, 83, 93, 141, 144, 147, 164,
166, 178, 191, 203, 217, 271, 298, 345,
349, 350, 396, 404, 421, 428, 429, 436,
443, 473, 474, 475, 565, 574, 585, 588,
605, 606, 624, 625, 641, 647, 699, 702,
750, 752, 772, 778, 804, 817, 822, 879,
895, 902, 941, 946, 954, 970, 975,
1009, 1028, 1030, 1031, 1041, 1073,
1089, 1091, 1092, 1098, 1100, 1104,
1106, 1152

GEOGRAPHIC INDEX

To facilitate the use of available literature by researchers, all references have been cross-indexed by geographic area. Alaska and Yukon Territory are treated generally while British Columbia and Washington State have both general and specific categories (see maps for each area).

Additional categories, which have no specific geographic identity, but relate generally to the area covered, have been included. These are:

1. General literature, which includes all references of general interest. Subjects here include introductory texts, field guides, handbooks, dictionaries, regional checklists, bibliographies, taxonomy, systematics, evolution, history, longevity, vocalizations, identification, keys, collecting methods, capture and marking techniques, killing and preserving agents, laboratory methods, handling procedures, laws and regulations, introductions, human attitudes, lore, snake bites, controls, cookbooks, management, communicable diseases, and care and maintenance of reptiles and amphibians as pets.

2. Additional literature, which includes a selection of articles written outside of our area but dealing with species (see page 127 found within Alaska, Yukon Territory British Columbia and Washington.

The six categories are: General Literature
Alaska
Yukon Territory
British Columbia
Washington
Additional Literature

GENERAL LITERATURE

47, 62, 63, 68, 83, 93, 108, 110, 111, 120, 143, 178, 181, 218, 219, 220, 222, 227, 228, 239, 266, 267, 268, 277, 286, 287, 296, 298, 359, 361, 362, 363, 365, 430, 436, 458, 471, 472, 473, 474, 475, 476, 481, 487, 499, 572, 625, 635, 641, 643, 650, 651, 668, 669, 670, 671, 672, 684, 687, 690, 701, 702, 703, 709, 710, 713, 765, 776, 778, 780, 786, 801, 804, 805, 808, 809, 811, 812, 817, 818, 823, 824, 864, 869, 871, 892, 896, 905, 906, 917, 919, 922, 926, 928, 933, 936, 937, 942, 944, 952, 953, 954, 962, 964, 967, 972, 973, 977, 980, 1014, 1025, 1026, 1028, 1031, 1032, 1033, 1036, 1037, 1039, 1040, 1041, 1042, 1055, 1056, 1057, 1058, 1060, 1063, 1067, 1068, 1069, 1070, 1072, 1074, 1075, 1079, 1080, 1087, 1088, 1090, 1091, 1096, 1097, 1098, 1099, 1101, 1102, 1103, 1105, 1106, 1107, 1108, 1112, 1113, 1114, 1115, 1116, 1117, 1118, 1119, 1120, 1121, 1123, 1125, 1126, 1128, 1133, 1136, 1137, 1144, 1148, 1149, 1150, 1151, 1152, 1154, 1155

ALASKA

2, 5, 7, 9, 27, 63, 64, 83, 86, 88, 89, 117, 146, 157, 212, 297, 298, 299, 300, 304, 313, 319, 321, 335, 344, 351, 472, 474, 475, 491, 541, 542, 543, 550, 551, 552, 553, 554, 556, 570, 608, 647, 653, 661, 676, 684, 702, 711, 722, 724, 746, 780, 842, 1061, 1089

YUKON TERRITORY

7, 9, 21, 83, 157, 212, 293, 556, 570, 676, 722

Province of British Columbia
Ministry of Environment

NATIONAL TOPOGRAPHIC SYSTEM

BRITISH COLUMBIA INDEX

British Columbia is divided into 89 major grids (1° latitude by 2° longitude). Each grid (see opposite page) is listed in numerical/alphabetical order: Map Grid 82E, Map Grid 82F, Map Grid 82G, etc. (For example, Vancouver is found on Map Grid 92G; Cranbrook, on Map Grid 82G; and Fort Nelson, on Map Grid 94J.

However, many articles contain information for much larger, ill-defined or general areas of the Province; therefore, five additional categories have been included:

    1.   British Columbia General
         – general references to British Columbia

    2.   Northern Interior British Columbia
         – north of latitude 55°

    3.   Southern Interior British Columbia
         – south of latitude 55°

    4.   Coastal British Columbia
         – area west of the line drawn through the Coast Mountain summits

    5.   Pelagic British Columbia
         – off-shore to 200 miles

The inset shows these areas for British Columbia and Washington. Each of these categories should be searched in addition to referring to the grid areas.

BRITISH COLUMBIA GENERAL

14, 59, 146, 167, 171, 269, 294, 296, 297, 298, 302, 304, 313, 350, 463, 473, 475, 476, 481, 482, 497, 498, 568, 588, 610, 637, 641, 642, 647, 649, 653, 656, 657, 815, 816, 860, 1027, 1029, 1038, 1043, 1045, 1046, 1047, 1049, 1050, 1055, 1066, 1076, 1081, 1082, 1089, 1091, 1108, 1110, 1122, 1129, 1146, 1147, 1149

NORTHERN INTERIOR BRITISH COLUMBIA (NORTH OF 55° LATITUDE)

9, 63, 73, 83, 299, 300, 610, 676, 700, 702, 711, 722, 852

SOUTHERN INTERIOR BRITISH COLUMBIA (SOUTH OF 55° LATITUDE)

9, 10, 13, 14, 36, 59, 62, 63, 83, 90, 161, 296, 297, 298, 299, 300, 313, 329, 333, 395, 434, 456, 474, 476, 477, 478, 481, 482, 485, 488, 489, 497, 591, 610, 647, 654, 657, 678, 685, 700, 702, 711, 721, 722, 724, 726, 730, 731, 733, 743

COASTAL BRITISH COLUMBIA (WEST OF COAST RANGE)

2, 9, 13, 23, 32, 36, 39, 42, 50, 53, 59, 62, 63, 72, 83, 91, 111, 120, 161, 169, 234, 238, 242, 283, 296, 297, 298, 299, 300, 302, 313, 320, 321, 333, 339, 344, 349, 350, 351, 353, 422, 436, 441, 453, 456, 472, 474, 475, 476, 481, 482, 487, 497, 537, 538, 579, 587, 588,

General Geographical Divisions for British Columbia and Washington

COASTAL BRITISH COLUMBIA
   (WEST OF COAST RANGE) (cont'd)

610, 616, 618, 643, 647, 649, 659, 700,
702, 703, 706, 711, 714, 719, 724, 725,
726, 727, 730, 732, 743, 804, 1061,
1124, 1145, 1153

MAP GRID 82E

  2, 6, 9, 12, 13, 14, 15, 18, 25,
27, 28, 43, 63, 64, 72, 81, 82, 107,
109, 122, 235, 237, 242, 264, 299, 300,
301, 302, 322, 352, 353, 479, 483, 502,
573, 587, 661, 695, 696, 700, 851,
1048, 1139, 1140

MAP GRID 82F

  9, 12, 13, 14, 63, 64, 72, 107,
213, 214, 263, 264, 302, 350, 351, 489,
503, 504, 507, 526, 555, 587, 661, 851,
938, 1139

MAP GRID 82G

  1, 11, 13, 43, 64, 72, 82, 88, 107,
383, 384, 661, 851, 1059

MAP GRID 82J

  14, 43, 64, 302, 661

MAP GRID 82K

  5, 14, 43, 72, 88, 242, 352, 521,
661

MAP GRID 82L

  2, 6, 9, 11, 14, 25, 43, 64, 72,
88, 106, 107, 111, 154, 235, 237, 242,
263, 264, 284, 289, 301, 302, 313, 319,
346, 351, 353, 479, 483, 489, 490, 502,
508, 509, 510, 511, 512, 518, 519, 522,
525, 555, 573, 576, 577, 660, 661, 1139

MAP GRID 82M

  386, 519, 577, 661, 819, 820

MAP GRID 82N

  9, 12, 13, 43, 63, 72, 242, 319,
350, 351, 489, 555, 661, 804, 819,
1059, 1139

MAP GRID 83D

  9, 11, 64, 72, 204, 242, 351, 353,
370, 371, 386, 501, 634, 661

MAP GRID 83E

  9, 64, 72, 204, 242, 351, 353, 371,
661, 852

MAP GRID 83L

  852

MAP GRID 92B

  2, 8, 9, 11, 13, 14, 24, 27, 28,
29, 38, 40, 41, 43, 44, 45, 48, 49, 56,
57, 63, 64, 67, 71, 72, 74, 78, 82, 83,
85, 88, 106, 107, 156, 158, 236, 240,
241, 242, 243, 250, 255, 256, 258, 261,
263, 288, 299, 302, 322, 335, 351, 353,
356, 357, 489, 530, 536, 555, 573, 591,
637, 645, 661, 700, 720, 733, 799, 848,
851, 852, 932, 938, 949, 968, 974, 982,
1022, 1044, 1139, 1140

MAP GRID 92C

  6, 14, 28, 30, 33, 46, 64, 72, 83,
155, 206, 242, 243, 261, 331, 356, 564,
637, 661, 968, 1029, 1059

MAP GRID 92E

  9, 14, 33, 41, 51, 64, 72, 76, 111,
224, 237, 322, 341, 350, 358, 637, 661,
716, 1029

MAP GRID 92F

  9, 10, 11, 14, 18, 20, 24, 27, 37,
41, 42, 43, 51, 52, 64, 72, 79, 82,
106, 107, 122, 207, 235, 237, 238, 242,
250, 264, 291, 292, 295, 297, 299, 309,
314, 319, 322, 335, 341, 350, 351, 355,
356, 372, 373, 374, 375, 376, 377, 378,
379, 380, 381, 382, 385, 489, 505, 514,
564, 573, 591, 637, 655, 661, 693, 845,
849, 850, 851, 932, 934, 949, 1022,
1053, 1059, 1086

MAP GRID 92G

  2, 4, 9, 10, 11, 13, 14, 17, 19,
20, 22, 26, 27, 28, 29, 34, 38, 41, 43,
54, 60, 61, 63, 64, 69, 72, 85, 88, 95,
96, 97, 98, 99, 102, 103, 105, 106,
107, 111, 151, 152, 153, 156, 170, 193,
221, 225, 226, 229, 230, 234, 237, 242,
243, 251, 253, 254, 257, 259, 260, 262,
263, 277, 295, 299, 302, 310, 311, 319,
322, 331, 335, 346, 350, 351, 353, 354,
368, 470, 483, 506, 516, 517, 533, 539,
555, 597, 615, 616, 637, 644, 645, 658,
661, 696, 700, 720, 733, 738, 770, 792,
803, 806, 813, 851, 852, 889, 931, 938,
966, 1022, 1023, 1024, 1029, 1044,
1050, 1077, 1078, 1084, 1085, 1086,
1093, 1134, 1138, 1139, 1140, 1142, 1156

MAP GRID 92H

  2, 6, 9, 11, 12, 13, 14, 16, 18,
26, 27, 28, 29, 40, 43, 64, 71, 72, 74,
85, 88, 106, 107, 128, 156, 193, 242,
285, 306, 311, 319, 331, 335, 346, 350,
351, 353, 367, 470, 474, 491, 500, 532,
538, 567, 597, 616, 637, 647, 653, 661,
696, 698, 700, 771, 826, 844, 851, 852,
1059, 1093, 1109, 1111, 1140

MAP GRID 92I

9, 11, 13, 14, 25, 26, 64, 72, 88, 106, 107, 111, 242, 264, 299, 301, 302, 309, 322, 335, 341, 350, 479, 483, 502, 513, 524, 661, 696, 700, 851, 852, 1059, 1127, 1129, 1130, 1131

MAP GRID 92J

9, 13, 14, 27, 28, 64, 72, 263, 264, 302, 322, 661

MAP GRID 92K

9, 11, 13, 14, 66, 72, 226, 309, 661, 721, 733, 1059

MAP GRID 92L

12, 13, 14, 27, 33, 42, 64, 77, 223, 309, 350, 647, 661, 720, 853, 1059, 1065

MAP GRID 92M

27, 29, 64, 264, 351, 661

MAP GRID 92N

640

MAP GRID 92O

64, 72, 242, 308, 351, 353, 661

MAP GRID 92P

9, 11, 13, 14, 43, 63, 64, 72, 80, 115, 235, 242, 290, 319, 351, 353, 386, 387, 556, 634, 661, 851, 1059

MAP GRID 93A

14, 80, 386, 387, 634

MAP GRID 93B

14, 72, 84, 851, 1059

MAP GRID 93C

640, 661

MAP GRID 93D

9, 13, 14, 27, 29, 64, 72, 112, 115, 117, 242, 299, 300, 319, 322, 335, 350, 351, 640, 661, 700, 852, 1059

MAP GRID 93E

9, 64, 72, 640, 661, 1059

MAP GRID 93F

9, 661

MAP GRID 93G

700, 1059

MAP GRID 93H

72, 556, 1059

MAP GRID 93K

43

MAP GRID 93L

520, 1059

MAP GRID 93M

9, 21, 64, 88, 242, 264, 319, 351, 366, 556, 661, 1059, 1083

MAP GRID 93O

661, 1059

MAP GRID 93P

13, 35, 63, 64, 157, 299, 315, 556, 661, 724, 1059

MAP GRID 94A

7, 13, 33, 63, 64, 157, 299, 315, 556, 563, 661, 1059

MAP GRID 94D

1035

MAP GRID 94F

527

MAP GRID 94J

157, 1059

MAP GRID 94K

7, 661

MAP GRID 94M

3, 293, 523

MAP GRID 94N

7

MAP GRID 102I

72, 75

MAP GRID 102P

12, 13, 27, 29, 64, 264, 661

MAP GRID 103A

27, 29, 64, 335, 661

MAP GRID 103B

33, 83

MAP GRID 103G

27, 29

MAP GRID 103H

29, 64, 335, 661

5

MAP GRID 103I

    157, 369, 851, 1059

MAP GRID 103J

    9, 13, 27, 29, 64, 71, 72, 116, 117, 242, 297, 298, 313, 335, 351, 474, 491, 647, 661, 1059

MAP GRID 103K

    64, 72, 242, 319, 351, 661

MAP GRID 103O

    1029

MAP GRID 103P

    13, 14, 556

MAP GRID 104G

    9, 11, 13, 21, 64, 72, 88, 242, 319, 351, 556, 661, 711, 724

MAP GRID 104H

    1035

MAP GRID 104M

    9, 13, 63, 64, 72, 242, 293, 351, 661

MAP GRID 104N

    9, 72, 242, 293, 351, 556

MAP GRID 114P

    293

WASHINGTON INDEX

Washington is divided into 38 counties. Each county is listed in alphabetical order. Three additional categories have been included:

1. Washington General
     – general references to Washington

2. Coastal Washington
     – west of Cascade Mountains

3. Interior Washington
     – east of Cascade Mountains

Each of these categories should be searched in addition to referring to counties.

State of Washington Counties

WASHINGTON GENERAL

36, 83, 91, 94, 107, 111, 144, 146, 149, 211, 269, 313, 329, 333, 421, 426, 428, 429, 431, 436, 454, 456, 463, 472, 473, 476, 481, 482, 486, 487, 497, 498, 540, 549, 565, 589, 592, 603, 605, 635, 641, 647, 649, 653, 654, 656, 657, 678, 685, 696, 702, 703, 711, 713, 724, 726, 743, 771, 802, 804, 821, 822, 834, 836, 851, 863, 870, 998, 1055, 1076, 1089, 1091, 1129, 1146

COASTAL WASHINGTON
(WEST OF CASCADE MOUNTAINS)

36, 59, 62, 63, 72, 90, 92, 161, 167, 169, 170, 171, 264, 304, 313, 332, 339, 350, 359, 423, 426, 441, 444, 453, 469, 474, 475, 483, 491, 500, 538, 547, 555, 616, 628, 712, 714, 716, 717, 720, 721, 723, 725, 727, 730, 731, 732, 733, 1145

INTERIOR WASHINGTON
(EAST OF CASCADE MOUNTAINS)

13, 18, 32, 36, 59, 63, 90, 92, 161, 171, 192, 264, 304, 350, 423, 474, 475, 477, 478, 479, 485, 488, 491, 609, 636, 662, 699, 723, 730, 731, 733, 734, 854, 872, 885, 965

ADAMS COUNTY

587, 604, 606, 707, 876

ASOTIN COUNTY

88, 213, 350, 351, 483, 594, 604, 606, 660, 707, 876, 996

BENTON COUNTY

483, 594, 604, 606, 707, 740, 876, 1034

CHELAN COUNTY

81, 88, 131, 141, 179, 194, 198, 350, 351, 420, 437, 439, 470, 483, 604, 606, 660, 698, 707, 876, 996

CLALLAM COUNTY

11, 27, 88, 116, 126, 136, 201, 319, 322, 331, 335, 341, 350, 351, 439, 444, 453, 470, 588, 604, 606, 607, 637, 646, 698, 707, 860, 994, 996, 1089

CLARK COUNTY

10, 201, 331, 335, 350, 351, 438, 567, 594, 604, 606, 698, 707, 996, 1089

COLUMBIA COUNTY

88, 188, 194, 198, 322, 341, 350, 351, 590, 593, 600, 604, 606, 707, 785, 876, 879

COWLITZ COUNTY

88, 126, 137, 159, 194, 198, 201, 331, 332, 349, 350, 438, 440, 466, 594, 604, 606, 637, 698, 707, 855, 996, 1005

DOUGLAS COUNTY

88, 141, 483, 604, 606, 707, 876

FERRY COUNTY

604, 606, 707, 876

FRANKLIN COUNTY

81, 131, 483, 604, 606, 684, 707, 876, 996

GARFIELD COUNTY

88, 604, 606, 707, 876

GRANT COUNTY

81, 88, 139, 141, 147, 166, 174, 211, 213, 313, 329, 483, 491, 604, 606, 707, 810, 857, 876, 996

GRAYS HARBOR COUNTY

11, 88, 126, 201, 313, 319, 331, 340, 341, 350, 351, 470, 546, 604, 606, 637, 698, 707, 865, 875, 974, 994, 996, 1017

ISLAND COUNTY

88, 588, 594, 604, 606, 607, 653, 707, 882, 995

JEFFERSON COUNTY

126, 201, 263, 265, 319, 331, 335, 350, 351, 470, 567, 591, 604, 606, 607, 637, 698, 707, 994, 995, 996, 1017

KING COUNTY

10, 11, 32, 36, 69, 70, 88, 113, 141, 145, 149, 166, 170, 249, 252, 319, 322, 331, 335, 341, 346, 349, 350, 351, 359, 360, 363, 391, 445, 447, 448, 544, 588, 591, 594, 604, 606, 607, 637, 642, 653, 707, 848, 860, 961, 994, 995, 996, 1008, 1017, 1033

KITSAP COUNTY

11, 88, 210, 331, 341, 350, 351, 561, 588, 591, 604, 606, 607, 653, 707, 876, 884, 996

KITTITAS COUNTY

88, 123, 124, 141, 148, 166, 172, 263, 335, 350, 351, 359, 363, 424, 439, 483, 598, 604, 606, 698, 707, 810, 843, 857, 875, 876, 996

KLICKITAT COUNTY

81, 88, 129, 141, 147, 193, 263, 335, 350, 351, 437, 464, 483, 593, 594, 599, 601, 604, 606, 707, 728, 729, 876, 883, 996

LEWIS COUNTY

69, 88, 126, 313, 319, 331, 332, 335, 350, 351, 439, 441, 453, 470, 602, 604, 606, 627, 637, 664, 698, 707, 996, 1000

LINCOLN COUNTY

11, 81, 88, 350, 351, 437, 604, 606, 707, 876, 996

MASON COUNTY

11, 88, 113, 119, 126, 149, 194, 198, 201, 313, 319, 322, 331, 332, 350, 351, 439, 441, 470, 491, 545, 569, 588, 604, 606, 607, 637, 698, 707, 856, 883, 993, 994, 995, 996, 1002, 1003

OKANOGAN COUNTY

81, 88, 125, 141, 213, 350, 351, 420, 424, 435, 483, 604, 606, 649, 660, 707, 876, 996

PACIFIC COUNTY

126, 141, 173, 314, 319, 331, 335, 341, 350, 351, 453, 567, 591, 604, 606, 637, 707, 715, 875, 996

PIERCE COUNTY

10, 11, 32, 69, 88, 111, 113, 118, 126, 132, 136, 141, 142, 146, 169, 182, 313, 319, 331, 332, 335, 340, 341, 349, 350, 351, 425, 427, 439, 441, 453, 457, 470, 483, 491, 536, 537, 544, 588, 591, 594, 595, 596, 604, 606, 607, 627, 637, 646, 660, 664, 707, 860, 867, 873, 883, 927, 972, 994, 995, 996, 1000, 1002, 1004, 1089

PEND OREILLE COUNTY

88, 604, 606, 707, 858, 876, 996

SAN JUAN COUNTY

32, 141, 184, 263, 322, 335, 341, 350, 351, 441, 588, 604, 606, 607, 707, 848, 995, 996

SKAGIT COUNTY

11, 32, 170, 210, 335, 350, 359, 439, 447, 561, 588, 594, 604, 606, 607, 707, 848, 877, 996

SKAMANIA COUNTY

88, 128, 185, 194, 201, 332, 350, 351, 438, 439, 453, 479, 594, 604, 606, 637, 698, 707, 748, 868, 943, 963, 996

SNOHOMISH COUNTY

11, 32, 36, 88, 160, 193, 306, 322, 331, 341, 346, 350, 351, 439, 470, 604, 606, 637, 707, 840, 856, 860, 974, 996, 1005

SPOKANE COUNTY

81, 88, 131, 213, 319, 350, 351, 437, 457, 483, 587, 591, 604, 606, 660, 707, 876, 878, 881, 974, 996, 999, 1001

STEVENS COUNTY

18, 81, 88, 114, 319, 322, 341, 350, 351, 483, 587, 604, 606, 660, 707, 876, 996, 1017

THURSTON COUNTY

10, 88, 331, 351, 441, 594, 596, 601, 604, 606, 707, 859, 860, 861, 862, 873, 974, 996

WAHKIAKUM COUNTY

126, 346, 351, 440, 604, 606, 637, 698, 707, 996

WALLA WALLA COUNTY

11, 18, 88, 141, 208, 294, 319, 320, 322, 341, 342, 349, 350, 351, 434, 457, 483, 491, 567, 590, 591, 593, 604, 606, 616, 660, 697, 707, 876, 879, 883, 996, 1089

WHATCOM COUNTY

32, 88, 125, 141, 162, 194, 198, 210, 319, 322, 335, 350, 412, 422, 483, 528, 561, 588, 594, 604, 606, 607, 637, 660, 674, 696, 707, 814, 848, 856, 860, 866, 874, 921, 995, 996

WHITMAN COUNTY

11, 81, 88, 121, 127, 133, 137, 141, 163, 179, 213, 264, 314, 322, 341, 350, 351, 483, 587, 591, 594, 604, 606, 660, 707, 876, 887, 888, 900, 950, 996, 997, 1002, 1017, 1062

YAKIMA COUNTY

11, 88, 141, 193, 213, 335, 349, 350, 351, 439, 457, 470, 483, 603, 604, 606, 660, 707, 876, 883, 994, 996

31,   65,   87,   100,   101,   104,   138,
140,   183,   186,   187,   189,   190,   191,   195,
196,   199,   202,   205,   216,   231,   232,   233,
276,   280,   281,   303,   305,   312,   316,   317,
318,   323,   324,   325,   327,   328,   330,   336,
337,   338,   345,   347,   348,   388,   389,   390,
392,   393,   394,   396,   397,   398,   399,   400,
401,   402,   403,   404,   405,   406,   407,   408,
409,   410,   411,   413,   414,   415,   416,   417,
418,   419,   432,   433,   446,   449,   450,   455,
456,   459,   460,   461,   462,   465,   467,   468,
480,   484,   492,   493,   494,   495,   496,   498,
529,   531,   534,   535,   548,   562,   565,   566,
571,   574,   575,   578,   580,   581,   582,   583,
584,   585,   586,   626,   629,   630,   632,   633,
638,   639,   648,   649,   652,   653,   655,   666,
667,   675,   677,   679,   680,   681,   682,   683,
686,   689,   691,   692,   704,   705,   708,   735,
736,   737,   739,   741,   742,   744,   745,   747,
749,   750,   751,   752,   753,   754,   755,   756,
757,   758,   759,   760,   761,   762,   763,   764,
766,   767,   768,   769,   772,   773,   774,   775,
777,   779,   781,   782,   783,   784,   787,   788,
789,   790,   791,   793,   794,   795,   796,   800,
807,   825,   827,   828,   829,   830,   831,   832,
833,   835,   837,   838,   839,   846,   847,   880,
886,   890,   891,   893,   894,   895,   897,   898,
899,   901,   902,   903,   904,   907,   908,   909,
910,   911,   912,   913,   914,   915,   916,   918,
920,   923,   924,   925,   929,   930,   935,   939,
940,   941,   945,   946,   947,   948,   951,   955,
956,   957,   958,   959,   960,   967,   970,   971,
975,   976,   978,   979,   981,   983,   984,   985,
986,   987,   988,   989,   990,   991,   992,
1006,   1007,   1009,   1010,   1011,   1012,
1013,   1015,   1016,   1018,   1019,   1020,
1021,   1030,   1051,   1052,   1054,   1064,
1071,   1073,   1092,   1094,   1095,   1100,
1104,   1132,   1135,   1141,   1143

AUTHOR INDEX

Authors, including co-authorship combinations, are listed alphabetically by surname. Names are presented in the fullest form associated with an article. Where changes or misspellings have occurred, the most recent name is listed.

ADLER, KRAIG
917

AINSCOUGH, BRIAN
47

ALDRIDGE, ROBERT D.
955

ALCORN, GORDON D.
132

ADAMS, ELLEN
101, 219

ALGARD, F. T.
258

ALLAN, DOUGLAS M.
909

ALLEN, ANNE L.
1044

ALLEN, BENNET M.
694

ALLISON, ALLEN
411

ALTIG, RONALD
278, 398, 402, 720, 723, 740, 765, 797

ALVARADO, RONALD HERBERT
854, 965

AMARAL, AFRANIO DO
434

ANDERSON, CRAIG THORNTON
993

ANDERSON, J. R.
695

ANDERSON, JAMES D.
401, 712, 714, 789

ANDERSON, RUDOLPH MARTIN
1099

ANDERSON, WILLIAM J.
966

ANDRE, JOHN B.
970

ANONYMOUS
46, 48, 71, 74, 235, 352, 503, 576, 656, 657, 681, 685, 844, 936, 1042, 1060, 1081

ANTONELLI, ARTHUR L.
159, 855

ARBOGAST, R.
828

ARNOLD, STEVAN J.
652

AUEN, EDWARD L.
910

AUGHEY, SAMUEL
663

AVERY, DAVID F.
217

AWBREY, FRANK T.
708

BACHMANN, MARILYN D.
956

BAIRD, SPENCER F.
690

BAKER, M. R.
529, 534

BALL, DAVID J.
671

BALLINGER, ROYCE E.
959

BALLOU, W. H.
776

BANDY, P. J.
1111

BANTA, BENJAMIN H.
585

BARBOUR, ROGER W.
1087

BARBOUR, THOMAS
313, 474, 475

BARKER, WILL
1040

BARKLEY, WILLIAM D.
510

BATTS, BILLY S.
184

BEATTY, JOSEPH J.
648

BECHTEL, ELIZABETH
635

BECHTEL, M. BERNARD
635

BEECHER, KITT
928

BEERY, DON
870

BEHLER, JOHN L.
1098

BEIRNE, MARYANN B.
856

BEISWENGER, RONALD E.
418

BELTON, DESMOND
516

BELTON, JOHN C.
622

BENNETT, ALBERT F.
772, 774, 837

BENNETT, WILLIAM H.
283

BENTLEY, DAVID L.
950

BERGER, T.
1137

BERNARD, STEPHEN R.
822

BERRY, JAMES F.
916

BETHEA, CYNTHIA L.
413

BIDER, J. R.
801

BISHOP, SHERMAN C.
297, 612, 688

BLACK, JEFFREY HOWARD
215

BLAIR, W. FRANK
305, 1129, 1141

BLANCHARD, FRANK NELSON
114, 458, 486

BLANEY, RICHARD M.
728

BLEAKNEY, SHERMAN
892

BLEDSOE, BOB
1016

BOGART, JAMES P.
1077, 1127

BOGERT, CHARLES MITCHILL
684, 1104

BOLS, NIELS CHRISTIAN
65, 228, 253

BONNER, L.
520

BOOTH, ERNEST S.
589

BOPP, TERESITA E.
1085

BOULENGER, GEORGE ALBERT
294, 1102, 1108, 1122, 1125, 1126, 1128

BOWLER, J. KEVIN
1118

BOWMAN, IRENE
1027

BOYD, CLAUDE E.
1071

BRADBURY, WILLIAM A.
840

BRADFORD, JACK
205, 857

BRAGG, ARTHUR N.
678, 701

BRANDON, RONALD A.
748

BRATTSTROM, BAYRD H.
176

BRIGGS, JEFFREY L.
419, 767

BRITISH COLUMBIA FISH AND WILDLIFE BRANCH
610, 1043

BRODIE, EDMUND D.
195, 278, 281, 619, 637, 673, 715, 716, 717, 718, 758, 759, 802, 807

BRONS, H. A.
825

BROWN, CHARLES WALTER
339, 588

BROWN, GREGG
662

BROWN, HERBERT A.
162, 412, 528, 674, 836

BROWN, KENNETH F.
822

BROWN, VINSON
702

BROWN, WALTER CREIGHTON
995

BRUNSON, ROYAL BRUCE
215

BRYANT, HAROLD C.
457, 745

BUFFAM, FRANK
378, 511, 512

BURCH, ARTHUR B.
327

BURGESS, T. E.
1138

BURGGREN, WARREN
531

BURGHARDT, GORDON M.
795

BURKHOLDER, GARY L.
794

BURNS, DOUGLAS M.
185

BURRAGE, BRYAN R.
902

BURT, CHARLES E.
1028

BURY, R. BRUCE
200, 405, 638, 725, 727, 963, 1001, 1069

BUTLER, ROBERT W.
291, 370

BYRNE, JAMES J.
858

CAHALL, ANNA MARIE
859

CALEF, GEORGE WALLER
105, 153, 311

CAMPBELL, CRAIG
1142

CAMPBELL, JAMES B.
766

CAMPBELL, R. WAYNE
37, 41, 206, 358, 379, 380, 385,
506, 563, 806, 851, 852, 1082, 1093,
1110, 1134

CANNINGS, ROB
376, 501

CANNINGS, SYDNEY
371

CAREY, CYNTHIA
915

CARL, G. CLIFFORD
8, 12, 13, 14, 24, 25, 26, 28, 29,
30, 38, 43, 45, 51, 53, 66, 67, 75, 77,
79, 80, 155, 156, 234, 236, 288, 356,
367, 1140

CARLSON, DENNIS S.
421

CARPENTER, CHARLES C.
788

CARR, ARCHIE F.
62, 791

CARR, CATHERINE M.
261

CASE, SUSAN M.
433, 548, 631

CIE, JOSE M.
1132

CHANDLER, ASA C.
244

CHRISTIANSEN, JAMES L.
918

CLAESSEN, HUGO
953

CLARK, GLEN W.
205

CLARK, WILLIAM H.
930

CLARK, WINNIFRED HEATHER
222

CLARKE, RAYMOND D.
280

CLAUSSEN, DENNIS L.
831, 832

CLOTHIER, GLEN W.
160

COCHRAN, DORIS M.
491, 1041

COHEN, NICHOLAS
1135

COLLINS, JAMES P.
1011

COLLINS, JOSEPH T.
93

COMMITTEE   ON   RESOURCES   IN
HERPETOLOGY
94, 178

CONANT, R.
672

CONTE, F. P.
55

COOK, FRANCIS R.
2, 293, 564, 1050, 1056, 1059, 1066

COOK, SHERBURNE F.
536

COOK, STANTON A.
821

COOKE, CEDRIC VINCENT
994

COPE, EDWARD DRINKER
538, 555, 568, 616, 618, 641, 643,
778, 780, 781, 804, 812, 823, 1089

COSS, RICHARD G.
586

COWAN, IAN McTAGGART
20, 23, 28, 29, 35, 72, 471

COWLES, RAYMOND BRIDGMAN
1104

CRESO, IRENE OWENS
860

CUELLAR, ORLANDO
1009

CULLEY, DUDLEY D.
417

CUNNINGHAM, JOHN D.
451, 752

CZOPEK, JULIUSZ
187

DANIEL, RONALD S.
1006

DAUGHERTY, CHARLES H.
988, 1077

DAUGHERTY, LYNN B.
988

DAVIS, DWIGHT D.
476

DAVIS, JOHN
939

DAVIS, WILLIAM C.
190

DAWE, NEIL K.
207, 383, 849, 850, 853, 1053

De JONGH, H. J.
971, 1064

DENNIS, DAVID M.
189

DERICKSON, W. KENNETH
829

DESSAUER, HERBERT C.
974

DETHLEFSEN, EDWIN S.
580

De VILLIERS, C. G. S.
312

De VLAMING, VICTOR L.
405

DEYRUP, MARK
926

DICE, LEE RAYMOND
590

DICKERSON, MARY C.
472

DICKMAN, MIKE D.
96

DIETZ, THOMAS HOWARD
636, 673

DILL, LAWRENCE M.
532

DILLER, J. S.
682

DILLER, LOWELL V.
164

DITMARS, RAYMOND L.
296, 473, 497

DOBIE, J. FRANK
1025

DOBIE, JAMES L.
1136

DODD, C. KENNETH
943, 963

DODSON, STANLEY I.
691

DODSON, VIRGINIA E.
691

DOLE, JIM W.
629, 692, 924, 925

DORNFELD, E. J.
55

DOW, DOUGLAS D.
1024

DOWLING, HERNDON G.
1095, 1096, 1097, 1101, 1103, 1106,
1113, 1114, 1117, 1120, 1133

DRAYCOT, W. M.
239

DROGE, DALE L.
959

DRONEN, NORMAN OBERT
999

DRYNESS, C. T.
821

DUBE, IAN
368

DUELLMAN, WILLIAM E.
710, 1133

DUMAS, PHILIP C.
36, 90, 720, 723, 724

DUNLAP, DONALD G.
272, 863

DUNN, EMMETT REID
27, 81, 117, 120, 295, 615, 627, 645

DUVALL, DAVID
984

EAGLESON, GERALD WAYNE
262, 533, 1156

EAKIN, RICHARD M.
330

EATON, THEODORE H.
130, 321, 979, 981

EBERHARDT, CHAR
859

EDWARDS, JAMES L.
911

EDWARDS, STEPHEN R.
92

EFFORD, IAN E.
34, 98, 889

ELKAN, E.
903, 906

ELLIOT, D. G.
547

ELLMAN, NIKKI
859

EMLEN, STEPHEN T.
620

ENGEL, STEVE
862

ERNST, CARL H.
726, 727, 904, 913, 1087

ERNST, EVELYN M.
913

ERSPAMER, VITTORIO
1132

ETHERIDGE, JACK
861

ETHERIDGE, RICHARD
191, 736

EVANS, KENNETH J.
624

EVENDEN, FRED G.
10

FANGHELLA, CHARLES
217

FANNIN, JOHN
1139

FARBER, J.
1064

FARNER, DONALD S.
175, 270

FAXON, GLENDA
821

FEDER, JULIANA H.
614, 1012

FELLERS, GARY M.
914, 963

FERGUSON, DENZEL E.
5, 88, 711, 753, 937

FERGUSON, GARY W.
920

FERNALD, ROBERT L.
325

FERNER, JOHN W.
1151

FERRANCE, MICHAEL R.
762

FERRANS, VICTOR J.
756

FEUER, ROBERT C.
1144

FISH, JOSEPH LEROY
864

FITCH, HENRY S.
129, 150, 167, 263, 264, 303, 304,
322, 329, 468, 498, 1030, 1092, 1146

FITZGERALD, KEVIN T.
1054

FITZ-GIBBON, JOYCE
384

FLYNT, ALEXANDER W.
599

FOOTTIT, ROBERT G.
385, 506

FORBES, RICHARD B.
58

FORD, B.
1035

FORRESTER, C. R.
33

FORS, SUSAN ROBIN
865

FOSTER, SUSAN ANN
768

FOSTER, WOODBRIDGE A.
755

FOWLER, HENRY W.
615, 645

FOX, WADE
171, 333, 449

FRANCIS, MICHAEL G.
890

FRANKLIN, JERRY F.
821

FRAZER, J. F. D.
1032

FRAZZETTA, T. H.
975

FRIEDMANN, G. B.
56, 57, 250, 255, 258, 530

FROOM, BARBARA
302, 1029

FROST, DEANNA
861

FUNKHOUSER, ANNE
768, 948

GAIGE, HELEN THOMPSON
545

GANS, CARL
971, 1064

GANTERT, ROBERT
896

GARRICK, LESLIE D.
400

GAUDIN, ANTHONY J.
392, 735, 784

GEHLBACH, FREDERICK R.
654

GEMMELL, D. J.
907

GENTRY, ALAN F.
540

GERMYN, DAWN
516, 517

GIBSON, LINDA S.
758

GIGUERE, LOUIS
644

GILBOA, ITZCHAK
1094, 1107, 1114

GILCHRIST, CATHY
1022

GITHENS, THOMAS S.
677

GLOYD, HOWARD K.
488, 1037

GNAEDINGER, LESLIE McKAY
168

GOIN, COLEMAN J.
1041, 1088

GOIN, OLIVE B.
1088

GOLDBERG, STEPHEN R.
388, 632, 783

GOODYEAR, C. PHILLIP
1071

GORHAM, STANLEY W.
286, 287, 1036

GORMAN, GEORGE C.
638

GOVE, DORIS
1019

GOW, JACK A.
220

GOWARD, TREVOR
507

GRADWELL, NORMAN
249, 785

GRANT, JAMES
1, 289

GRASS, AL
290, 386, 803

GRAY, RANDALL L.
960

GREEN, DAVID MARTIN
514, 519, 577, 655, 813, 851, 934, 1063, 1077

GREGORY, PATRICK T.
154, 261, 573, 799, 852, 932, 949, 1049, 1086

GREGSON, JOHN DOUGLAS
85, 106, 243

GRESS, FRANKLIN
638

GRIFFIN, JOHN
1068

GRUNDHAUSER, WALTER
186

GUERRA, LADISLAO A.
709

GUIGUET, CHARLES J.
40, 75, 77, 156, 367, 1140

GUILLETTE, LOUIS J.
1054

GUPPY, RICHARD
42, 50, 52, 238

GUTHRIE, DAN JAMES
900, 1002

GUTTMAN, SHELDON I.
404, 929, 1131

HADLEY, RAYMOND S.
542

HAERTELL, JOHN D.
769

HAILMAN, JACK P.
912

HALL, E. RAYMOND
1123

HALL, JAMES D.
821

HALL, JAMES L.
571

HALL, RUSSELL J.
964

HALLOWELL, E.
689

HANELINE, PATRICIA G.
433, 811

HANLIN, HUGH G.
648

HANLIN, SUE W.
648

HANSEN, RONALD RAE
500

HANSON, W. J.
443

HARD, ROBERT PAUL
846

HARDIN, EDITH
866

HARDY, GEORGE A.
39, 78, 80, 353, 354, 355, 367

HARESTAD, ALTON S.
309, 1065

HARLAN, RICHARD
687

HARLESS, MARION
1057

HARRIS, MARTIN J.
163

HARRIS, MELANY
861

HARRIS, MORGAN
324

HART, JOHN LAWSON
17

HASSELL, SHARON
1084

HAZELWOOD, W. GRANT
527, 640, 1035

HEATH, ALAN G.
987

HEATH, JAMES EDWARD
338

HEBARD, WILLIAM BARTLETT
32, 170, 445, 447, 448, 848

HECKEL, DAVID G.
1014

HENDERSON, BRYAN A.
4, 99

HENDERSON, J. G.
777

HENDERSON, N. LYDIA
505

HENRY, WILBUR V.
142

HENSLEY, MAX
642

HERHENREADER, PETER
750

HERRIED, CLYDE F.
3, 554, 608

HERBIG, RAYMOND J.
867

HERZOG, HAROLD A.
795

HESS, GEORGE L.
990

HEUSNER, A. A.
828, 958

HIBBS, RICHARD G.
756

HICK, WILLIAM BERNARD MARTIN
104, 471

HIGHTON, RICHARD
453, 628, 977

HILLMAN, PETER ERIC
869

HILLMAN, STANLEY S.
923

HILTON, WILLIAM A.
444, 446, 611, 704, 705, 744, 746

HIRTH, HAROLD F.
749, 1148, 1149

HOCK, RAYMOND J.
550

HODGE, ROBERT PARKER
157, 592, 609, 676, 871, 927

HOEK, W.
801

HOLBROOK, JOHN EDWARDS
1154

HOLLAND, GEORGE PEARSON
107

HOLLE, PAUL A.
450

HOLLISTER, N.
204

HOLMAN, J. ALAN
947

HOLMES, CHARLES OLIVER
868

HOLMES, S. J.
317, 318

HONEGGER, RENE E.
668

HORSEMAN, NELSON D.
417

HOTTON, NICHOLAS
271

HOUCK, W. J.
739

HOWARD, CHRIS
1067

HOWARD, JAMES H.
986

HOWIE, RICK
1109

HOWSE, HAROLD D.
756

HOYER, RICHARD F.
161, 796

HUDSON, GEORGE E.
179

HUEY, RAYMOND B.
687, 961, 972

HUHEEY, JAMES E.
93

HUMPHREY, D. G.
839

HUMPHRIES, ROBERT L.
556

HUTCHINSON, VICTOR H.
762

JACOBS, GEORGE J.
1115

JAMES, MIRIAN STOKES
328

JAMESON, DAVID L.
177, 180, 193, 306, 346, 469

JAMESON, E. W.
389, 411, 828, 958

JANES, RALPH G.
138

JAREMOVIC, RENATA V.
224

JENKS, BRUCE GRIFFIN
1155

JESSUP, DAVID A.
1015

JEWETT, TIM
662

JOHANSEN, KJELL
86, 552

JOHNSON, CLIFFORD RAY
742

JOHNSON, JUDITH A.
281

JOHNSON, MURRAY L.
31, 144, 441, 593

JOHNSON, MYRTLE E.
316

JOHNSON, T. S.
55

JOHNSTON, J. A.
942

JONES, DAVID R.
773

JONES, J. KNOX
7

JONES, RICHARD E.
1054

JONES, STEVEN M.
959

JOSLIN, PAUL
1045

JUELSON, THOMAS C.
840

KARDONG, KENNETH VICTOR
847, 950

KARLSTROM, ERNEST L.
337, 551

KARSTAD, LARS
666

KASAHARA, MICHIKO
347, 367

KASINSKY, H. E.
65

KAUFFELD, CARL F.
633

KEDDIE, GRANT R.
308

KELLER, ANDY
859

KELLY, J. PADGETT
797

KENNEDY, KEN
368, 376

KENNEDY, MURRAY JAMES
102, 539

KEPHART, DONALD G.
952

KERMODE, FRANCIS
76, 938, 968

KERSTETTER, THEODORE HARVEY
834, 872

KESSEL, BERTA B.
582, 583, 584

KESSEL, BRINA
89, 553

KESSEL, EDWARD L.
581, 582, 583, 584

KEZER, JAMES
175, 270

KIESTER, A. ROSS
430

KING, F. WAYNE
1098

KINNEY, STEPHEN BALDWIN
543, 554, 608

KIRK, JAMES L.
732, 1145

KIRSCHNER, LEONARD B.
834, 965

KIRTON, MICHAEL PAUL
541

KLAUBER, LAURENCE M.
301, 463, 464, 477, 478, 479, 483,
492, 493, 494, 495, 496, 649, 743

KLICKA, JOHN
835, 990

KLOTZ, SALLY A.
873

KNIGHT, JAMES L.
93

KNOWLTON, G. F.
443

KNOX, CAMERON
139

KNUDSEN, JENS W.
182

KOHLER, ANTHONY J.
1055

KORSMO, PAUL S.
874

KOWALEWSKI, BRUCE W.
895

KREBS, JOHN R.
260

KRUSE, KIPP C.
890

KULLMAN, CAL
845

KURKO, KEITH W.
840

LAIS, P. MIKE
733, 734

LAMBERT, LEWIS H.
625

LANDE, SUSAN PRITCHARD
929

LANDESMAN, RICHARD H.
100, 562

LANDRETH, HOBART F.
753

LANGEBARTEL, DAVID A.
910

LANGILLE, BRIAN LOWELL
232

LARDIE, RICHARD L.
425, 427

LARSEN, ALLAN
977

LARSEN, JOHN HERBERT
362, 364, 613, 887, 900, 1062

LASH, RUTH
982

LASZLO, JOZSEF
670

LAWSON, ROBIN
974

Le BROCQ, DEBRA
368

LEGLER, JOHN M.
893, 985, 989

LEHMAN, GRACE C.
969

LEHMANN, DONALD L.
245, 246, 247

LEM, DONNA
958

LEVITON, ALAN E.
1091

LEWIS, THOMAS H.
147, 166

LEWKE, ROBERT E.
888

LICHT, LAWRENCE E.
54, 60, 61, 103, 151, 152, 257, 277, 310, 658, 738, 754

LICHT, PAUL
772, 774, 837

LILLYWHITE, HARVEY B.
833, 838

LINDBORG, ROBERT G.
935

LINDQUIST, SARAH B.
956

LINDQUIST, TYRA
861

LINDSEY, C. C.
95

LINER, ERNEST A.
1112

LIU, CH'ENG CHAO
790

LIVEZEY, ROBERT L.
265, 267, 275

LOCKINGTON, W. N.
824

LOEB, TIMOTHY G.
875

LOGIER, E. B. S.
16, 64, 242, 661, 967

LOMBARD, ERIC
898

LOOMIS, RICHARD B.
7

LORD, JOHN KEAST
1153

LOW, BOBBI S.
1130

LOWE, CHARLES H.
169, 332

LUCKENBACH, ROGER A.
1001, 1069

LYNN, W. GARDNER
750

MacASKIE, I. B.
33

MACARTNEY, JAMES MALCOLM
579, 949

MacCOLL, M.
520

MacINTYRE, D. H.
1047

MACKEY, JAMES P.
346, 763

MACKIE, AUSTIN
502

MacMAHON, JAMES A.
970

MADSON, SARAH J.
873

MADISON, HAROLD L.
1070

MAGUIRE, FRANCES MARGARET
110

MAHMOUD, I. Y.
621, 835, 990

MANWELL, CLYDE PAT
361

MARCELLINI, DALE
763

MARTAN, JAN
748

MARTIN, KATHY
693

MARTIN, P. J.
435

MARTIN, ROBERT F.
782

MARTIN, WILLIAM F.
686, 1143

MARTOF, BERNARD S.
556, 722

MARX, HYMEN
484, 549, 646

MASER, CHRIS
821

MASON, E. R.
741

MASON, GRANT A.
571

MATHIAS, JACK A.
35, 221

MAUGHAN, O. EUGENE
395

MAYHEW, WILBUR W.
1090

MAYR, ERNST
143

MAXSON, LINDA R.
414, 432, 628

McAULIFFE, JOSEPH R.
415

McCARTNEY, EUGENE S.
703

McCURDY, HARRIET M.
248, 256, 258

McDIARMID, ROY W.
996

McKEOWN, B. A.
533

McINTOSH, A. G. DUNCAN
154, 932

McKENZIE, DONALD S.
639, 787, 800

McKEY-FENDER, DOROTHY
58

McLAIN, ROBERT BAIRD
1017

McLEAN, ROBERT G.
279

McLEAY, DONALD JAMES
108

McNICHOLL, MARTIN K.
292

MEADE, SHAWNA
1023

MEDICA, PHILIP A.
396, 895

MEEK, S. E.
547

MEMMLER, VIOLA H.
465

MERRELL, DAVID J.
983

MERRICK, GEORGE
44

METCALF, MAYNARD M.
818

METTER, DEAN EDWARD
188, 192, 194, 198, 408, 431, 600, 721, 876

MEYER, GENE R.
1121

MILLER, MALCOLM R.
345, 347, 348, 467, 891

MILLER, PAMELA A.
873

MILLICHAMP, N. J.
1080

MILLS, R. COLLIN
9

MILSTEAD, WILLIAM W.
1100

MILLZNER, RAYMOND
460, 461

MILSON, WILLIAM KENNETH
233, 1051

MINTON, SHERMAN A.
1120

MITTLEMAN, M. B.
11, 470

MIX, MICHAEL C.
787

MOLL, EDWARD O.
918

MOORE, FRANK L.
830

MOORE, J. E.
459

MOORE, ROBERT E.
737

MORLOCK, HENRY
1057

MORRIS, PERCY A.
1031

MORRIS, RONALD L.
214

MOUNTJOY, JOHN
306

MUELLER, CHARLES F.
406, 737, 764

MULLALLY, DON P.
451

MULLEN, TERRY L.
877

MULROY, MICHAEL
467

MURPHY, JAMES B.
944, 1116

MUSACCHIA, X. J.
186

MUSTAFA, TARIQ
773

MYERS, GEORGE S.
146, 314, 470

MYHRMAN, HERMAN M.
1004

NACE, GEORGE W.
669

NATIONAL RESEARCH COUNCIL
572

NEAL, G. MORLEY
218

NEISH, IAIN CHARLES
97, 230

NELSON, R. WAYNE
509

NICHOLS, RAY JANNEY
455

NIETFELDT, JOSEPH W.
959

NIGRELLI, ROSS F.
566

NOBLE, G. K.
119, 578, 741, 805

NORRIS, DAVID O.
984

NORTHCUTT, R. GLEN
480, 1021

NUSSBAUM, RONALD A.
159, 160, 161, 164, 201, 205, 282, 393, 698, 759, 760, 761, 802, 1005

O'BRIEN, SISTER MARY CYRILLA
750

O'DAY, DANTON H.
227

O'FARRELL, THOMAS P.
1034

OLIPHANT, L. W.
252

OLIVER, MARLENE GAIL
158, 241, 256

OLSON, RICHARD LEE
878

ORCHARD, STAN A.
815, 816, 1046, 1119

ORRICO, LEO
237

ORTENBURGER, ARTHUR IRVING
696

ORTON, GRACE L.
268

OSGOOD, WILFRED H.
1124

OSMOND-JONES, E.
520, 1035

OWCZARZAK, ALFRED
622

OWEN, ROBERT P.
141

OWINGS, DONALD H.
586

PACE, ANN E.
697

PALERMO, R. V.
1047

PARKER, B. J.
942

PARKER, WILLIAM S.
203, 617, 632

PARKIN, T. W.
521, 526

PARSONS, THOMAS S.
976

PATCH, CLYDE L.
6, 15, 21, 115, 659

PAUKEN, ROBERT J.
198, 431

PAULEY, GILBERT B.
998

PAULSON, DENNIS
428, 429

PEABODY, FRANK E.
336

PEACOCK, ROBERT L.
393

PENDLEBURY, GEORGE B.
786

PERKINS, C. B.
481, 482

PERRY, ALFRED E.
879

PETERS, JAMES A.
569, 1105

PETERS, RALPH I.
880

PETERSON, ERNST A.
751

PETERSON, PHIL H.
1033

PETTERSON, CYNTHIA M.
881

PETTUS, DAVID
623

PIANKA, ERIC RODGER
203, 365

PICKWELL, GAYLE
298

PIMENTEL, RICHARD A.
894

PISANI, GEORGE R.
92, 397, 1150

POPE, CLIFFORD H.
111, 485

POST, DOUGLAS D.
623

PRESCH, WILLIAM
196

PRESTON, WILLIAM BARTON
109

PRITCHARD, PETER C.
1147

PURDUE, JAMES R.
788

PUTNAM, PHILLIPS, GRISWOLD
119, 1003

QUAY, W. B.
978

RABB, GEORGE B.
484

RAHN, HERMANN
140

RAUCH, JOSEFINE C.
535

REED, CHARLES A.
    168

REID, D. B.
    1079

REID, T. C.
    523

REIMER, WILLIAM J.
    335

REIMKING, LARRY N.
    988

RESNICK, LINDA E.
    469

RHODIN, ANDERS G. J.
    811

RICHES, ROBERT J.
    1074

RICHMOND, ROLLIN C.
    346

RICKER, WILLIAM E.
    16

RIE, IVO P.
    919

RITLAND, RICHARD M.
    992, 1018

RIVARD, DONALD H.
    949, 1059

ROBBERSON, DOUGLAS L.
    998

ROBINSON, DOUGLAS A.
    997

ROBINSON, HARRY B.
    326

RODGERS, THOMAS L.
    329, 465

ROOFE, PAUL GIBBONS
    571

ROSEGHINI, M.
    1132

ROSENBERG, HERBERT I.
    991

ROSENBERG, KAREN
    901

ROSSMAN, DOUGLAS A.
    973

ROUF, M. A.
    199

ROUGHGARDEN, JONATHAN
    1014

ROYCE, G. JAMES
    1021

RUBEN, JOHN A.
    675, 899

RUNYAN, CRAIG S.
    770, 1078

RUTHVEN, ALEXANDER G.
    489, 591, 808

RYAN, MICHAEL J.
    945

RYDER, GLEN R.
    84, 792

SAGE, RICHARD D.
    1013

SALO, LEO J.
    840

SAMIS, STEPHEN C.
    1044

SAMOLLOW, PAUL B.
    1010

SATHER, M.
    520, 1035

SAVAGE, JAY M.
    68, 565, 809

SCHAUB, DAVID L.
    613

SCHECHTMAN, A MANDEL
    323

SCHMIDT, ANTHONY JOHN
    360, 578

SCHMIDT, KARL P.
    476, 647

SCHONBERGER, CLINTON F.
    149

SCHROEDER, PAUL C.
    1062

SCHUELER, FREDERICK W.
    1059

SCHULTZ, RICHARD H.
    843

SCOTT, A. FLOYD
    1136

SCUDDER, G. G. E.
    1048

SECOY, D. M.
    416

SEELIGER, L. M.
    537

SEIDE, RICHARD L.
    830

SEIDEL, MICHAEL E.
    935

SELANDER, ROBERT K.
    1013

SELLERS, JEFFREY C.
    954

SHADDUCK, JOHN A.
    944

SHALER, N. S.
    775

SHEPARD, TERESA
    369

SHINE, RICHARD
    630, 916

SHINN, ELIZABETH A.
    629, 692

SHRODE, C. J.
    399

SIMPSON, DAVE
    862

SIMPSON, ROBERT EDWARD
    226

SIRK, GEORGE
    524

SIVULA, JANICE C.
    787

SLATER, JAMES R.
    31, 116, 118, 126, 128, 131, 136,
    437, 438, 439, 440, 588, 594, 595, 596,
    597, 598, 601, 602, 603, 604, 605, 606,
    607, 707, 1000, 1076

SLEVIN, JOSEPH R.
    341, 342, 351

SLIPP, JOHN W.
    26

SMITH, ARNOLD J. M.
    423, 933

SMITH, B.
    520

SMITH, CRAIG A.
    417

SMITH, DAPHNE F.
    873

SMITH, GERTRUDE M.
    225

SMITH, HARLAN I.
    112

SMITH, HOBART M.
    59, 93, 216, 1026, 1054, 1055

SMITH, MARGARET F.
    433

SMITH, PHILIP W.
    315

SMITH, STANFORD D.
    159

SMITH, VIVIEN
826

SNOW, JONATHAN E.
940

SNYDER, GREGORY K.
683

SNYDER, RICHARD C.
69, 70, 653

SNYDER, WADE F.
193

SORENSON, DWIGHT C.
882

SOTTOVIA-FILHO, DAGOBERTO
390

SPECKER, JENNIFER L.
830

SPELLERBERG, IAN F.
1073

SPERRY, DAVID G.
908

SPRULES, W. GARY
254, 259

STANLAKE, ELIZABETH A.
1044

STANWELL-FLETCHER, JOHN F.
366, 1083

STANWELL-FLETCHER, THEODORA C.
1083

STEBBINS, ROBERT C.
83, 183, 299, 326, 331, 332, 334,
1152

STEINWASCHER, KURT
1020

STEJNEGER, LEONHARD
313, 474, 475, 499, 544, 546

STELMOCK, JAMES JOSEPH
223, 1065

STEPHENSON, N. G.
664

STEWART, DORIS MAE
883

STEWART, GLENN R.
409, 730, 747, 1006

STEWART, JAMES R.
957

STICKEL, WILLIAM H.
650, 651

STIRLING, DAVID
41, 358, 373, 374, 508, 518, 525,
1109

STOKELY, PAUL S.
450

STORER, TRACY I.
18, 122, 319, 320, 1075

STORM, ROBERT M.
173, 436, 442, 452, 639, 715, 716,
717, 718, 757, 759, 767, 769, 793, 800

STRICKLAND, E. H.
459

STRONG, KENNETH V.
1038

STROTHER, WILLIAM F.
394

STROUD, DENNIS C.
960

STUART, BRADLEY H.
394

STULL, OLIVE GRIFFITH
91, 490, 660

SVIHLA, ARTHUR
121, 123, 124, 125, 127, 133, 134,
137, 139, 145, 148, 172, 174, 181

SVIHLA, RUTH DOWELL
123, 124, 127

SWANSON, LLOYD
830

SWARTH, HARRY S.
344, 1061

SWEENEY, STEVEN J.
840

SWIFT, PAT
513, 522

SWITAK, K. H.
667

TANNER, VASCO M.
208, 209, 212

TANNER, WILMER W.
209, 210, 211, 213, 214, 217, 561, 794

TAYLOR, EDWARD H.
587

TAYLOR, E. J.
443

TAYLOR, J. MARY
700

TAYLOR, W. EDGAR
779

TAYLOR, WILLIAM
306

TEST, FREDERICK CLEVELAND
567

THACKER, T. L.
82, 285

THETIS PARK NATURE SANCTUARY ASSOCIATION
357

THOMAS, ROBERT A.
817

THOMPSON, GEORGEANNA B.
884

THORSON, THOMAS BERTEL
359, 363

TIHEN, JOSEPH A.
226, 276, 456, 713

TINKLE, DONALD W.
699

TOBIASON, FRED L.
922

TODD, TERESE
240

TONER, G. C.
64, 661, 967

TRAUTH, STANLEY E.
954

TSUMURA, KANJI
98, 889

TURNER, FREDERICK B.
273, 274, 307, 396, 895, 724

TWINING, HOWARD
150

TWITTY, VICTOR C.
142, 190

UNDERHILL, J. E.
504

VALENTINE, BARRY D.
189

VAN DENBURGH, JOHN
340, 466, 341, 342, 343, 349, 454, 842

VAN EEDEN, J. A.
1052

VAN TETS, GERARD FREDERICK
372

VAN WINKLE, KATHERINE
113

VASLIT, FRANK H.
980

VINCENT, TOM K.
410, 416

VITT, LAURIE J.
391, 420, 422, 426, 814, 921, 946

VOGT, RICHARD C.
962

VON DER LINN, KAREN
859

WADE, CARSON
375

WADE, KEITH
634

WADDICK, JAMES W.
216

WAGNER, ERNIE
424

WAKE, DAVID B.
462, 614, 628, 706, 719, 886, 897, 898, 951, 1008

WALDO, ALLEN E.
1062

WALDSCHMIDT, STEVE
941

WALKER, RICHARD F.
413

WALLACE, RICHARD L.
986

WARREN, JAMES W.
176

WASSERSUG, RICHARD J.
626, 652, 901, 908, 1007

WATNEY, GERTRUDE M. SMITH
19, 22

WATSON, MARY R.
49

WEARY, G. C.
1072

WEATHERS, WESLEY W.
683

WEIGMANN, DIANA L.
398

WIENS, JOHN A.
679

WEISS, BURTON A.
394

WELCH, PAUL S.
703

WELLS, KENTWOOD D.
680

WERNZ, JAMES G.
407, 757

WEST, NIGEL HUGH
231

WESTERBORG, BETTY
377

WETMORE, STEPHEN P.
853

WHITAKER, JOHN O.
403

WHITE, CHARLES A.
827

WHITE, H.
905

WHITE, ROBERT L.
165

WHITEHOUSE, F. C.
284

WHITNEY, CARL LINN
229, 260, 665, 931

WICKHAM, MARVIN GARY
395, 885

WIEWANDT, THOMAS A.
197

WILHOFT, D. C.
978

WILLIAMS, ERNEST E.
976

WILLIAMS, M. Y.
73

WILSON, A. C.
432

WILSON, LARRY DAVID
731

WINOKUR, ROBERT M.
985, 989

WINTERBOURN, MICHAEL J.
251

WIT, LAWRENCE C.
954

WITHERS, PHILIP C.
923

WOLFE, MICHAEL
381, 382

WOLFHEIM, J. H.
1001

WOOD, SHERWIN F.
135

WOOD, STEPHEN C.
202

WOODS, JOHN G.
819, 820

WOOLERY, DONALD L.
810

WORTHAM, J. W. EDWARD
748

WORTHINGTON, RICHARD D.
897, 1008

WRIGHT, ALBERT HAZEN
63, 265, 267, 269, 300, 487, 1039,
1058

WRIGHT, ANNA ALLEN
63, 269, 1039, 1058

WRIGHT, DEBRA L.
950

WRIGHT, RICHARD T.
387

WURST, GLORIA Z.
614

WYATT, TIM
862

WYLLIE, GILBERT A.
275

WYNNE-EDWARDS, V. C.
570

YARROW, H. C.
771

ZUG, GEORGE R.
574, 575

ZWEIFEL, RICHARD G.
87, 729

ADDRESSES OF COMPILERS

R. Wayne Campbell
Vertebrate Zoology Division
British Columbia Provincial Museum
Victoria, British Columbia
V8V 1X4

Michael G. Shepard
Vertebrate Zoology Division
British Columbia Provincial Museum
Victoria, British Columbia
V8V 1X4

Present address:

Swiftsure Tours Limited
645 Fort Street
Victoria, British Columbia
V8W 1G2

Brigitta M. Van Der Raay
College of Forest Resources
Wildlife Science Group
University of Washington
Seattle, Washington   98195
U.S.A.

Present address:

United States Forest Service (USDA)
Gifford Pincho National Forest
Route 1, Box 369
Amboy, Washington   98601
U.S.A.

Patrick T. Gregory
Department of Biology
University of Victoria
Victoria, British Columbia
V8W 2Y2
